explained. When necessary, consult the text materials for aid in revising your writing.

out-6	improper single subheading	423–424
out-7	inconsistent form	424
P	faulty punctuation	283–315
P-1	omitted comma(s)	285–296
P-2	unnecessary comma(s)	293–295
P-3	omitted or misused colon	302–303
P-4	omitted or misused semicolon	300–302
P-5	omitted or misused dash	296–298
P-6	omitted or misused quotation marks	303–308
P-7	omitted or misused end punctuation	284–285
¶	undeveloped paragraph	57–59
no ¶	improperly divided paragraph	57–58
new ¶	run-together paragraphs	93
paral	faulty parallelism	162–165
pl	incorrect plural form	
pred	faulty predication	159–162
prim	primer style, choppy sentences	118–119, 123
PV	shift in point of view	175–176
ref	unclear reference	178–181
rep	unnecessary repetition of ideas	80–82
RS	rambling or overloaded sentence	119–120
RTS	run-together sentences or comma splice	295–296, 300
shift	faulty shift in number, person, voice, tense, or mood	170–177
SP	misspelling	
SS	mixed or confused sentence structure	156–157
sub	faulty subordination	116–117
syl	improper syllabic division of word	
tr	improper transition	45–48, 96–107
unity	mixed paragraph, irrelevant material	93–96
V	weak use of passive voice	114–115
verb	incorrect verb form or tense	315–328
W	wordiness, deadwood	108–114
WW	wrong word, incorrect diction	226–234
∧	omission	
?	questionable statement or usage, lack of clarity	
X	careless error	

Structure, Style, and Usage

The Rhetoric of Exposition

HULON WILLIS

Bakersfield College

Structure, Style, and Usage

The Rhetoric of Exposition

Second Edition

HOLT, RINEHART and WINSTON, INC.
New York   Chicago   San Francisco   Atlanta
Dallas   Montreal   Toronto   London   Sydney

Preface

There are many valid approaches to the teaching of the course called Freshman Composition. Even within one college, one section of English 1A (or English 100, or whatever) may bear little relationship to another section. The course may be—legitimately, according to circumstances—one in semantics, or logic, or linguistics, or rhetorical principles, or usage, or even the history of ideas. Often several of these approaches are combined. I have no quarrel with any of them—have, indeed, used various approaches myself from semester to semester.

This book, however, is for those who feel that Freshman Composition should most strongly emphasize the rhetoric and logic of exposition as it is written—or should be written—by college students. For this reason, though the book has more in it than one instructor can teach in one semester, I have limited the book to the basic principles of expository writing. All the material on logic, semantics, and linguistics is designed to pertain directly to the writing of exposition. It does not have sections on the writing of narration, description, or impressionism. I have tried to present teachable principles that apply to student writing rather than to present theoretical rhetorical classifications. I hope Chapters 2 through 5 (organization, paragraphing, sentence composition, diction) will be both interesting and useful to all students; the use to be made of Chapter 6 on conventions of usage will depend on the nature of individual classes.

Since in the composition course time is limited and instructors have various teaching methods, I have designed the book so that much of its materials can be (1) used for classroom teaching, or (2) assigned as homework without class explanations, or (3) used individually by students for reference. All sections of the book cannot, of course, operate on all three levels, but many can; and thus I hope that most instructors will find the book adaptable to their methods.

In matters of usage and linguistic descriptions, I have maintained a liberal point of view. In consonance with this viewpoint, I have tried to present interesting, though elementary, comments about the nature of language, particularly in the discussions of those conventional aspects of usage which are normally quite dull to students and teachers alike.

I have included plentiful exercises, knowing of course that no instructor can assign them all. I have tried to design the exercises so they can be discussed in class or handed in for grading or just handed in as evidence of work done. I have prepared an instructor's manual for all the exercises, but in many cases my answers represent just one of several valid possibilities.

In many of the exercises and the illustrative sentences in the text, I have tried to use words that will enlarge the students' vocabularies. I have tried to avoid oversimplified exercises and illustrative materials.

I owe a large debt to Richard Beal of Boston University for help in preparing this book. I am also grateful for the perceptive suggestions given me by Richard Dodge of Santa Monica City College, John R. Grace of El Camino College, Donald J. Gray of Indiana University, James T. Hayes of Murray State University, John Jordan of Berkeley, George Levine of Indiana U., Youra Qualls of the Tuskegee Institute, Amy K. Richards of Wayne State, Martin Steinmann of the University of Minnesota, and R. B. Thomas of Lamar State College of Technology.

And of course all writers of composition texts, however much originality they put into their own work, are indebted to those who have written texts before them. I therefore gratefully acknowledge the influence of my predecessors and hope that some future writers of composition texts may feel some indebtedness to me.

H.W.

Bakersfield, California
October 1968

Contents

For all a Rhetorician's Rules,
Teach nothing but to name his Tools.
—HUDIBRAS

Structure, Style, and Usage

The Rhetoric of Exposition

CHAPTER 1

Introduction to the Principles of Expository Composition

Writing is one of man's most complex activities. Its purposes and varieties are manifold. It may be designed to amuse, to inspire, to persuade, to inform, to deceive, to guide, to enlighten. It may be a one-sentence memorandum or a volume of philosophic discourse; an indulgence in self-expression or a work of impersonal objectivity; a workaday report of simplicity and directness or a masterpiece of subtlety and suggestion. Its creation may be a source of pride and joy or of anxiety and frustration. Its content is subject to a fallible human scrutiny for inaccuracy and bias; its quality is subject to widely varying value judgments; its correctness depends on social conventions and prejudices as well as on the logic of grammar. Though an indispensable tool in the educational process, it often presents the greatest challenge to the student, for it is so various, so complex, so subjectively masked that it is difficult for two people—especially an expert and a novice—to focus on the same aspect of it in the same way at the same time. Thus composition is one of the most difficult college courses. But it also may be one of the most rewarding.

The goals of any English course are various: to expand the student's intellectual horizons, to deepen his moral awareness, to whet his esthetic sensitivities, to develop further his social potential, and *to teach him skills in the use of his native language.* In freshman composition, the prime objective is to give the student an understanding of and an adeptness in applying the principles of expository composition.

Expository writing—or **exposition,** as it is also called—is that which expresses facts, opinions, and ideas. The term excludes narrative, descriptive, and impressionistic writing (though techniques from these areas may be used in exposition), and it also excludes persuasive and argumentative writing based on emotional appeal rather than on orderly, sound, and open-minded examination of facts and suppositions. Expository writing is analytical, critical, logical—not imaginative, bombastic, cunning, intimate, or freewheeling. The word *exposition* comes from the same root as *expose,* which means to uncover or make clear. Thus expository writing is used to explain or analyze, to reason out or make clear.

Teaching you the principles of expository writing is the chief objective of your freshman composition course because your success in college will depend to a surprising degree on your ability to write clear, precise, intelligible exposition. In your courses in the social sciences, the life sciences, the natural sciences, the humanities, and professional areas such as business administration, agriculture, and engineering, you will be required to write definitions, essay exams, term papers, book reports, and technical reports. During every week of your college career some expository writing will be demanded of you. Whether you anticipate or fear the prospect of writing, you must adjust to its fundamental role in college education.

Your writing of exposition in college, then, has a limited purpose and a limited audience. Its purpose is to explain clearly and logically information that you know or opinions that you think are sound. Its audience is your instructors, who are interested in the subject matter of your exposition and the clarity of its expression.

Though both in college and later you will write with other purposes and for other audiences, your immediate success in college will be partially dependent on how well you write exposition for your instructors. And if later you enter the business or professional world, your writing there will have a similar purpose and an equally critical audience. Thus your study of the principles of exposition is one of the most important aspects of your college work.

But though you study exposition primarily for its practical value, you will find in this kind of writing personal satisfaction that you thought only imaginative writing could give. The factual and logical, rather than imaginative, nature of exposition does not mean that it is wholly impersonal in tone or rigidly structured. Good exposition is, in fact, rich and varied, not lusterless and monotonous. In a sense it is just as "creative" as narration or description, for out of the raw materials of facts and opinions the writer creates new form—form that utilizes many of the elements that make imaginative writing interesting and exciting. Though clarity, precision, and coherence are its chief goals, exposition is not void of rhythm, variety, color, warmth, vividness, concreteness, and vigor. The writer of exposition can indeed exercise as much creativity as he possesses.

To get an over-all view of the plan of your course, you should very carefully study—even memorize—the following outline of the principles of exposition and learn in general terms what each heading means. The rest of the book will be devoted to a detailed explanation of how you can improve your own performance in each of these principles.

PRINCIPLES OF EXPOSITORY COMPOSITION

1. Adequate subject matter
   A. Range of thought
   B. Soundness of ideas
   C. Appropriateness of ideas

II. Organization of the whole paper
   A. Logical sequence of main ideas
   B. Suitable introduction and conclusion
   C. Coherence between paragraphs

III. Organization and development of paragraphs
   A. Fullness of development
   B. Orderly arrangement of details

      C. Unity in subject matter
      D. Coherence between sentences

IV. Mature and effective sentence composition
      A. Terseness and vigor in structure
      B. Variety in structure
      C. Clarity in structure

V. Effective diction
      A. Flexible and extensive vocabulary
      B. Precise and vigorous word choice

VI. Correct usage

These six main principles form the basis of expository writing, whether a book, a long paper, or a theme assigned in your composition class. To write a good theme, you must—consciously or unconsciously—apply all six. As your instructor grades your themes, he judges them on the basis of all these separate principles, each of which is in itself highly involved.

Principle I—adequate subject matter—is the most important of the six, for the purpose of exposition is to explain facts, opinions, and ideas. The range of your subject matter is adequate when you have covered all the pertinent material directly related to your topic. Then your reader will feel a sense of completeness as he finishes your paper. Your ideas are sound when everything you say is truthful and reliable, or at least is based on open-minded investigation and reasonable supposition. When you are successful in this respect, your reader will not be left with a feeling of skepticism. Your ideas are appropriate when everything you write pertains to your announced topic. Then your reader will not feel that you have wandered from your topic or deceived him as to your purpose.

In preparing term papers and reports and in answering essay questions, the adequacy of your subject matter will be determined by the extensiveness of your research and your study of your text materials. The subject matter of some of your themes may also be gathered through research. But to write most of your themes, you will need to draw on information that you brought to college with you and that you are acquiring as you pursue your college work. To help you broaden your range of ideas, your English course may require a textbook of expository essays. Beyond that, you will gradually increase the range and soundness of your ideas through systematic study, class lectures, unassigned reading, student associations, and campus cultural affairs. Your whole program of college education will, in effect, contribute to your having something to say in your English themes.

The range of your general knowledge is probably more extensive than you realize. You will usually have much more to say about an assigned topic than, at first glance, you will think you have. In preparing a writing assignment, you need to develop the habit of canvassing your mind thoroughly to seek out pertinent facts, opinions, and ideas stored there. Chapter 2 of this text, on organization of the whole paper, will include guidelines on how to search through your mind in an orderly fashion.

The first of our six principles has to do with what you write, the next five with how you write it. These five principles are the subject matter of this text. In order to be prepared to understand each principle in detail as you study the following chapters of your text, you should first acquire a general understanding of the meaning of each.

Principles II and III—organization and paragraphing—have to do with the **structure** of an expository paper. The first requisite of a good paper is that the topic be in proper focus. There should be no doubt in your reader's mind as to what your exact topic is. The boundaries of your whole topic and of each of its main points should be sharply etched, just as there is the correct focus in a photograph. Proper focus in exposition is achieved when the main points of a paper are clearly distinguished, logically arranged, suitably divided into paragraphs, and coherently welded together. Chapter 2 deals with this aspect of structure.

Just as an orderly arrangement of paragraphs gives focus and structure to the whole paper, an orderly arrangement of sentences gives focus and structure to each paragraph. Contrary to what you might expect, the structure of a paragraph is usually more complex than the structure of a whole paper. An analogy may be drawn between these two aspects of structure and the final assembly of an automobile. At the end of the assembly line the body, chassis, and power complex are put together to form the final structure. But the assembly of these three components into one whole car is much less complex than the original assembly of any one of the three. Putting the parts of the power complex together, for example, is a much more intricate process than building a car out of the three major components. Similarly, the making of a paragraph is often more involved than assembling several paragraphs to make a whole paper.

Principles IV and V—sentence composition and diction—are the ones that have most to do with what is called **style.** Whether a paper is smooth or awkward, precise or vague, lively or dull, fresh or trite, terse or rambling, colorful or drab, sharp or bland, vivid or abstract, clear or ambiguous, appropriate or offensive, flowery or simple, pretentious or unassuming—whether a paper reflects one or the other of these characteristics, or a degree between any two, depends primarily on the quality of its sentence composition and its diction. The few subheadings for these principles given in the outline above do not truly reflect their involved nature. But it should be noted that it is a writer's style, more than anything else, that expresses his unique individuality. Developing a competent style is a complex—but, again, a most rewarding—undertaking.

Principle VI—correct usage—has to do with the **social acceptability** of writing. Included under this principle are such matters as spelling, capitalization, the use of the apostrophe, verb forms, pronoun forms, modifier forms, agreement, and punctuation. These aspects of writing (except punctuation for clarity) have little to do with the clarity, truthfulness, or interest of what you write; but they have a great deal to do with how educated readers accept your writing.

All mechanical aspects of writing are conventions. In this sense, a **convention** is a habit agreed upon by a certain group. Conventions of writing are just matters of form agreed upon by people who write. For example, in German all nouns are capitalized but in English only proper nouns are capitalized. Thus in English you make a mistake if you capitalize *table*, but in German you make a mistake if you don't capitalize it. It's all a matter of convention—agreement among those involved. For us, the phrase "those involved" means educated Americans whose agreements about the rules of conventions are the best for us to abide by. Such conventional agreements are, of course, necessary for orderliness and efficiency in language, just as agreements about rules of the road are necessary for orderly and efficient driving.

Correctness in writing is one thing; effectiveness is another. Do not confuse good writing with correct writing. As an educated person you will be expected to be reasonably correct in your writing, and correctness is a quality not especially hard to achieve. Chapter 6 of this text deals with matters of conventional usage that may give you trouble. If necessary, you will want to study the rules so that you can be adequately correct in your writing. But you should never think that mere correctness is the most important aspect of writing. It is really the least important. Your instructor may choose to teach you various sections of Chapter 6 early in the course, but he will not do so because he thinks correctness is more important than the other principles of composition.

In summary, then, Principles I, II, and III have to do with the subject matter of a paper and its structure, Principles IV and V with clarity and that complex element called style, and Principle VI with the social acceptability of writing, or usage.

The alert student has already noted that Principles II, III, IV, and V of our outline proceed from the largest element of writing (the whole paper) through intermediate elements (the paragraph and sentence) and on to the smallest (the individual word). In studying these principles, it might seem logical to start with the smallest unit and then proceed up the scale to the largest. But, since you will not write just single words and sentences at the beginning of your course and whole papers only at the end, that is not a logical approach. You will write whole papers at the beginning of the course, for you already know a good deal about all the principles of exposition. You can already write whole papers, paragraphs, and sentences of some competence. The purpose of this text is to teach you a great deal **more** about each of these principles. Hence it is logical for you to study in descending order the principles of organization, paragraphing, sentence composition, and diction. Instruction in correct usage can, of course, be spread out through your whole sequence of study.

EXERCISE 1. Review

DIRECTIONS: *Answer the following questions succinctly.*

1. Define *exposition*.
2. Why is a study of the principles of expository writing important in your college career?

3. What are the six general principles of expository writing and what is the nature of each?
4. What is a *convention* as it applies to writing? Why are correct writing and effective writing not necessarily the same?
5. Define *style*.
6. Why is it logical to study organization, paragraphing, sentence composition, and diction in descending rather than ascending order?

CHAPTER 2

Organization of the Whole Paper

THE MEANING OF ORGANIZATION

Some of your compositions may be assigned on topics that require research, some on topics about which you already have information and opinions. Some may be narrowly limited for you; some you may need to limit further yourself. In any case, you can plan your whole paper only after you have a limited topic and after the raw materials are in your mind. We will assume that your mind is stocked with materials adequate for any sufficiently limited topic assigned to you. Now, to write successfully, you must plan your whole paper before you actually begin composing sentences.

The word *organize* is composed of the suffix *ize*, which means to make into, and the root *organ,* which originally meant a whole instrument or machine made up of interdependent parts. To organize, then, means to make into a whole, or to arrange interdependent parts into a whole structure. And this is exactly what you do when you organize a piece of writing; you arrange parts so that they form a clearly constructed whole.

Organization, of course, does not apply just to the whole paper. A good paragraph requires intricate organization, for its parts—the sentences—must be carefully arranged so that the reader may proceed smoothly and with understanding through an involved sequence of details and ideas. A good sentence, too, is intricately organized. In fact, a mature sentence is more complex in structure than most short papers, the parts of a sentence variously being such constructions as subjects, verbs, objects, subjective complements, adjectives, adverbs, a wide variety of phrases and clauses, conjunctions, subordinators, logical connectives, transitional phrases, absolute phrases, and probably constructions as yet unidentified. In short, a mature sentence generally has more parts than a short paper has paragraphs, and the logical relationships of its parts are more complex than the logic expressed between paragraphs in a paper. And beyond the sentence, even the organization of a word can be carried right down to the individual vocal sounds called phonemes, though such a process has no direct bearing on the study of exposition. In Chapter 2 we will be concerned only with the organization of the whole paper. Chapters 3 and 4 are devoted to the organization of paragraphs and sentences. Though in a sense the organization of a whole paper is less complex than that of a mature sentence, you nevertheless need, in all probability, more training in organizing whole papers, for you have already unconsciously learned a great deal about organizing sentences.

The parts that you arrange in organizing a whole paper are the introduction, the conclusion, and all the main points or central ideas that you develop in-between. It is these main points that give structure to your paper. You must know what they are before you begin writing. Your problem in organizing, simply put, is to think of the main points of your paper and to give them order and development.

Some writers can organize with magical ease. They just seem naturally to arrange and develop their subject matter so that a reader can glide effortlessly through whatever involved sequence of ideas they have to present. Most of us, however, have to work diligently to organize well. We need to proceed systematically and to check and recheck our work frequently. We can seldom indulge in freewheeling organizational tactics.

You must not think, however, that organization of a whole paper is mathematically rigid. It yields to variety just as writing itself does. Even in exposition, multiple approaches to organization exist; and narrative, descriptive, and impressionistic writing have various modes of their own. At times, even, a deliberate flouting of organization can be effective. The more adept a writer you become, the more you can vary your organization.

But it is widely acknowledged among composition teachers (and teachers in all academic subjects, for that matter) that most students do not have a sufficient grasp of organization. Therefore in the sections following you will be given instruction in one simple, systematic technique of organization that will stand you in good stead both in writing themes and reports and in answering essay questions. Though not a magic formula, the basic system of organization presented here will serve for most of your college writing, and on it, if you pursue the craft of writing, you can build more variable and subtle systems of organization. But you must master fundamental organization before you can undertake subtle variety. As Alexander Pope wrote:

> *True ease in writing comes from art, not chance,*
> *As those move easiest who have learn'd to dance.*

HOW TO PLAN THE MAIN POINTS OF A PAPER

The distinction between a title and a topic

The first lesson to be learned in organizing an expository paper is the distinction between the **title** and the **topic.** The meaning of the title may not be clear to the reader until he has read most of the paper; but the topic must be fully clear to you before you begin to write. Consider the title "Art and My Personality." From this title the reader can get only a general understanding of the content of the paper, but that is no drawback, for he will read the paper. The writer, on the other hand, had to know much more specifically than this title indicates just what his whole paper was to be about. In short, the writer started with a topic, from which he derived a title which he hoped would please the reader. The topic which this writer began with was this: "Discuss the social uses of a knowledge of art." For the purposes of organization the writer needed to consider his topic rather than his title. Of course a title is often very similar to its topic.

Consider another title: "Professor, Think Young." Here the writer has composed a clever title that will not mean much to the reader until he is partly through the paper. The topic on which this writer based his organization was this: "Write an essay giving advice to college teachers." Here is another clever title that means little to one who has not read the paper: "Pony Riders on the Campus." The writer of this paper organized from a topic stated like this: "Discuss the methods of cheating that you have observed in your college classes."

The first step in organizing an expository paper, then, is to get the topic stated clearly. A title may be little more than a clever or pretty heading for the paper; a topic must be more fully and precisely expressed. Composition students are often required to state in one sentence the "controlling idea" of a paper or to write a "thesis sentence" for it. For example, this sentence states the central idea of a theme of the kind often assigned in composition: "A member of the Peace Corps should have knowledge and skills that will help him be of practical assistance to the population of the underdeveloped area to which he is assigned." A thesis sentence of this sort is really a statement of the topic of the paper. In briefer form, the topic might be stated in this way: "Discuss the knowledge and skills that will help a Peace Corps member give practical assistance in an underdeveloped area." Without such a precise statement of topic, you cannot plan an effective organization.

If an assignment is given to you in the form of a cute or clever title, you yourself must transform it into a topic before you begin to organize. For example, here is a writing assignment suggested in one class: "That's My Tax Money You're Spending." Before planning such a paper, you would need to restate the title into a clear topic, perhaps one like this: "Discuss some of the ways in which your county government wastes tax monies." The above title may be satisfactory as a heading, but you as the writer must have a clearly stated topic to work from.

Clues to organization

As stated above, organizational approaches vary with kinds of writing. In narration, a time element is implicit, and thus narrative organization is likely to be built around a sequence of events in time. In description, a spatial element is likely to dominate, for different aspects of an entity will be described in order. The subjective organization of impressionistic or personal writing depends on the modes of thought of any particular writer. *The objective organization of exposition is usually built around logical divisions of the topic, or main points.* Of course in exposition there is room for a subjective, imaginative touch, but for the most part its organization calls for a logical plan. In approaching a theme topic, then, you need a system for discovering the main points inherent in it.

One widely advocated method of organizing advises the student to jot down every single idea that he can think of pertaining to his topic—usually a list of twenty or thirty points. Then he is to reconsider the list and cross off those points which, on second thought, do not seem pertinent. Next he separates the remaining points into major and minor categories. Finally he tries to place the minor points under the appropriate major points. Such a method is workable, but a simpler and more effective method is available for discovering the main points embodied in a well-stated topic.

After you have your topic clearly stated, your next step is to analyze it for clues to meaningful over-all organization. Your task is to discover the main points that will give structure to your paper. You try to keep details out of your mind until you have the main points formulated. If your topic is well stated, it will usually contain a specific clue to guide you in expressing these points in scratch outline form so that you will have a basic organization to work from as you write your paper.

The clue to organization in a well-stated topic is an important plural noun that, in a sense, can be divided. For an example, look again at this topic: "Discuss the social uses of a knowledge of art." In this topic the important plural noun that is subject to division is *uses*. Note the plural form, which means that more than one use is implied. This noun, then, can be divided into as many parts as there are general uses involved. It is this kind of key plural noun in a fully stated topic that will guide you in planning a basic organization for your paper.

Now let's see specifically how you use such a noun in planning a paper. You are to write about "social uses of a knowledge of art." You begin by identifying in your own mind just what these uses are. In a sense, you divide the plural noun *uses* into several singular nouns: *this use, that use, another use,* and perhaps *another use.* You must think clearly and sharply so that you can identify real uses that do not duplicate each other. As you think of separate, broad uses, you list them in scratch outline form, like this:

1. Gives one topics of conversation
2. Gives one the means to belong to a special group
3. Provides one with a means of enjoying himself when alone
4. Helps one to adjust better in a complex society

Now you have a basic organization for your paper: four main parts that, with an introduction and a conclusion, will form a whole. Only at this point are you ready to begin writing.

The main points that you have expressed are **generalities.** You will convert each into a developed paragraph through the use of details and examples or logical explanation.[1] *The important point to learn here is that you must first plan your basic organization before you begin writing detailed paragraphs.* Your most practical approach to such a plan is to look for the special noun in your topic that will guide you in thinking of your main points. This approach will provide satisfactory organization for many if not most college writing assignments and for many kinds of business and professional writing.

Now look at another example of this method of organization, using this topic: "Discuss some of the ways in which your county government wastes tax monies." The plural noun subject to division here is *ways.* (Actually, not just the noun but the whole phrase "ways in which your county government wastes tax monies" is the plural unit out of which several main points can be extracted.) You can plan a basic organization by thinking of three or four *general*

---

[1] Chapter 3 on paragraph development is designed to improve your ability to organize and develop full paragraphs. A fuller discussion of the difference between generalities and specific details, which you should perhaps study now and also later, is contained on pages 59–63.

ways in which the county wastes money. You should state these generalities in scratch outline form like this:

1. By supporting recreational projects used by only a few people
2. By giving welfare funds to deadbeats and bums
3. By hiring unneeded white-collar workers
4. By maintaining private farm roads

Now you have the parts that, with an introduction and conclusion, can be assembled into a whole structure.

The most practical approach to organizing an expository paper, then, is to find in the topic a plural noun that can be divided into several singular units and then to jot down in scratch outline form the three or four main points (generalities) that this noun suggests to you. Note how each of the following topics has such a word in it:

> Describe in detail the habits of some wild or domestic animal that you have observed.
> The college student has many problems not encountered in high school. What are some of these problems and how can they be solved?
> Discuss the three or four most important lessons about life that one should have learned by the time he is eighteen.
> Analyze as precisely as you can some of the personality traits of someone you dislike.

Perhaps the most effective approach to organizing papers on topics like these is to convert the plural noun into several main points.

Now take a further step in understanding this process of organization. In the examples given above, each topic had a clearly stated plural noun that contained the clue to organization: *uses, ways, methods, habits, problems, lessons, values, advantages,* and so on. But many good topics, you will discover, do not have nouns of this sort. Consider, for example, this topic: "Write an essay giving advice to college teachers." In this topic there is no plural noun like *uses, habits,* or *problems.* Where then is the clue to organization?

If you look more closely, you will see that the noun *advice* does suggest the kind of division we have been talking about. We use the phrase "pieces of advice," and *pieces* is just the kind of plural noun that can suggest an organization. So before writing on this topic, you should enumerate in scratch outline form the separate, general "pieces of advice" you will give college teachers:

1. To try to understand better the freshman's limited background
2. To state clearly rules about absences, late work, and no work
3. To review important material and to give frequent quizzes
4. To have more personal interviews

With this simple division of the topic into separate pieces of advice, the paper is planned. Next come detailed paragraphs explaining each of these general points (plus, of course, an introduction and conclusion).

Here is another topic without a stated plural noun to provide a clue to organization: "Every community has a personality, just as a human being has a personality. Write an essay about the personality of your home town." The key noun of this topic appears to be *personality,* but that word is apparently not divisible into several singular units. It doesn't take much thought, however, to see that the noun *personality* implies *traits* or *characteristics.* For a basic organization, then, you just need to think of three or four general traits of personality your home town has. You might produce a scratch outline like this:

1. Is stuffy and prudish
2. Is proud without sufficient reason
3. Is intolerant of eccentric behavior
4. Demands more than it is willing to give

With a fully developed paragraph of details about each of these general traits, you would produce a well-planned and effective essay.

A similar example is involved in this topic: "Discuss the meaning of the sentence, 'After all, I'm only human.'" On first glance it is not clear just how this topic can be divided into three or four main points. But if you are to write an effective paper on this topic, you must organize it. A little thought will lead you to the implied phrase "*characteristics* of being human," which can be divided into singular units: *this characteristic, that characteristic,* and so on. So you can prepare a simple and clear basic organization by thinking of three or four general characteristics of being human:

1. Human beings are subject to temptations
2. To making mistakes
3. To inconsistency
4. To imperfect reasoning

By examining the topic closely, you found an implied plural noun from which you could extract a basic organization of main points, points about which detailed paragraphs can be written.

As a last example, consider a more difficult topic: "Attack or defend the view that the best way to preserve peace is to prepare for war." Again you must infer a plural noun for division into singular units, and it doesn't seem easy to think of one. This topic, however, is of a common type that has the noun *reasons* or *grounds* implied in it. You might say, "I will defend this view on these *grounds*." Or, "I will attack this view for these *reasons*." Once you see that your basic organization will consist of the chief *reasons* why you think as you do, you should not find it too difficult to prepare your basic organization of main points. For this topic you might scribble down reasons why you will defend the above view:

1. Because disarmament plans of the past have failed
2. Because modern weapons will surely be a deterrent to war
3. Because unilateral disarmament would incite aggression

You would still be faced with the task of writing well-developed paragraphs about these main points. *But you must have main points in mind before you can make any sort of adequate beginning. The importance of preparing a basic organization cannot be overemphasized.*

It should be clear now that organization is the first requirement of any extended piece of expository writing, whether an English theme, an essay exam, a term paper, a technical report, a business report, or any similar piece of writing. The simplest approach to such organization is to state the topic clearly and then to find a plural noun in the topic. If no such noun is apparent, there will usually be implied such phrases as "*reasons* why I believe . . .," "*steps* that I will take . . .," "*grounds* on which I will defend . . .," "*ways* in which something can . . .," or "*characteristics* of. . . ." The division of such a noun into singular units will give you the main points on which you can base your organization.

Additional organizational patterns in exposition

The term *logic* has been used above without definition. Though it is so complex a term that whole books and college courses are devoted to it, you have a general understanding of its meaning and have not, so far, been confused by its use. But a specific definition of the term as used in this text is now in order.

Basically, logic has to do with the interrelationship of facts and ideas. When there is no relationship between facts or ideas, logic is not involved. For example, there is no logic implied between these facts:

Babe Ruth hit sixty homers in 1927.
President Hoover was elected in 1928.

But there may exist logic between these facts:

The Great Depression started in 1930.
President Hoover was defeated for re-election in 1932.

To express this logic (if he believed it exists) a historian might compose this sentence: "Because of the Great Depression that started in 1930, President Hoover was defeated for re-election in 1932." Logic is evidenced in writing, then, when some sort of relationship is expressed between facts or ideas. If the relationship expressed is valid, the logic is sound; if the relationship is not valid, the logic is faulty. In the above sentence the word *because* expresses the logic of cause and result.

Though there are various subvarieties of logical relationships, six basic kinds appear in exposition. The most common is a **cause-and-result** relationship (*because, since, therefore, as a result,* and so on.) The next most common is a relationship of **contrast,** which includes opposition, antithesis, contradiction, paradox, and qualification (*although, but, however, in contrast,* and so on). This is the kind of logic which says that *even though* one fact is true, another apparently contrasting fact is also true. The other four logical relationships are **manner** or **method** (*as . . . as, as if, as though*), **condition** (*if, unless, otherwise*), **time** (*when, after, before, then,* and so on), and **addition** or **accumulation** (*and, moreover, furthermore, also,* and so on). Often two kinds of logic (for example, time and cause-and-result) are expressed by the same connective word.

The whole field of logic is far more complex than this simple explanation suggests. Many learned treatises have been written about induction (reasoning from the specific to the general), deduction (reasoning from the general to the specific), and other aspects of logic. In a study of the principles of exposition, however (that is, a study of how to express what you have already thought), it is important to understand the above simple logical relationships. The organization of whole papers, of paragraphs, and of complex or compound sentences depends on a proper expression or implication of logical relationships. Whether or not the logic is sound is, of course, all-important, but sound logic may be encompassed in bad writing if the writer does not know how to express his logic clearly in good expository style.

Only one pattern of logic has been utilized in the basic organizations of the topics discussed earlier: the main points of each have been related to each other by a logic of addition or accumulation. For example, the pieces of advice in the third topic, though not necessarily of equal importance, are expressed coordinately, as "I advise teachers to do this, *and* to do that, *and* to do something else." Or, for another example, any topic which asks for a discussion of the advantages of something would, regardless of the relative value of each advantage, have main points connected by the logic of addition: "Such-and-such has this advantage, *and* this advantage, *and* also this advantage." In some topics, however, the main points have a more complicated logical relationship than mere addition or accumulation.

Some topics call for main points connected with a logic of addition plus time. The sequence of points in such an organization is not "this, *and* this, *and* this," but "this, *and then* this, *and then* this." Consider, for example, this good topic: "If you were to educate yourself without instruction, but with access to a good library, how would you proceed?" In this topic there is no plural noun to suggest organization, but one can easily be inferred. Inspect the topic closely and you will see that the word *proceed* implies *steps*— we usually proceed in steps. Thus the topic is really asking "What steps would you take?" To arrive at a basic organization, you would identify the major steps you would take in the process of self-education. You might prepare a scratch outline like this:

1. First decide which fields to concentrate on
2. Then plan a balanced program of reading
3. Then take notes and review them at planned intervals
4. Then arrange to talk with educated people to test myself

Of course different writers might decide on different sets of steps; the important point to understand is that you must evolve **some** plan before you can write a competent paper.

The logic of the above organization is one of steps in a time sequence, not just an accumulation of points of equal value that could be rearranged without loss of logic. Each step of the process is logically derived from the preceding one and no steps can be rearranged without a collapse of logic. Many, many college writing assignments, especially essay questions in such subjects as history and anthropology, call for this kind of basic organization. The familiar "how to . . ." theme topic is also of this type.

Sometimes a topic calls for an organization in which the first main point establishes a central thesis to be supported by the succeeding main points. Consider this topic: "someone once said, 'You can tell the ideals of a nation by its advertisements.' What impression would a visitor from Mars get of America from its advertising?" Note that the topic says *impression* and not *impressions;* therefore we should not derive a basic organization by enumerating several different impressions. Instead, we extend the topic in this way: "What are the *reasons* why the visitor from Mars gets his impression?" Then the basic organization becomes the statement of the first main point, which is the impression the visitor gets, followed by other main points to support the first one. A scratch outline of the basic organization might take this form:

1. From our advertisements a visitor from Mars would get an impression of a materialistic culture.
Because (logic of cause-and-result)
2. Most of our ads are for things.
3. Most of our ads are for goods not essential to healthy survival or spiritual fulfillment.
4. Many of our ads are based on snob appeal.
5. Our ads indicate planned obsolescence in hard goods.

The opening paragraph (or paragraphs) of this paper would define materialistic culture and the Martian's impression of it, and the remaining coordinate points (logic of addition) would be used to support or illustrate this central idea. Note that all the main points are generalities that call for detailed development.

Here is another such topic: "What is the primary purpose of college? Describe an experimental college you would like to establish to achieve this purpose." In order to find a plural noun to guide your organization, you might alter the topic in this way: "What are the *ways* in which your experimental college can achieve its primary purpose." Now your basic organization will center around your defining the primary purpose of college (first main point) and then identifying the ways an experimental college of your own would achieve that purpose. Your scratch outline might be as follows:

1. The primary purpose of a college is to lead students out of error and ignorance into truth and knowledge.

My experimental college would achieve this purpose by

2. Abolishing grades so as to motivate students to seek knowledge rather than grades.
3. Eliminating marginal courses that have little to do with knowledge.
4. Integrating closely related courses, such as history, economics, and geography.
5. Establishing a tutorial rather than a class system.

Your opening paragraph (or paragraphs) would then explain your first main point, which would be supported by the next four points. The logic is one of result followed by four causes (which are given a logic of addition).

Another kind of basic organization is composed of sequential main points, each connected to the preceding one by a logic of cause-and-result. Consider this topic: "Explain why Americans are less individualistic now than in the nineteenth century." The implied plural noun from which a basic organization can be derived is "what are the *reasons*. . . ." This topic can, of course, be organized into a few accumulated main points, such as these:

1. Americans are less individualistic now than in the nineteenth century.

Because

2. The frontier has disappeared.
3. Mass production has replaced self-sufficiency.
4. Our political structure has become much more centralized.
5. Public and private education has become more uniform.

The logic here is again a statement of result followed by four causes.

But the topic might also be organized with a sequential logic of cause-and-result. Your scratch outline might take this form:

1. Americans are less individualistic now than in the nineteenth century.

Because

2. In the nineteenth century sharp increases in population created a demand for industrialization.

3. Which brought division of labor and an end to self-sufficiency.
4. Which decreased the individual's sense of his own worth and purpose.
5. Which led him into a social structure of conformity rather than individualism.

Points 2, 3, and 4 are each the cause of the next main point, or, to put it another way, points 3, 4, and 5 are each the result of the preceding main point. A sequential logic of cause-and-result, rather than one of accumulation, is embodied in this kind of organization. Note that each main point is a generality calling for detailed development. Also note that in this structure the conclusion or thesis of the topic—that Americans are less individualistic now than in the nineteenth century—is established as the opening point. It could be expressed in the closing paragraph; then the causes would be expressed first and the result last.

The main points of some topics can show a logic of contrast to each other. Consider this topic: "Should one do his own religious thinking or should he rely on a trained clergyman?" This is one of the "*reasons* why . . ." topics. A basic organization such as this can be formulated:

1. An individual must be responsible for his own religious thinking.
However
2. Everyone is bound to a cultural tradition.
3. And also, religious thought is too complex for one mind to master.
Therefore
4. One should use the guidance of a clergyman as a starting point for his own thought.

Each of these points is a generality that would need at least one full paragraph for even scant development. Note that the logical relationship between the points is not just one of accumulation but involves a contrast between points 2 and 3 and point 1, and a cause-and-result relationship between points 2 and 3 and point 4. Points 2 and 3 are derived from the plural noun *reasons* implied in the topic.

Some topics require a basic organization in which one main point is a qualification of another. (The logic of qualification is also one of contrast.) Consider this topic: "In the professional world, what are a woman's chances of success in competition with men?" This is a deceptive topic because the plural noun *chances* does not offer the best clue to organization. A better clue appears when the topic is restated like this (assuming the writer takes this position): "What are the *reasons* why a woman does not have an equal chance of succeeding in the professional world in competition with men?" A basic organization such as this can be prepared:

1. Because there is a lingering prejudice against women in the professions.
2. But that prejudice has been greatly weakened and may soon disappear.
3. Because women are more limited physiologically.
4. But they can partially overcome this limitation through will-power and intellectual energy.
5. Because women can't travel alone for business as easily as men.
6. But individual safety is becoming more assured for women.
7. Conclusion that a woman's chances of success are not equal to a man's but are improving.

Points 2, 4, and 6 qualify points 1, 3, and 5. The logic of the whole basic organization is one of contrast as well as of accumulation (points 1, 3, and 5 have a logic of accumulation).

The simple method of organization presented here—developing main points from clues in the topic—is satisfactory for most short expository papers. In fact, if you master these elementary techniques, you will greatly improve your college work, for essay questions as well as theme topics lend themselves to this kind of organization. But the longer and more enriched a paper is, the less it can depend wholly on this simple approach. The above instruction is introductory only. It will see you through your first years of college, but it is no more than a foundation (though a necessary one) for subtlety and variety in organization, which must come through individual insight and maturity, not from textbook instruction.

The distinction between main points and specific details in organization

When you are preparing your basic organization, the main points that you put into your scratch outline must be general statements rather than specific details.[2] Each will form one large part of your

---

[2] For a fuller discussion of generalities and details see pages 59–63.

paper—a paragraph if the paper is no more than 500 to 1000 words. For example, suppose you are preparing a basic organization for this topic: "The *habits* of a wild animal." You would prepare a scratch outline something like this:

1. Eating habits of the jackrabbit
2. Sleeping habits
3. Mating habits
4. Habits relating to self-preservation

You would not prepare a scratch outline of just specific details, such as this:

1. Eats sagebrush
2. Sleeps during daylight
3. Mates in the fall, and so forth

Each of the main points in the first scratch outline is a general statement that can be developed with details, but in the second outline none of the points is subject to full paragraph development, for each is only a single detail.

To organize well you must learn to distinguish between main points and specific details. As you plan your basic organization by dividing a key plural noun into several singular units, you should think in terms of main points only. These will be generalities, which will cover many specific details. To make a distinction between main points and mere details requires hard thinking, for which there is no substitute in writing good exposition.

To see how a careless thinker can arrive at a mixed basic organization, examine this topic: "What makes a good community junior college?" In order to get a key plural noun to divide, our writer restated the topic in this way: "What *attributes* should a good community junior college have?" Then he jotted down this basic organization, thinking that he was dividing *attributes* into several coordinate main points:

1. A wide offering of transfer and terminal courses
2. A well-trained faculty
3. A well-planned extracurricular program
4. Good English teachers
5. Good football and basketball teams
6. A democratic student government
7. An attractive and functional college plant

How did our author go wrong? Quite clearly he should not have put points 4, 5, and 6 into his basic organizational plan. Point 4 is a detail to be developed under main point 2, and points 5 and 6 similarly belong under main point 3. The writer did not keep his mind directly on the main points suggested by the key plural noun in his topic. Points 1, 2, 3, and 7 form a good basic organization for the topic.

As you examine a topic for clues to a basic organization, keep your mind on main points only. They will be general statements that you will explain through the use of details or logical analysis as you write your paragraphs. It will be much easier for you to think of details after you have planned your basic organization than vice versa. In papers of from 500 to 1000 words, two to five main points will almost always be sufficient. You cannot develop many main points in so few words.

One more point. After you have divided your key plural noun into the two to five main points that will form the parts of your paper, you should of course arrange them in a proper sequence, for your mind will not always think of main points in the order in which they should appear in your paper. If your main points show a logic of addition, you should arrange them in the most effective sequence. If their logic is one of time or of cause and result or of contrast, you are necessarily bound to one sequence of main points.

EXERCISE 2. **Distinguishing between Main Points and Minor Details**

DIRECTIONS: *In preparing a basic organization for each of the following topics, the writer has put down points that duplicate each other or that are minor details which do not belong in a basic organization. For each topic, first determine the important plural noun (stated or implied) that provides a clue to organization. Then indicate by letter which points should be kept for a basic organization.*

1. *Topic:* "What is the best profession for a woman to enter? Why?" (The writer selects teaching.)
   Points: a. offers financial security
   b. offers good vacation periods
   c. nowadays pays better than many other jobs for women
   d. offers a kind of work congenial to most women

       e. tenure makes the job permanent
       f. long summer gives chance to do other things
       g. can save enough money to travel
       h. women like to teach children
       i. work is varied and so not boring

2. *Topic:* "What do you, as a representative member of your generation, consider to be your chief aims and ambitions?"
   Points: a. to establish a secure financial future
         b. to maintain a well-adjusted family and love life
         c. to have a good-paying job
         d. to see that my family is well provided for
         e. to avoid becoming a mere conformist cog in mass culture
         f. to establish individual taste in music and art
         g. to own a boat and two cars
         h. to read enough to make up my own mind about important affairs
         i. to get off the beaten track in taking my vacations
         j. to own a large, comfortable house with swimming pool

3. *Topic:* "Describe a social disaffiliate."
   Points: a. dresses and grooms himself in an unusual fashion
         b. doesn't wear clean clothes
         c. has odd language habits
         d. affects avant-garde movements in the arts
         e. begins every sentence with "like"
         f. likes to associate with others like himself
         g. appears to listen very intently to music
         h. very seldom seen alone
         i. writes incomprehensible poetry
         j. likes slang rather than standard English
         k. wears a beard and long, uncombed hair

4. *Topic:* "Municipal improvements my home town should make."
   Points a. needs to improve streets and alleys
         b. main street needs resurfacing
         c. a playground for young children
         d. needs more and better recreational facilities
         e. a new school in the El Monte District
         f. needs to relieve overcrowded schools
         g. some tennis courts
         h. needs to fire incompetent employees in city hall
         i. tax assessor shows partiality
         j. some street lights broken
         k. swimming pools not cleaned often enough

5. *Topic:* "Identify and discuss the chief motivations that affect college students in their pursuit of higher education."
   Points: a. to develop cultural assets
         b. to learn how to make more money
         c. to improve taste in music and literature
         d. to prepare for life's vocation
         e. to develop social assets
         f. to learn better conduct at dances and such
         g. to have a good time in college activities
         h. to participate in and watch sports events
         i. to learn how to carry on a better conversation
         j. to participate in student government
         k. to maybe get engaged

EXERCISE 3. Preparing Basic Organizations for Theme Topics

DIRECTIONS: *First identify the key plural noun (stated or implied) in each of the following topics that, when divided into singular units, will provide a basic organization. Then prepare a basic organization for two or more topics by writing out three or four main points suggested by the noun you choose to divide.*

1. What improvements in practice could be made in American democracy?
2. What are some of the advantages of not being a well-adjusted person?
3. What are the characteristics of an ideal children's story?
4. If your college had to eliminate either intercollegiate sports or plays and concerts, which should it eliminate and why?
5. Discuss the merit of fining or jailing parents for crimes committed by their minor children.
6. Are there valid reasons why ours should be called the age of anxiety?
7. Is equality for women in the business and political world desirable?
8. How to avoid a divorce.
9. Some justifiable uses of lying.
10. Attack or defend the emphasis on athletics at the college level.
11. There is often controversy between teachers and parents over novels assigned in high school. Explain and evaluate the issues involved in such a controversy.
12. What specific measures do you think should be taken to conserve

one important natural resource—soil, forest, wildlife, or water—that is being depleted in our country?

13. If you have visited a foreign country, discuss the advantages or disadvantages of living there over living in the United States.

14. It has been said that the quality of higher education would be improved if universities and colleges gave neither grades nor degrees. Defend or attack this statement.

15. Discuss the values and attitudes expressed in one comic strip, such as "Pogo."

EXERCISE 4. Organizing Answers to Essay Questions

DIRECTIONS: *The following are actual essay examination questions that were given to college students. Decide which plural noun (stated or implied) could guide the student in organizing an answer for each question. Of course you are not expected to give answers to these questions, but you should be able to suggest main points for one or two.*

1. What are the criticisms that George Gaylord Simpson gave of the gladiatorial theories of evolution?

2. Discuss the methods used for measuring astronomical distances.

3. What are the significant contributions of the Saxon system of local government to the present British system?

4. What are the evidences of human habitation in the New World before 15,000 B.C.?

5. What are the principal differences between the American and British civil services?

6. Discuss the characteristics of polypeptides.

7. Discuss the functions of the Judicial Committee of the Privy Council.

8. What are the chief differences between Lamarckian and Darwinian theories of evolution?

9. What advantages did Lincoln have in the election of 1860?

10. What objections have been lodged against Hoyle's theory of continuous creation?

11. Discuss the factors of Russia's geographical position that might influence her foreign policy.

12. Describe the various approaches for dealing with problems of mental health.

13. Why did England develop free institutions so far in advance of the other countries of the world?

14. How did Lenin's "New Economic Policy" differ from the "War Communism" of 1917–1921?
15. Why is there a tendency for government to gradually increase its powers of control over the economy?
16. How does Parkinson lampoon modern bureaucracy? What particular features in bureaucracy deserve his criticism?
17. Discuss the techniques and themes of Hawthorne's short stories.
18. Contrast the philosophic outlooks of Robinson and Frost.
19. How does Romanticism differ from Neoclassicism?
20. Attack or defend the kind of poetry that is known as "modern."

INTRODUCTIONS AND CONCLUSIONS

The introduction and the conclusion of an expository paper are parts of its organization because they are concerned with the structure of the paper rather than with the individual details or logical analysis which make up its subject matter. Thus, though both introductions and conclusions may be separate paragraphs, a discussion of them belongs in Chapter 2 on organization rather than in Chapter 3 on paragraph development.

Effective introductions in expository writing.

Many students, judging from the time they spend composing an opening sentence, find the introduction of a theme the very hardest part to write. They often feel that if they can just get the paper underway, the rest will be easy. A good basic organization should make the rest of the paper easy to write—or at least not overwhelmingly difficult—but an introduction itself should not be the cause of aimless diddling while one waits for inspiration. Once their nature is understood, introductions are not difficult to compose.

The first purpose of an introduction in exposition is *to lead the reader directly into the topic* at hand so that he will know at once the general nature of what he is about to read. This purpose is especially true of term papers, essay questions, and other kinds of college (as well as business and professional) writing, including most themes. The purpose, in short, is to clarify the topic, not to tease the reader or to hold him in suspense.

The clue to writing an introduction that fulfills this purpose, like the clue to a basic organization, is in the fully stated topic. *Before trying to write your opening sentence or sentences, examine your topic closely so that you can compose an introduction that tells the reader substantially what the topic tells you.* Of course you want your opening to sound smooth and literary, not blunt like a class assignment. But the substance of the topic and of the introduction should usually be similar. (Some variations will be noted below.)

Consider, for example, this topic and basic organization from a prior section: "Discuss the social uses of a knowledge of art."

1. Gives one topics of conversation
2. Gives one the means to belong to a special group
3. Provides one with a means of enjoying himself when alone
4. Helps one to adjust better in a complex society

The basic organization provides the main points to be developed in the paper but does not suggest an introduction. That is suggested by the fully stated topic itself. Thus when beginning a theme you should examine your topic carefully and compose one or more sentences (the question of length will be discussed below) that tell your reader what the paper is to be about. For example: "A knowledge of art is not an airy, useless element in one's mental storehouse, but has practical uses of considerable social value." Note that the core of the topic—with an added literary flourish—is stated in the introduction. It is this core that leads the reader into the general topic of the paper and prepares him for the first main point.

Here are some other examples of short introductions based on a close scrutiny of fully stated topics:

Topic: Discuss some of the ways in which your county government wastes tax monies.

Opening: Though a high degree of economic efficiency cannot be expected in an organization with many disbursing departments and numerous near-autonomous department heads, the officials in my county government seem determined to waste more of the taxpayers' money than can be condoned by those most tolerant of human frailties.

Topic: Write an essay giving advice to college teachers.

Opening: Many college teachers exhibit deficiencies in teaching techniques that they could easily eliminate if they just knew the truth of their students' impression of them. I shall pretend that I, in masked anonymity, have all the teachers of my college assembled for a lecture of advice.

Topic: Every community has a personality, just as a human being has a personality. Write an essay about the personality of your home town.

Opening: As I sit in my dormitory room, lonely and home-sick, I think not only of the human beings I left behind, but also of my home town itself. For now I see it as a personality, a whole being with many moods and odd behavioral patterns.

Topic: Defend the view that the best way to preserve peace is to prepare for war.

Opening: Many good-willed people think that only an aboli-tion of all armaments can preserve peace, but a realistic look at world politics convinces me that only readiness for war can give any assurance of peace.

These examples show how the core of a well-stated topic can be smoothly and appropriately expressed in the introduction to a short paper. *The clue to writing an introduction, like the clue to basic organization, is in the topic.* If you find a paper particularly hard to open, try restating the topic or stating it more fully. Then you can spot the core idea that you will want to work into your introduction.

Besides leading directly into the topic, an introduction should also *arouse the reader's interest* so that he will want to continue reading. There is a widespread misapprehension, however, about what arouses interest in expository writing. Many writers have the impression that no matter what their topic, they must open with some gimmick—either suspenseful, shocking, or colorful—to capture the reader's interest. Then, after attracting him with artificial bait, they give him the information which, apparently, they feared he might not be interested in. In truth, however, it is the subject matter of exposition, not a cute gim-mick, which arouses initial interest, and thus the second purpose of an introduction is to a considerable degree achieved by the first. A clear statement of the subject matter to follow will usually arouse the interest of those who can be interested. A cute or suspenseful or startling introduction is not only not necessary in exposition, but often is offensive to a sophisticated readership, for it has the insincere ring of the come-on technique.

As examples of a phony or come-on technique, consider these openings from articles in one of America's most famous expository magazines:

He had no antennas, no green scales, not even a plastic helmet or a space suit. Yet I distinctly heard him say:

"Telephone? Of course. My number is Craters of the Moon 2."—*National Geographic.*

About three o'clock in the morning something woke me, and I lay listening. Lizards rustled in the thatch of our hut, but it wasn't that. A strange rumbling came from somewhere out in the night.

"Are you awake?" Jinx whispered softly.—*National Geographic.*

The teeth were projecting from the rock face, smooth and shiny and quite obviously human.—*National Geographic.*

Now none of these openings is poorly written, but they try to capture reader interest in a phony way. You perhaps expect the first to continue as a science fiction story; the second might be a bedroom scene in a love story; the third sounds like the opening of a Rover Boys' adventure.

Actually, the articles that follow these openings are expository and contain factual information of considerable interest. The first is about volcanic formations in southern Idaho; the second is about a wild game preserve in Africa; the third is about the discovery of an ancient human fossil. The authors (or editors) seemed to feel that no one would be immediately interested in the mere factual material and that therefore their openings needed folksy, human-interest angles and narrative gimmicks. The result was that the articles became less interesting to those who simply wanted the absorbing information available instead of intimate insight into the personality of Jinx.

Now examine some openings of expository articles from other famous American magazines:

A series of recent discoveries has linked prehuman primates of half a million years ago with stone tools.—*Scientific American.*

Men with chins, relatively small brow ridges and small facial skeletons, and with high, flatside skulls, probably appeared on earth in the period between the last two great continental glaciers, say from 150,000 to 50,000 years ago.—*Scientific American.*

Compare these openings with the third example in the last group. For people truly interested in the ideas involved, these are far more attractive openings than the narrative-descriptive attempt involving the shining teeth.

Or note the simple, direct approach to his topic used by this author:

> For a long time I have had the urge to speak up about the misleading impression the public is being given about cancer research—and for that matter, medical research in general.—*Harper's.*

This is just a direct, simple explanation of what the article following will be about; yet considerable interest is aroused. Here is another opening from the same magazine:

> Last year I was elected to the Kentucky legislature after paying off many of the citizens in my district with the money and whiskey they demanded in return for their votes. Many of the men who sit with me as legislators were elected in the same way.

This opening does have some shock value, but only as much as the subject warrants, and it does lead directly into the topic of the essay.

The foregoing, however, is not to be taken as a blanket condemnation of all narrative-dramatic openings for expository papers. When tastefully used, such openings can be effective, for storytelling can be a natural way to arouse reader interest. The following, for example, is an introduction used for an essay on euthanasia:

> On his way to the hospital a minister stops at a house near his church to say a word of personal sympathy to a couple sitting on the porch with their family doctor. Upstairs the man's mother is in bed, the victim of a series of small cerebral hemorrhages over the last eleven years. Her voice went two years ago and there is now no sign that she hears anything. Communication has ended. Says the son, with a complex question-asking glance at his wife, "My mother is already dead."—*Harper's.*

This is a narrative-dramatic opening in good taste. The writer was not too folksy or sentimental—to put it plainly, phony—in his attempt to lead into his expository topic. The example he used suggests directly the subject matter of his essay; it is not an inconsequential detail nor an artificial gimmick designed to trap the reader. A narrative opening can be effective if it is tastefully used and is related directly to the core subject matter of the article. But you should avoid opening many of your papers with this technique.

The mere statement of a topic is not in itself sufficient to arouse strong reader interest. In addition to this, an introduction (like the rest of the paper) *should be pleasingly phrased,* for good style as well as subject matter stimulates reader interest. A realization of the importance of style is probably the origin of the misconception that a catchy or unusual opening is needed to arouse reader interest. But in an introduction to an expository paper it is the core idea of the topic, not some cute or startling or insignificant detail, that should be artfully and pleasingly phrased.

Compare the effectiveness of the following introductions:

Topic: Explain why 12- and 13-year-olds should not go steady.

Opening as mere statement of the topic: There are many reasons why 12- and 13-year-olds should not go steady.

Gimmick opening: Have you as a parent ever experienced the terror of having a teen-age daughter in trouble?

Opening as stylistically pleasing statement of the topic: On the junior high school campus and at private parties I have seen flushed pleasure on the faces of 12- and 13-year-old sweethearts; but I have also seen enough anxiety on the same faces to convince me that children this age should not go steady.

Topic: Discuss the reasons why superior high school students should not be separated into special classes.

Opening as mere statement of the topic: In this paper I will show why superior high school students should not be separated into special classes.

Gimmick opening: It is 1975, and the once brilliant high school student is jobless, broke, and wearing off a hangover in a cheap flophouse. Why?

Opening as stylistically pleasing statement of the topic: Though when superficially considered the segregation of brilliant high school students into special classes seems an obvious means of providing them with superior instruction, in actual practice this system is seen to have many defects.

In these examples the first opening is too flat to be effective, the second too bizarre. A direct but pleasingly phrased introduction is usually best for a short paper.

In addition to expressing the topic in a pleasing fashion, an introduction should also *establish a proper tone* for the whole paper. One weakness of the gimmick opening is that it establishes a wrong tone for expository writing. Since the primary purpose of exposition is to inform, its tone should be objective, quiet, reasonable, open-minded. The tone should suggest to the reader that there is something to be learned or an important issue to be explained or an interesting point of view to be considered. A startling or extravagant tone adversely affects the informative nature of exposition. An argumentative, overbearing, pompous, or overly assertive tone brings the writer's open-mindedness into question. A smug or smirking tone will alienate readers.

A personal tone need not be avoided either in an introduction or the body of a paper; the pronoun *I* is not out of place even in the highest level scholarly exposition. But in exposition the personal tone should not lapse into diffuse impressionism. A tone of amusement may also be utilized provided it does not mask the informative nature of the exposition. In general, the tone should suit the subject matter; it should not be excessively dramatic or assertive.

Compare the effectiveness of the following introductions:

> *Topic:* Account for the wide appeal that personal advice columns have in the United States.
>
> *Overly assertive tone:* Nothing more clearly demonstrates the low-level intelligence, taste, and social awareness of Americans than their silly addiction to personal advice columns.
>
> *Reasonable tone:* The wide appeal that personal advice columns have in the United States is not due to one simple trait or flaw in human nature, but to a variety of complex human traits, some of which may even be praiseworthy.

> *Topic:* It has been traditionally asserted that sports help develop good character. What undesirable traits of character, if any, do they develop? Why?
>
> *Extravagant tone:* All the mouthing that coaches and P.E. teachers make about sports developing good character is a lot of baloney. Varsity sports teach all sorts of bad habits.
>
> *Reasonable tone:* Though most people agree that varsity sports have much character-building potential, there is some evi-

dence that bad traits of character may also result from athletic participation.

A moderate or reasonable tone is much more likely to attract reader interest than an extravagant tone, as these examples illustrate.

Length is another troublesome aspect of introductions. A general misapprehension is that a successful paper is built around an introduction-body-conclusion structure with each of the three sections given equal weight, or with at least a full paragraph for both introduction and conclusion. Of course the introduction and conclusion should by no means be equivalent in length to the subject matter of the paper. Consider, for example, a 400-page book: what impression would it make with a 100-page introduction and a 100-page conclusion? An introduction should be just long enough to announce the topic of the paper in an interest-arousing fashion, and that means a short introduction for most college writing assignments. An overlong introduction dissipates reader interest.

When a one- or two-sentence beginning is sufficient to get a paper underway, the introduction should not form a separate paragraph. Instead, it should be combined with the first paragraph, which will be a discussion of the first main point of the paper. Consider, for example, this topic and basic organization:

> *Topic:* Discuss the *principles* underlying the campaign of nonviolent resistance that Southern Negroes are using to win their civil rights.
>
> 1. Belief in the sacredness and effectiveness of Christ's principles of returning good for evil and of nonviolence
> 2. Belief that right will triumph if publicly demonstrated
> 3. Belief that steadfastness of purpose will defeat the opposition in a struggle of wills
>
> *Opening:* The campaign of nonviolent resistance that Southern Negroes are using to win their civil rights is based on a few principles which sound idealistic in theory but which are surprisingly effective in practice. The chief of these is Christ's injunction to return good for evil and to resist not evil. . . . [continuation in the first paragraph of an explanation of this main point]

For this topic a one-sentence introduction is sufficient, and that sentence should be a part of the first main paragraph, not a separate paragraph by itself. A brief separate introductory paragraph tends to give a paper a bad appearance.

Occasionally, however, even a short paper needs a separate introductory paragraph. When the introduction requires as many as two long or three ordinary sentences, they may be given separate status without damaging the appearance or structure of the paper. Consider, for example, this topic: "What criticisms would you make of the reading program in your most recent high school literature course?"

> *Opening:* A reading program for high school seniors is difficult to organize, for not only are seniors in general in an in-between stage of development, but they also vary more widely than is thought in their individual maturity. If adult books are assigned, some students may be damaged psychologically; if childish books are assigned, most students will lose interest in literature. The problem is difficult to solve, but I believe that on the basis of my experience in Literature 12A I have some valid suggestions to make.

An introduction of this length necessarily needs separate paragraph status of its own. The more usual short introduction should not be separated from the first main paragraph.

There are several kinds of **stock openings** that students frequently use but should be warned against, for they often do not lead directly into the topic of the paper, they seldom set an appropriate tone, and they never arouse any reader interest at all. One of the most commonly used and inept of these is the opening that depends on the title for its meaning. An opening should not contain a pronoun or phrase that refers to the title; instead, a paper should begin just as though a title were not stated. Consider such openings as these:

> I have thought a good deal about this problem.
> This is something I have read a lot about.
> You can't play a winning game without knowing the odds.

With such introductions, the reader is sent immediately to the title to see what *this,* or *something,* or *game* means. Such openings do not directly announce the purpose of the paper, and they do not arouse any interest at all. You should make it a cardinal rule never to refer to your title in your opening sentence.

Another weak introduction that the unthinking writer often

resorts to is the mere repetition of the assignment. In effect, he passes the buck in order to get started. Such openings as these are examples:

> The question has been asked, "Why are Americans so disliked in many foreign countries?"
> In this paper I will discuss the relationship between the sales of hydrogen peroxide and the marriage rate.
> I have been asked to write about my favorite ecdysiast.

It is true that such openings announce the topic of the paper, but they are stylistically so dull and routine that they do little to arouse interest.

The apologetic opening should also be avoided, for it has a wet-blanket effect just at the point that the reader's interest should be attracted. Here are some examples of these dull and flabby openings:

> I'm not much of an expert in cybernetics, but I will try to tell you something about that science.
> I haven't worked very long as a shoestring-tip stapler, but I think the work will be interesting.
> Why dictators can come to power is a very hard subject to write about.

An introduction, rather than being apologetic, should be sure-handed and give the impression that the writer has a good command of his subject.

The "both sides" opening is a stock introduction that some students rely on whenever they are faced with a topic that calls for them to choose one of two points of view. Such topics usually ask the writer to "discuss the advantages or disadvantages of" or "to attack or defend." Rather than taking a stand and composing a brisk, interesting introduction, many a student composes a wishy-washy beginning that pays homage to both sides. Here are two examples:

> There are both advantages and disadvantages in having an exceptionally beautiful wife.
> In some ways I think it would be best for our country to disarm unilaterally, but in other ways I don't think it would be a good idea.

Such openings are indecisive and lacking in vigor.

Direct quotations, including dictionary definitions, generally make weak openings. For the most part, they not only fail to lead directly into the topic but also give the impression that the writer could not use his own words to get started. Such weak openings are more likely to appear in long term papers than in short themes.

Finally, it should be noted that students tend to overuse rhetorical questions as introductions. The method itself is not necessarily ineffective, but two common weaknesses frequently attend its use. First, the question itself often sounds like just a repetition of the assignment (which it often is). For example, consider these two openings:

> Can one trust his conscience to show him what is right?
> Is conformity to the thinking of the majority a safe road to happiness?

The reader seems to hear the instructor speaking rather than the writer. The second weakness is that the writer often fails to make a smooth transition between the question and the next sentence. Too often he resorts to a clumsy transition like this:

> Given time, will scientific advancements solve all human problems? This is a question that concerns us all.

You should be wary about using a rhetorical question as an opening. You should choose such a method only if you are sure of its effectiveness, not because it is the only way you can think of to get started.

Effective conclusions in expository writing

The conclusion is also a part of the structure, or organization, of a paper. Like the introduction, it is often misunderstood. A long expository paper may justifiably have one or more separate concluding paragraphs that summarize the whole substance of the paper. But a short paper, such as a 500-word theme, should not have such a conclusion, for in a short paper the points have been so recently made clear to the reader that he does not need a summary of them. After all, it doesn't make much sense to write, say, three paragraphs explaining three main points and then a fourth paragraph explaining the three points you have just made.

The conclusion of an ordinary theme usually should not be a

separate paragraph, but should be the last sentence of the final paragraph of development, just as the introduction is often the first sentence of the initial paragraph of development. Also like the introduction, the conclusion is a general rather than a specific statement, for it has to do with the general idea of the whole paper, not with just one specific detail. For example, suppose you have written a theme on this topic: "Discuss the disadvantages of having an exceptionally beautiful wife." At the end of the paragraph that makes your last point you could conclude the paper with this general statement of summary: "A beautiful wife, then, is a dream on the honeymoon, a showpiece for the first year of marriage, but often a cross to bear during routine married life." Or suppose your topic was this: "Discuss the challenges and rewards of some unusual job you have had." Your concluding sentence, attached to your final main paragraph, might be this: "I may find my job monotonous later, but after two years I still find shoestring-tip stapling challenging and gratifying." Or you might have written on this topic: "Discuss the trials and tribulations of dieting to lose weight." A satisfactory concluding sentence might be this: "So I have decided that a man losing weight is a frustrated, irritable, hungry man." Such concluding sentences should not be given separate paragraph status, for usually a one-sentence paragraph at the end of a paper gives it a bad appearance, just as a one-sentence opening paragraph usually appears structurally unsound.

In a paper designed to prove a point or reach a valid conclusion after an investigation of pertinent evidence, the conclusion will, of course, be a statement, long as is necessary, of the point proved or the conclusion reached. If the paper is short, such as a theme of 500 to 1000 words, such a conclusion may be briefly stated as the concluding sentence of the final paragraph of development; or, if it takes as much as two long or three ordinary sentences, it may constitute a separate paragraph. If the paper is a longer term paper or research project, the conclusion will always be a separate paragraph or paragraphs following the final developmental paragraph. For example, consider this topic: "Build a case for the existence of psychic phenomena." The concluding paragraph might be this:

> In spite of the fraud and charlatanism surrounding psychic phenomena, the authentically documented evidence we have cited

can only lead to the conclusion that phenomena beyond the explanation of contemporary physics and chemistry do exist. Whether, as Rhine thinks, these phenomena are supernatural, or whether, as Stevenson asserts, they will have an ultimate scientific explanation cannot yet be known. But that they exist cannot be doubted.

Whether a conclusion is a one-sentence addition to the final paragraph of development or a full paragraph of its own like this example, it is a part of the structure rather than of the development of a paper.

The concluding sentence or sentences of an expository paper should be emphatic, though not bizarre or unduly startling. A piece of fiction may use a shock technique in its conclusion, but the tone of an expository conclusion should be consonant with the tone of the whole paper. An emphatic conclusion will leave the reader with the dominant (general) idea of the paper. It will not be concerned with some minor detail or triviality; nor will it suddenly bring in an afterthought or irrelevancy. For example, consider this topic: "A bit of advice frequently heard on college campuses is, 'Don't let your studies interfere with your education.' Discuss the merits of this idea."

> *Trivial ending:* Oh yes, a college student might also learn something from conversing with a custodian.
> *General ending:* Thus we can see that the vast complexity of college life means that the educational process is strongly active outside the classroom.

As the second example here illustrates, a conclusion should be emphatic enough to make the whole purpose of the paper appear to be fulfilled. That is the reason the conclusion is a part of the paper's structure: it shows the wholeness of the paper and keeps it from appearing fragmentary or at loose ends.

Students are often advised to develop the most important point of a paper last so that the conclusion can be emphatic. But the final point of a paper is not the conclusion; it is a part of the development of the subject matter. The points of a paper should be developed in their most logical order, which may, indeed, mean that the most important comes last. But the conclusion is another thing, even if it consists of only one sentence, and it should carry its own emphatic note.

A good conclusion will have an air of finality about it: it will **sound** like an ending, just as an introduction sounds like a beginning. In narration, an air of finality is not hard to achieve, for a story has a natural ending. But in exposition, it often seems difficult to wrap up the topic and give the reader a sense of completion. If, however, you have prepared a basic organization for your paper, you will be able to discuss the last point as though it is the last, and this will naturally leave the reader with an impression that you have covered all the points that you intended to cover. Then you should add a sentence or sentences that, as illustrated above, state the general idea of the paper in the tone of a conclusion. This will leave the reader with a sense of completion.

In summary, then, the composition of an expository paper is the building of a whole structure. The introduction starts the structure by expressing the core idea to be discussed. The so-called body of the structure consists of a detailed development of main points, which, in college writing, can be treated openly as main points and not concealed for esthetic purposes by subtle and subjective organizational modes. The conclusion shows that the structure is finished.

EXERCISE 5. Plain and Fancy Introductions

DIRECTIONS: *The following introductory statements came from expository articles published in well-known American magazines. Decide which are plain or direct openings and which are fancy or cute. Comment on the quality of each. One good approach in judging is to decide just on the basis of the opening whether you are about to read a factual article, a piece of fiction, or just some human-interest piece of journalism. (All the articles* **are** *factual.)*

1. Most people are unaware of how widespread smoking is and of the pattern it takes among American people.
2. Almost until the present turn in human affairs an expanding population has been equated with progress.
3. Hatless and feeling out of place in my city clothes, I squeezed my way through the Wild West mob.
4. The girl clerk in the Seattle bookstore was comely and seemed to be intelligent, which made it all the worse.

5. The behavior of monkeys and apes has always held great fascination for men.
6. A kind of dream world enveloped us, a blank white waste of sodden snow patterned with shallow lakes and swirling melt streams.
7. Man's knowledge of the nature and structure of stars rests on a complex interplay between observation and theory.
8. The lady wore a sunsuit, wedgies, and a bemused expression.
9. I am finishing an enjoyable meal with my wife Simone and a tableful of good companions in a snug lodge we have built in a remote and primitive part of the world.
10. The moment when it first becomes apparent that one's marriage was a mistake is the beginning of probably the longest, darkest period in the human lifetime.

EXERCISE 6. Effective and Weak Introductions

DIRECTIONS: *Following are ten theme topics with introductory sentences. First decide which plural noun (stated or implied) in each topic would guide you in preparing a basic organization. Then explain why each of the introductions is or is not effective. Rewrite one or more of the openings that you consider unsatisfactory.*

1. *Topic:* "Should capital punishment be abolished?"
   Opening: This is something you hear a lot about nowadays. I think both sides have many good points, but I don't see much use for it.

2. *Topic:* Is TV chiefly an instrument of education or of escape?
   Opening: It can be both, depending on how you look at it.

3. *Topic:* What are the virtues or defects of one imported car that you are familiar with?
   Opening: Arunhrunhrunhrunh. (pause) Arunhrunhrunhrunh. (pause) Arunhrunhrunhrunh. (pause) "Confound this &G%$#@ *¢ sardine can, anyway."
   Every morning at about the time my father should be leaving for work, the above noises jolt me out of a sound sleep.

4. *Topic:* What special markets and advertising techniques have been developed for the teen-age consumer?
   Opening: I don't have much money to spend myself, but I look at all the advertisements in the best known teen-age magazines.

5. *Topic:* Explain the care and nurture of a commercially valuable plant, fish, or animal.
Opening: Since they are sensitive and delicate, Burmese cats require more attention and medical care than ordinary alley cats. Yet if a Burmese queen is properly managed, she can bring her owner several hundred dollars profit a year.

6. *Topic:* Discuss the contention that jazz has been America's most significant contribution to world culture.
Opening: It has been stated that jazz has been America's most significant contribution to world culture. In this paper I will support this contention.

7. *Topic:* What characteristics of Americans make us disliked in some foreign countries?
Opening: First, I think, because we are so selfish.

8. *Topic:* Do any minority groups in the United States suffer as much discrimination as Southern Negroes?
Opening: A general assumption in European countries, and among many Americans too, is that racial discrimination in America is confined to Southern Negroes. A few months' residence in Brooklyn and Manhattan, however, will reveal to you other complex patterns of racial discrimination.

9. *Topic:* Why have so many new democratic governments in Asia and Africa recently been supplanted by military dictatorships?
Opening: I don't know anything about those countries, but I imagine it is because they were not ready for democracy.

10. *Topic:* What foreign country (besides Russia) has, in recent years, had the most influence on the United States in one particular field (for example, transportation, art, or politics)?
Opening: I would say France has had more influence on our movies than any other country. They sure seem to be getting Frenchy.

EXERCISE 7. Writing Introductions

DIRECTIONS: *Following are five theme topics. First decide which stated or implied plural noun would guide you in preparing a basic organization for each topic. Then write a one- or two-sentence opening for at least three of the topics.*

1. What do you consider the most important single course or activity that college offers? Why?

2. Explain and refute some common misconceptions about members of a particular racial, national, religious, or political group.
3. Should college grading standards be sufficiently high to eliminate students who do not have above-average intelligence?
4. Discuss some ways in which the social and economic status of migratory agricultural workers can be improved.
5. Discuss the reasons why the study of a foreign language should not be required of all junior high and high school students.

COHERENCE BETWEEN PARAGRAPHS

Heading II, C of our outline of the principles of exposition in Chapter 1 states that coherence between paragraphs is a part of the organization of the whole paper. The word *coherence* comes from the Latin *co,* meaning together, and *haerere,* meaning to stick. Hence coherence literally means a sticking together. In writing, it means the quality of being integrated, consistent, and intelligible. The paragraphs of a paper are coherent when they are closely and logically joined together.[3]

Two paragraphs are coherently joined when there is clear transition between them. The word *transition* means a carrying across. In writing it refers to some specific, logical linkage between two elements (clauses, sentences, paragraphs). Coherence is most often effected by three common methods of transition.

The use of transitional devices between paragraphs

One common method of transition is the use of transitional words or phrases, such as *also, another, next, finally, in addition to,* and *on the other hand.* When a word or phrase of this sort (there are dozens) appears at the beginning of one paragraph, it signals to the reader's mind a continuation of the thought of the previous paragraph, thus keeping the writing integrated and intelligible.

A second method is the repetition near the beginning of one paragraph of an important word from the preceding paragraph. The repetition of this word (usually a noun) also signals a continuation of the thought of the previous paragraph. When the reader's

---

[3] Coherence within a paragraph, also essential, is discussed in Chapter 3.

mind encounters the signal, it recognizes familiar material and feels the coherent union of the two paragraphs.

A third method is similar to the second. It involves the use of a pronoun near the beginning of one paragraph to refer to a noun in the preceding paragraph. Such a pronoun, too, acts as a signal to keep the reader's mind focused on the writer's line of thought. It integrates the two paragraphs.

Though there are other means of achieving coherence (such as parallelism of sentence structure), these three are by far the most common, and one or another of them usually appears between paragraphs in clear, coherent exposition. They make for smoothness and clarity. When the signals are present, the reader can proceed rapidly and extract full meaning from the writing. When the signals are not present, he may stumble or lose his train of thought. You should learn to examine your own paragraphs to see if there is always clear transition between them. Incoherent writing is never good writing, no matter how truthful or profound.

For examples of transitions between paragraphs, inspect this section of your text. Paragraph two is joined to paragraph one by the repetition of the words *paragraph* and *coherence*. Paragraph three is linked to two by the repetition of the phrase *common method of transition*. Paragraph four continues the transition with the phrase *a second method*. Number five begins with *a third method*. Number six uses the transitional word *other* and the key noun *transition*. Number seven repeats *transitions between paragraphs*. All of these repetitions are transitional signals that make for coherence. You are hardly aware of them because they are there. If they were not, you would find the writing disjointed and hard to follow.

EXERCISE 8.   Analyzing Transitions between Paragraphs

DIRECTIONS: *Choose any selection from your textbook of expository essays and identify the means of transition (transitional words, repeated key words, pronoun reference) that appear between all the paragraphs. Be prepared to explain how these transitional elements act as signals to keep the reader's mind focused on the writer's train of thought.*

The use of transitional paragraphs
in long papers

In long papers whole paragraphs are sometimes used for transitional purposes. Such paragraphs are a part of the organizational structure of a paper rather than of its development because they are used just to connect ideas rather than to introduce new ones. Short papers seldom have a need for transitional paragraphs, but term papers and long reports often require them. They are used when a simple transitional element will not suffice.

A transitional paragraph, usually quite short, is most frequently used to summarize the ideas of one part of a paper in preparation for the beginning of another part. Thus it forms a transition between two large parts of a paper. The following one-sentence paragraph is an example from a term paper entitled "The First Battle of Bull Run":

> These skirmishes, however, were only a prelude to the savage battle that followed.

This transitional paragraph helped the reader see the preceding paragraphs as one unit and the succeeding ones as another. It was, in fact, both a concluding and an introductory statement and was helpful in making clear the over-all organization of the paper.

Following is another example of a well-used transitional paragraph, from a term paper entitled "Some Oddities of Eighteenth-Century Medicine":

> Such fantastic remedies were, of course, just passing fads and were soon abandoned; but stranger fads were soon solemnly adopted by leading physicians.

This short transitional paragraph clearly signals a turn in thought. It ties up in a bundle for the reader one set of ideas and also prepares him for another. It does not introduce new material but serves as an organizational signal for the reader.

Brief one-sentence paragraphs like the above are likely to be ineffective at the beginning or end of a paper, but as transitional paragraphs within a paper they can be useful. They prevent an abrupt shift of ideas by forming transitions between groups of paragraphs, just as words like *therefore, also, however,* and *finally* form transitions between sentences or paragraphs. Transitional paragraphs then are signals that keep the reader from losing his train of thought in a long paper just as transitional phrases, repeated nouns, and pronoun reference keep him from losing his train of thought from paragraph to paragraph.

EXERCISE 9. Review

DIRECTIONS: *Answer the following questions succinctly.*

1. Define *organization*.
2. What is the distinction between a title and a topic?
3. How can organizational clues be stated in a topic?
4. How can organizational clues be implied in a topic?
5. What is the difference between a general statement and a specific detail in the basic organization of a paper?
6. What are the purposes of an introduction in expository writing?
7. Why are excessively dramatic or startling openings out of place in exposition?
8. When can a narrative-dramatic opening be effective in exposition?
9. What are some of the stock openings that students should avoid?
10. When should an introduction be a separate paragraph and when should it not?
11. What are the qualities of a good conclusion to an expository paper?
12. Define the word *coherence*.
13. Define the word *transition*.
14. What are the common methods of effecting coherence between paragraphs?
15. Why is a transitional paragraph a part of a paper's organization?

CHAPTER 3

Paragraph Development

PRELIMINARIES OF PARAGRAPH DEVELOPMENT

What makes a paragraph

In the earliest days of writing by alphabet, neither spaces, marks of punctuation, nor paragraph indentations were used. All of the letters were placed together with no indication to the reader where a word, sentence, or paragraph began. Gradually writers began to space groups of letters to set off single words and to use marks of punctuation to indicate units of words. The most important development in punctuation was, of course, the use of the period to signify the end of a full unit of thought. Later, writers began to use the symbol ¶ in the margin to mark the beginning of a unit of writing larger than one sentence. Gradually the use of the symbol ¶ declined and in its place writers began to indent a line to show the beginning of a unit larger than a sentence. Such units became known as paragraphs, for the symbol ¶ stood for the word *paragraph,* which in English means "to write beside."

Thus indented units of writing are known as paragraphs. It is a mistake, however, to think that indentation alone makes a paragraph. (Does a period necessarily make a sentence?) The true identifying feature of a paragraph is its central idea, for it is this central idea and not indentation that makes a true unit of composition, the original meaning of the symbol ¶. A paragraph, then, is a series of sentences all pertaining closely to one central idea. This is the kind of unit that early writers set off with the symbol ¶.

The central idea of a paragraph is usually called its *topic,* which is just another word for *subject.* Thus a paragraph, like an essay or a sentence, should have a subject. The subject of an essay is what the essay is about; the subject of a sentence (in one sense) is what the sentence is about. Similarly, the subject (topic) of a paragraph is what the paragraph is about—its central idea. *Paragraph topics come, of course, from the main points of a paper's basic organization,* as explained in Chapter 2. In planning a basic organization for a short paper, you are, in effect, dividing your whole into separate units, and these units will form paragraphs. It is, then, not indentation but the central idea of a group of related sentences that makes a true paragraph.

Paragraph length

Since a paragraph is a unit of composition built around one central idea, your basic organization will determine how your pape⁻ is to be divided into paragraphs, for your basic organization is a list of central ideas. In a short paper you will plan, tentatively at least, to write one paragraph about each of your main points and not to write about two separate points within one paragraph. For example, you might prepare a basic organization like this for a short paper on "Artificialities in Present-Day Education":

1. Students required to learn some material before they use it.
2. Classroom situations do not imitate real life.
3. Fragmentation of subject matter keeps students from integrating what they learn.

For such a paper you would expect to develop three main paragraphs (plus opening and closing statements), one for each of the three artificialities to be explained.

Asking how long a paragraph should be, then, is somewhat like asking how large a swimming suit should be. A swimming suit should be large enough to fit its intended wearer; a paragraph should be long enough to explain its central idea. If a swimming suit is too small, its owner suffers. If a paragraph is so short that it does not cover its topic, the reader is not fully informed. Thus the length of a paragraph is determined by the amount of detailed explanation called for by the central idea, just as the size of a swimming suit is determined by the area it must cover.

But, you are already saying, the size of a swimming suit varies according to fashion as well as size of person. This is of course true, and in one respect paragraph length is also limited by fashion. The size of a person will keep the swimming suit from being too small; fashion will keep it from being too extensive. A full explanation of its central idea will keep a paragraph from being too short; the reader's need for frequent pauses should keep it from becoming too long. *So there is an upper limit to the length of a paragraph regardless of how much detailed explanation its central idea calls for.*

Therefore, as you undertake to explain in detail each main point of your basic organization, you should follow your plan of devoting one paragraph to each point only so long as you can develop each point in the space of one-half to three-quarters of a handwritten page—perhaps one page at most. (An average handwritten page contains about 200 to 250 words.) The reason for such a limitation is that a paragraph of exposition longer than this can become fatiguing or confusing to a reader, just as an overlong sentence can. Current reading fashion calls for fairly frequent pauses. Hence when the detailed development of one of your main points runs to more than three-quarters of a handwritten page (say about 175 to 200 words), you should arrange to divide into two parts what would normally be one paragraph so that your reader will have a convenient pause.

Even in high-level, learned exposition, a 250- to 300-word paragraph is now considered rather long, and in student writing, paragraphs are likely to be somewhat shorter since they will of necessity be somewhat less learned. You can make it a general rule of thumb to have two paragraphs or less per handwritten page but not more than one page for one paragraph.

When arbitrarily dividing a long paragraph for the convenience of your reader, you should find a suitable breaking place so that each of the two resulting indentations will have a natural beginning and ending. That is, you should not just divide a long paragraph into two equal parts. If a main point of your paper requires as much as a page of detailed development, it will usually provide you with a natural dividing point, just as a long sentence will have at least one natural point of division calling for punctuation. You may take advantage of this natural point of division in a long paragraph to give your reader a mental pause.

To give you an example of how a long paragraph may be arbitrarily divided for the reader's convenience, here is a single paragraph prepared from point 3 of the topic "Artificialities in Present-Day Education." This paragraph, though unified, coherent, and well developed (but not necessarily true), is rather long for a paragraph in a relatively simple piece of expository writing. It may be divided into two parts so that the reader will have a convenient pause. First see if you can spot its natural breaking point:

> One of the most conspicuous artificialities in modern education is the fragmentation of subject matter. This means the division of knowledge into separate subjects, such as geography, economics, history, government, literature, biology, etc. Life of course is not divided into separate small categories of this sort, but is one continuous whole. Therefore, since education is for life, it also should be one continuous whole and not divided into little fragments taught separately. When a student goes from a class in geography to one in economics and then to one in history, he is likely to think that these are totally separate categories of human knowledge or endeavor, whereas they are really so closely bound up with each other that they cannot be separated without some distortion of truth. You can't, for instance, have history without geography and economics; therefore geography, economics, and history should be taught together. This principle holds true for most other subjects as well. How, for example, can biology be taught without the use of chemistry, physics, and mathematics? Students, then, should be taught integrated rather than fragmented courses. In this way they would perceive human knowledge and activities as a whole rather than as separate fragments. Thus their education would be for life.

A natural breaking point in this paragraph comes after the fourth sentence; there might well be a second indentation at that point to give the reader a pause. The two resulting paragraphs, however, would still in essence be one paragraph, for only one central idea is developed. If the paragraph had gone into less detail, two identations would have given the paper fragmented paragraph structure.

Thus reading fashion has something to do with the length of a paragraph, just as esthetic or moral fashion has something to do with the size of a swimming suit. Basically, however, each is supposed to cover its subject.

To summarize: you should develop each main point of a paper in a separate paragraph and should not develop two main points in a single paragraph. For the convenience of your reader, however, you may divide a long paragraph, provided you find a natural breaking place. Most paragraphs in student papers should cover about one-half to three quarters of a handwritten page. A shorter paragraph is usually undeveloped; a longer one is usually fatiguing or confusing to the reader.[1]

Topic sentences

As we have seen, a paragraph should have a topic—what the paragraph is about. A topic sentence, then, is one that states in general terms the central idea of a paragraph. The central idea, in turn, is one of the points of a paper's basic organization. When you are preparing the organization of your paper, you state the main points briefly in scratch outline form. When you start writing, you restate each idea more fully so that it can serve as a topic sentence for a paragraph.

Now in the kind of expository writing you do as a student (themes, essay tests, reports, term papers), it is usually best for each of your paragraphs to have a topic sentence and for that sentence to come at or near the beginning of its paragraph. When you express the central idea of the paragraph in an initial topic sentence, you prepare your reader for the detailed explanation that will follow. His mind first focuses on the general statement in the topic

---

[1] Paragraphs in narrative and journalistic writing are often organized on different bases.

sentence and then shifts with understanding to the details that explain the general statement. Thus your topic sentence is an instrument of clarity. It helps your reader follow your line of thought.

Below are some topic sentences reproduced from student papers. Each of these clearly announces what its paragraph is to be about and thus prepares the reader to understand better the details of the paragraph. These student writers were wise to express their paragraph topics so clearly in initial topic sentences, for the effectiveness of expository writing depends a great deal on the clear statement of central ideas. Note that each of these topic sentences shows transition from a preceding paragraph.

> But in spite of their superstitious basis, a few old folk remedies have some therapeutic value.
> Worn piston rings, however, are not the only cause of excessive oil consumption in automobile engines.
> The T-formation is also more adaptable to quick surprise plays than is the single-wing formation.

You should try to develop skill in writing topic sentences like these, for they are especially valuable in answering essay questions and in writing term papers and technical reports. You will find that the more clearly you think out the basic organization of a paper, the easier it will be for you to compose clear and meaningful topic sentences. And you will also find that the more clearly you can state the topic of your paragraph in an opening sentence, the more effectively you will be able to develop a full, well-thought-out paragraph. The topic sentence is an important aid to clarity in exposition.

In professional writing, however, topic sentences are not as common as they are in college exposition. If you have ever hunted for topic sentences in professional essays, you probably found cases in which two or three sentences in a paragraph seemed to have equal, but not full, claim to being **the** topic sentence. You probably also found paragraphs that seemed to have no topic sentence at all. The truth is, simply, that the topic of a good paragraph is always there but is not always summed up in one topic sentence. This is especially true of professional writing because highly skilled writers, with their subtlety, learn to avoid some of the mechanical aspects of writing that are necessary to the amateur if his writing is to be clear and logical. You as a college student, not being a professional writer, will probably express yourself more lucidly and effectively if you will employ topic sentences for most of your paragraphs. (In fact, many professional writers would improve the clarity of their exposition if they would make more use of topic sentences.)

But even as an amateur writer you should not feel tightly bound to the concept of the topic sentence. Many times you will find that you can develop a good paragraph by gradually making the central idea clear rather than by stating it in a topic sentence. Such a practice is not only permissible but often desirable. The only dictum that you should abide by is to be sure that each of your paragraphs does have a central idea. You can make sure of this by planning a basic organization for each of your papers.

One more point should be made clear about topic sentences. It is often said that the topic sentence may appear anywhere in a paragraph—even last. Now it is true that a concluding sentence sometimes expresses the paragraph's central idea more fully than any other sentence. But such a sentence may more usefully be called one of **restatement**[2] rather than a topic sentence. A true topic sentence comes at or near the beginning of a paragraph because its purpose is to prepare the reader to understand better the details of the paragraph. A sentence of restatement may come later in the paragraph with the purpose of restating for emphasis the paragraph's central idea. Both are statements of generalities and thus are alike except for their position in the paragraph.

A topic sentence is not always first in a paragraph because transitional or introductory material may be used to open the paragraph. But the topic sentnce, if there is one, usually comes at the beginning of the paragraph's true development. Here is an example from a paper entitled "The Advantages of Early Marriage":

> There is one other advantage of early marriages that, so far as I know, has never been mentioned before. It is the reverse side of a coin frequently used to discourage early marriage. It is this: if a person avoids an early marriage because he wants to observe many potential mates before he chooses, he may miss the very person he should have married by not taking her when he had the chance. [The paragraph continued with an explanation of this general idea.]

---

[2] See pages 80–83 for a full discussion of restatement.

The first two sentences of this paragraph are simply preparation for the topic sentence. They form a transition between this paragraph and the one that preceded it and thus serve as an introduction to the paragraph. The topic sentence, though not first, comes before the true development of the paragraph topic, just as a real topic sentence should.

When the only general statement of a paragraph's central idea comes last, the paragraph has, in effect, an implied rather than a stated topic sentence. As the reader follows the paragraph's development, he gradually becomes aware of what the central idea is. The concluding sentence of restatement simply re-emphasizes that idea. It is not used to tell the reader at long last what he has been reading about. A topic sentence, then, comes at the beginning of the paragraph's detailed development; a sentence of restatement may come at or near the end.

EXERCISE 10. Writing Topic Sentences

DIRECTIONS: *Each of the following essay topics has its basic organization stated in scratch outline form. Write a clear and full topic sentence for several of the main points. Phrase each topic sentence as though it were to be the opening sentence of its paragraph.*

1. *Topic:* Discuss some of the ways in which poetry differs from prose.
    a. Rhythm more pronounced and regular than in prose
    b. Meaning more concentrated—few words deliver much meaning
    c. More use of devices for melody and tone—sounds more carefully chosen than in prose

2. *Topic:* Discuss some of the advantages of living in a fraternity house.
    a. More social contacts in living quarters—built-in friends
    b. More social prestige on campus—access to affairs
    c. Study help and study aids available

3. *Topic:* Discuss some of the personal benefits resulting from military training.
    a. Instills discipline—good for later life
    b. Gives contact with wide variety of people and their customs
    c. Involves practical instruction in care of equipment, improvising, roughing it, and so forth

4. *Topic:* Discuss some of the evils of inflation.
      a. Harms old people living on pensions, savings, annuities
      b. Costs always outrun wages, harming workers
      c. Makes planning for the future hard for everyone

5. *Topic:* Discuss some of the evils of censorship.
      a. Censors themselves can't be infallible—bad mistakes possible
      b. Censors would have to change—new ones might disagree with old
      c. Better to have some bad ideas than to kill good ones

PARAGRAPH FRAGMENTS

Incomplete paragraphs, or paragraph fragments, are one of the most common and serious weaknesses in student writing—much more common and serious than the much-abused sentence fragment, which can be an effective stylistic device. There are two kinds of paragraph fragments.

Excessive indentation

Indentation does not make a paragraph, just as a period does not make a sentence. When one complete sentence is punctuated with several periods, a disjointed effect occurs, like this:

> A sentence fragment. Is not a serious error. In composition.
> Unless it obscures clarity.

When one complete paragraph is given several indentations, a similar disjointedness occurs, like this:

> Some paragraphs are weakened because of the useless repetition of an idea that has already been made sufficiently clear.
> A paragraph, like a sentence, should be terse and direct rather than wordy and roundabout. Usually repetition in a paragraph occurs because a writer has trouble thinking of what should come next.
> Being unable to continue his train of thought, he resorts to a rewriting of his previous sentences in order to fill out his paragraph.
> Repetition for emphasis can be justified, but useless repetition is a serious weakness.

No student past the third grade would break a sentence into

fragments as in the first example above. But mature, capable college students still fragment paragraphs as illustrated. Such fragmentation is acceptable in certain kinds of journalistic writing, but not in the kind of more thoughtful and serious exposition of facts and ideas expected of college students and business and professional people. You can avoid this kind of fragmentation by remembering that you should write no more than one paragraph about each main point, unless you arbitrarily divide a long paragraph for the convenience of the reader. Excessive indentation as illustrated above is not a convenience for the reader but is actually quite distracting to him.

Incomplete paragraph development

In the above illustration, paragraph fragmentation occurred because the writer divided one good paragraph into four parts, thus distracting the reader, just as periods after each phrase in a sentence would distract him. Such a weakness can be easily corrected: the writer just needs to combine his fragments into one whole paragraph. But there is another kind of paragraph fragment which does much more damage to student writing. This is the paragraph left incomplete because of the failure of the writer to develop its central idea fully. To avoid this kind of paragraph fragment, you must first clearly distinguish in your own mind your paragraph topic. You do this by planning a basic organization for your paper. Then you must decide how you will develop that topic by using one of the methods of paragraph development described in the next section.

The most serious kind of paragraph fragment, then, is the undeveloped paragraph—the kind in which the writer suggests, often vaguely, a paragraph topic but fails to develop it in detail. This kind of paragraph is like a sentence subject without a predicate: it withholds desirable information from the reader and it mars the style of the writing. For example, suppose this subject-without-a-predicate posed as a complete sentence: "The most effective solution to the problem of overpopulation." The reader would be justly annoyed. First, the period would cause him to stumble in his reading, and second, he would certainly want to ask, "What *is* the solution?" He has learned that an effective solution exists, but he has not learned what it is. A unit of composition (here, a sentence) has been left incomplete.

In a similar fashion, paragraphs are often left incomplete. For example, consider this paragraph from a student paper entitled "My Choice for President":

> In his travels, Mr. Williams helped foreign relations. He has also stopped foolish wastefulness of foreign aid.

A critical reader would, of course, ask "how?" He has learned that Mr. Williams has helped foreign relations and has stopped wasteful aid, but he has not learned how the gentleman effected these remarkable accomplishments. The writer suggested two paragraph topics but did not say anything specific about either. His paragraph is a fragment just as surely as a sentence subject without a predicate is a fragment.

Here is another example, from a student paper on "The Advantages of Local Control of Public Education":

> A local school board knows better how to spend the money. They know what the schools need.

Again, a critical reader would be unsatisfied; he would say, "prove it." This writer left the topic of his paragraph undeveloped; the result was a paragraph fragment.

Usually a casual glance at a paper will tell whether or not it has paragraph fragments. An expository essay with four, five, or more indentations per page is almost sure to be full of paragraph fragments of one sort or another, for it is highly unlikely that four or five main points can be developed on a single page. Also a paragraph with only one or two sentences is likely to be a fragment, for full development of a main point will normally call for several sentences.

METHODS OF PARAGRAPH DEVELOPMENT

The distinction between generalities and specific details

Now we must consider various methods of achieving full paragraph development. Often a paragraph fragment takes the form of a generality (or generalization) without the support of specific details. The generality is the paragraph topic; the missing details would, if present, develop the topic and keep it from being a paragraph fragment. A generality then is a broad statement that covers many situations, events, or ideas. A specific detail covers just one situation, event, or idea.[3]

Following are some generalities and specific details placed side by side. Note that each generality is broad enough to cover many situations. Each specific detail, on the other hand, refers just to one instance. In each case the generality could serve as a paragraph topic; the detail could be used to help develop the topic:

Generality: A novel can be educational as well as entertaining.

Detail: By reading *Arrowsmith* you can learn how medical research is undertaken.

Generality: Even selfish politicians can do some good public service.

Detail: Senator Popov, who was convicted of taking bribes, introduced a bill designed to prevent commercial exploitation of Ginko National Forest.

Generality: Many intelligent people can't resist the lure of getting something for nothing.

Detail: Professor Nowall bought a set of the *Hot Rodder's Encyclopedia* from a salesman who wanted to "give" him a set "free" for advertising purposes.

Generality: Capital punishment is ineffective because it does not serve its purpose of deterring capital crimes.

Detail: In 1963 the rate of capital crimes in Wabash, a state without capital punishment, was 20 percent lower than the rate in Old Catawba, a state that retains capital punishment.

Students are sometimes advised to avoid generalizations and to use only specific details. But this advise is only half sound. A paragraph consisting only of specific details without a stated or clearly implied generality would be confusing. In exposition, the reader needs to focus his mind on a generality in order to understand the meaning of the details and their relationships to each other.

Generalities, then, are not to be avoided in expository writing; in fact, since they form paragraph topics (and thus often topic sentences), they are indispensable in it. But by themselves they are

---

[3] This discussion of generalities and details applies to expository writing only. Narrative and personal writing do not utilize generalities as much as exposition does.

not sufficient—for two reasons. First, a reader is not obliged to believe a generality unless he is given good cause to believe it, and second, a generality by itself is usually dull and does little to arouse a reader's interest. Look again at the paragraph fragments on page 59. Are we inclined to believe that Mr. Williams helped foreign relations? Do we find the mere statement that he did interesting? Or do we believe that a local school board "knows better how to spend the money"? Our answer to these questions is no. But we might have answered yes if the writers had cited specific details to show the truth of their generalities.

But a word of caution about generalities is needed. In your writing you should, of course, avoid unsound or overly broad generalities. Do not make sweeping statements that would still be questionable even when illustrated with a few specific instances. For example, generalities like these would be too broad and unconvincing even when supported by a few details:

> All political conservatives are just interested in keeping their money safe.
> Every varsity football player learns to become a good sport.
> The only reason coeds come to college is to find husbands.

If you used one of these statements as a paragraph topic, your fault would not be in using a generality, but in using an unsound generality. Generalities are necessary in expository writing; but they should be credible after they are illustrated with specific details.

You can guard against unsound generalities by using qualifying words or statements. *To qualify,* in this sense, means to restrict, limit, or modify. Thus qualifying words limit the range of a generality. For example, the generalities listed in the previous paragraph are qualified as they are rewritten here:

> Some political conservatives seem to be just interested in safeguarding their money.
> Good sportsmanship is an attribute that many varsity football players learn.
> Many college coeds seem to be more concerned with finding husbands than with becoming educated.

As your write your generalities in the form of topic sentences for your paragraphs, be sure to qualify them when necessary. Then your illustrative details will serve as convincing evidence for your generalities.

In essence, then, expository writing consists of the statement of sound generalities plus a suitable development of them. One means of development, as we will see, involves the use of details, and so it is important for you to understand the distinction between generalities and specific details.

EXERCISE 11. Distinguishing between Generalities and Details

DIRECTIONS: *Divide the following statements into three groups: (1) specific details; (2) generalities that do not need additional qualification; and (3) generalities that are unsound because they need additional qualification.*

1. Occasionally, a stitch in time saves nine.
2. Checking your car's tire pressure before a trip may prevent tire trouble on the trip.
3. Taking advance precautions will always save you trouble later.
4. Some TV programs are educational.
5. "Animal Secrets" is an informative TV program.
6. All TV programs are worthless claptrap.
7. All well-educated people know the history of their own country's literature.
8. "Uncle Remus" stories are interesting to adults as well as children.
9. Crickets will eat fabric and paper.
10. Insects vary widely in their diets.
11. All coeds are attractive.
12. Pamela is pretty enough to be Homecoming Queen.
13. Most freshman girls are good natured and sweet.
14. A knowledge of art may be a social asset.
15. My knowledge of cubism helped me make friends in France.
16. A person is not educated unless he has a knowledge of art.
17. The city officials of Bunksburg are all completely corrupt.
18. Our tax assessor took bribes from a real estate agent.
19. In most cities there is at least a small degree of corruption in city hall.
20. Most people find the prospect of space travel fascinating.

The two broad modes of paragraph development

Actually, there is an almost limitless variety of paragraphs in all the various kinds of writing that occur. Unless one specifies the kind of writing he is talking about, he can say little about the nature of a paragraph. For example, in dialogue every new speech is a paragraph; or in news reporting a new paragraph begins every sentence or so. But in the kind of expository writing we have been talking about, most paragraphs do have definite structure—that is, they are developed along set lines. Broadly speaking then, there are two modes of developing the generalities that make paragraph topics in exposition: (1) development through illustration, and (2) development through logical analysis or explanation. Various specific methods, explained separately in the following pages, fall within these two broad groupings.

First we will consider those methods that involve illustration. In general, these methods call for the use of specific details to give the generality an aura of truth and to make it interesting.

Development through an accumulation of specific details

One of the most common, simple, and effective means of paragraph development is the use of an accumulation of specific details and supporting data to make the generality more believable, interesting, and explicit in meaning. In order to understand better an example, first consider the following paragraph fragment, from a student paper entitled "The Differences between the Sexes":

> The thought patterns of the sexes differ also. A woman usually thinks differently from a man.

This is a paragraph fragment, of course. The topic is there, stated (twice) as a generality, but the reader is given no cause to believe it is true. Furthermore, the term "thought patterns" is not fully clear. The writer might have interested his reader, given him cause to believe the generality, and made the key phrase of the generality clearer if he had developed his paragraph topic with supporting details, as in this revision:

> Another major difference between the sexes is that their thought patterns vary widely. A woman is apt to think of the here and now; a man more often keeps his eye on the future. A woman's thinking usually centers around home, love, and security; a man's around adventure and sex. Small accomplishments will delight a woman, but a man is dissatisfied unless he can achieve major successes. In fact, there are few areas in which the thought patterns of the sexes mesh.

Now even the supporting details in the above paragraph are to some degree generalities. For example, the next-to-last sentence does not specify what sort of small accomplishments or what kind of major successes. However, they are still details in this particular paragraph, for they illustrate its central idea. If the whole paper had been on the subject of how the thought patterns of the sexes differ, then each of the details in the above paragraph would have become a general topic for a separate paragraph. In that case even more specific details would have been called for to develop those generalities.

For example, in a paper entitled "How the Thought Patterns of the Sexes Differ," the following two-sentence paragraph would be a fragment because the generality (paragraph topic) is not developed:

> The thought patterns of the sexes also differ in that women take delight in small accomplishments, while men like to achieve major successes. Men think bigger than women.

Such a paragraph fragment could be developed into a full paragraph by the inclusion of supporting details, as in this example:

> Another way in which the thought patterns of the sexes differ is that women take delight in small accomplishments whereas men are dissatisfied unless they can achieve major successes. Women, for example, love to make dresses for their daughters, to cook special dishes, and to grow rare plants. Men, on the other hand, want to add a room to the house, or to build a cabin in the mountains, or to establish a new civic organization. Women can be happy earning a few extra dollars selling Christmas cards; men want to make killings on big real estate deals. In short, women think small; men think big.

It is clear, then, that what is a specific detail in one paragraph may be a generality in another. For example, in the preceding paragraph even the detail about making killings on big real estate deals might be used as a general paragraph topic with specific details to explain what kind of deals. The important lesson here is that you must recognize what your paragraph generality is so that you can develop it properly.

Consider another paragraph fragment, from a student paper entitled "A Successful Date":

> Good manners are an asset to any girl. Properly introducing your date to your parents is only one of many opportunities that good manners have to shine.

The one supporting detail in this paragraph is not sufficient. The phrase "only one of many" indicates the opportunity to build a full paragraph. The writer might have made her paragraph more interesting, her central idea more believable, and her general term "good manners" clearer by adding more details, as in this revision:

> Good manners are an asset to any girl. Introducing your date to your parents, for example, is a simple act of politeness that will put everybody at ease. Allowing your date to order for you will give him a feeling of importance and manliness. Listening politely and not dominating the conversation will give your date and your friends a pleasing sense of your agreeableness. Good manners, indeed, are no bar to vivacity and insure quick acceptance on all occasions.

The use of details to illustrate a paragraph generality involves the logic of accumulation; each detail is independently related to the paragraph topic. Therefore in this method of paragraph development you can select details individually and can arrange them in any order. You should select interesting details which will make your generality believable, and you should arrange them in a natural, effective order.

Development through the use of extended examples

Another method of paragraph development is to illustrate a generality with one extended example rather than with a series of details. To understand better this method of development, first note the following paragraph fragment, from a student paper entitled "Advice to College Teachers":

> Another reason why intelligent college students sometimes fail is that the teachers often don't try to understand the student's problems. They don't seem to care.

The reader is given no cause to believe this generality nor to be interested in it. How could the writer have developed the idea so that it would be both interesting and believable? He might have cited several specific ways in which teachers fail to understand students. Then he would have been using an accumulation of details to develop his paragraph. Or he might have developed it through the use of one long example, as in the following revision of the paragraph:

> Another reason why intelligent college students sometimes fail is that their instructors don't try to understand their problems. For example, there is a brilliant lawyer in my home town who, even with an I.Q. of 140, flunked out of Torts University as a freshman. He had been compelled, because of illness, to enter college two weeks late, and in each of his classes the major assignments had already been made. Being somewhat shy, he was afraid to ask his professors what he needed to do to catch up, and so he drifted around without being sure just what was expected of him. Not a single professor even spoke to him personally. Consequently he never did get oriented and received an F in every subject for the first semester. He left Torts discouraged, but entered Blackstone University the next fall and established an outstanding record. Torts U. could have had the honor of being his alma mater if a professor or two had just spoken to a bewildered boy.

Note that length of example is the chief difference between the use of one extended example to develop a paragraph and the use of several supporting details. In both cases a paragraph generality is not left standing as a fragment but is illustrated. To realize the importance of such illustration, just suppose that nothing more than the following were written in a textbook about this method of paragraph development:

> Another method of paragraph development is the use of one extended example. This can make a paragraph topic more believable and interesting.

Would you feel that the author had done his job well? Or would you feel that he should have given an example to explain his meaning?

An example lends an aura of truth to a generality by serving as evidence. Therefore, in using an example you should choose one that seems typical, reasonable, and convincing, not one that, because of its oddity or unusualness, leaves the reader skeptical as to the validity of the generality. For instance, you should not try to demonstrate that soft drink producers add narcotics to their products because you know of a person who drank many soft drinks and then became a dope addict. On the other hand, few generalities can be absolutely proved, and so you may often feel satisfied that one example is enough to illustrate a generality.

Examples also serve to enliven a reader's interest. They do this by virtue of being specific and concrete and by adding a narrative quality to the paper. General statements tend to be dull because they are abstract and do not form concrete pictures in the reader's mind. But a specific example lets the reader's mind form a clear image so that he really has something to understand. For example, a general statement such as this does little by itself to stimulate a reader's interest: "Edgar Allan Poe had an analytical mind." But a specific example of his deductive abilities—for example, his exposure of the fraudulence of an automatic chess player that had fooled audiences for over fifty years—is sure to interest almost everyone. The mind can picture the concrete and specific but tends to lose interest in the abstract and general *unless they are followed by details.*

When using an extended example, you should make it appear to be a natural part of your paragraph. You should not force an example into a paragraph when it would seem out of place or uncalled for. Nor should you be heavy-handed in announcing that an example is to follow. Even the phrase "for example" need not be used, though neither should it necessarily be avoided. With a little practice you can learn to handle examples smoothly and easily.

How do you decide when to use a fairly long example? Usually you have a choice. The following two generalities could, for example, be developed through the use either of several short, specific details or of one long example. You would just have to decide which method would better suit your purpose.

> Most current communist dictatorships claim in theory to be democratic, but in practice ignore democratic principles.
> Often a writer who attracted little attention in his own lifetime becomes famous after his death.

The following generality, however, seems rather clearly to ask for development through one extended example:

> If a human being becomes overexcited by a sense of fear or urgency, he can often perform superhuman feats of strength.

The important point, of course, is for you to recognize your generalities and their need for development. You must find **one** suitable method of paragraph development and not leave a central idea standing as a paragraph fragment.

Development through the use of anecdote and allusion.

An anecdote or an allusion, like an example, can often be used to make a paragraph more interesting and fuller in its development. An anecdote is a brief story or joke; an allusion is a reference to some past occurrence or piece of literature. Generally, neither an anecdote nor an allusion will, by itself, be sufficient to effect full development of a paragraph's central idea; a single anecdote or allusion may, however, be a significant addition to a paragraph that has been partially developed by some other method.

To understand an example, first examine the following paragraph fragment, from a student paper entitled "Brains *v.* Brawn":

> Another common misconception is that short men are not only physically but also mentally inferior. There isn't any reason why anyone should think this. Many short men have done great things.

As is usual with paragraph fragments, this one is dull and uninformative because its generality is not developed. To be effective, this paragraph needs details. The writer might also have found use for an anecdote. The following revision shows how:

> Another common misconception is that short men are not only physically but also mentally inferior. Even people intelligent enough to read William Faulkner's novels are often surprised to learn that he was just over five feet tall; they marvel that such a short man could have written such great books. And no doubt there are millions of Americans who would sleep less soundly if they knew that our most important naval commander is only sixty-six inches tall. Actually, there is not a bit of anthropological evidence to show that there is any correlation between height and intelligence. Long legs may enhance basketball skill, but not intellectual powers. When Abraham Lincoln, renowned for his height and his genius, was asked how long a man's legs should be, he replied, "I've always felt they should be long enough to reach the ground."

The last sentence of this paragraph is an anecdote, a brief and humorous little story. It improves the clarity of the paragraph, not because it adds new information, but because it reemphasizes the writer's central idea—that height and intelligence are not related. It also makes the paragraph more interesting because it is witty. Relevant anecdotes of this sort can significantly improve paragraph development.

An allusion is somewhat different from an anecdote, but it serves approximately the same purpose in expository writing in that it adds clarity and interest to ordinary paragraph development. In order to better appreciate an example, first note the dullness and lack of information in the following paragraph fragment, from a student paper entitled "My Sports Favorites":

> From the reading I've done I believe that there were greater baseball players in the 1920s than in any other era. Babe Ruth, Walter Johnson, and Grover Cleveland Alexander are just a few of the greats of that time. They've never been equalled.

A more careful writer would have developed his paragraph with interesting details, and he might have seen the opportunity to use an anecdote or allusion or both. Compare this revision with the original:

> Though it can never be proved, it seems to me that the greatest baseball players were active in the 1920s. Everyone knows of Babe Ruth's record of sixty home runs in 154 games. Few know that he was also one of the greatest pitchers before he went to the outfield. Everyone also knows how Grover Cleveland Alexander saved the 1926 World Series after going on a binge the night before, when he thought his chores for the Series were over. When Walter Johnson was at his fastest, it was hard for a batter even to see the ball. Once when he was in his prime, Johnson faced a pretty good hitter who had just come into the American League. After the umpire had called the second straight strike, the batter started back to his dugout. "Wait," said the umpire. "You have another strike." "I don't want it," replied the batter. Truly, there were giants in the earth in those days.

This example paragraph has both an anecdote and an allusion. The last sentence is an allusion—a reference, in this case, to a familiar quotation from the Bible. Its use adds both a touch of clarity and of interest to the paragraph, for it reinforces the central idea and it also pleases the reader because it makes him feel superior for having recognized and understood the allusion. Allusions should be used in expository writing, then, only when they are clearly relevant to a paragraph's central idea and when they will be familiar to most of the intended readers. If an allusion is not aptly chosen, it will not add to the clarity of a paragraph; if it is not familiar to the readers, they will resent the encroachment on their ignorance.

Development through comparison, analogy, and contrast

A variation of the example method of paragraph development is the use of an extended comparison or contrast. This method is effective when you have expressed a generality that you simply want your reader to understand—that is, when you are not so much concerned with offering evidence for your generality as you are with making clear to your reader just what the generality means. You can often do this by comparing or contrasting the unclear generality with something with which the reader is familiar.

To understand an example, first examine the following paragraph fragment, from a paper entitled "The Care and Nurture of Honey Bees":

> Another problem facing a beekeeper is getting to know a newly arrived hive and getting it to know him. This is a delicate problem that calls for much know-how. It takes a lot of tact.

This is not only an incomplete but also a dull paragraph. The mere statement of a generality in abstract terms is seldom interesting or convincing. A concrete explanation of the generality, on the other hand, can form images in the reader's mind that will make the generality understandable and attractive to him.

The above paragraph, for instance, would have been fresh, original, and more understandable if the writer had explained his generality by comparing it with a situation more familiar to the reader. He might, for example, have written this:

> Another problem facing a beekeeper is getting to know a newly arrived hive and getting it to know him, a delicate problem that calls for much tact. The hive of bees is a unit in itself with its own personality; no strange bees are allowed in it and none of

its bees would venture into another hive. The keeper, too, is an individual personality. How shall the two personalities become familiar? The process is something like that of a young man becoming acquainted with a sensitive, slightly suspicious young lady. First he must let her know of his presence without getting too close or jarring her sensitivity. After she becomes aware of him, he will venture a very polite social call to her vicinity, say in a library, but still without getting close enough to touch her. Doubtless he will then go through a few characteristic actions so that she can identify him as a distinct individual. After two or three gentle approaches of this sort, he will become a little bolder and will engage her in polite social talk, or, in the case of the bees, in a little amiable cleaning of the hive or other close activity among the cloud of bees at the hive's mouth. Soon the two will be familiar with each other and chatting gaily like old acquaintances.

Such illustrative comparisons are used more for clarity than as evidence of the truth of a generality.

A short simple comparison may also be used in conjunction with some other method of paragraph development. For example:

Most composition textbooks illustrate the various modes of paragraph development with selections chosen from the writings of the best professional authors. These sample paragraphs are skillfully written and illustrate all the subtleties, refinements, and complexities of first-rate writing. And indeed they should, for they were written by first-rate authors. "There!" the textbook author says to the student. "That is how to write a real paragraph!" The student, however, feels a little baffled. *He* does not understand how to achieve such subtleties, refinements, and complexities. In fact, he cannot even recognize most of them. He is a beginner, not a professional. The textbook author has, in effect, acted like the piano teacher who ripped off a Chopin mazurka and then said to her beginning pupil, "There. That's the way to do it. Now you try it."

The last sentence of this paragraph contains the kind of comparison known as an analogy. It draws a parallel between two situations that have similar attributes in order to emphasize or make clearer the particular situation under discussion. In this case, the analogy clearly makes the point that beginning college students need to learn the fundamentals of good writing before trying to achieve professional subtleties and complexities. (Note, incidentally, that the above paragraph does not have a stated topic sentence. How would you express the topic of the paragraph?)

Next we will consider the second broad mode of paragraph development: the use of logic to explain a generality rather than the use of details to illustrate it. There are several variations of this mode. They represent a principle of development different from that in which supporting details or examples are used. You can consciously select details as to number and appropriateness, and on revision you may decide to drop one detail and add another. But in using logical development, you usually follow a fairly definite pattern of thought, for each idea is logically related to the previous one rather than just to the paragraph generality.

Development through a logical sequence of ideas

You may develop the central ideas of some paragraphs through presentation of a logical sequence of ideas that (in your mind, at any rate) demonstrates the truth of your generality. You try to build up a case for your generality by taking the reader step by step through a pattern of logic that will show why your generality is true. This kind of paragraph development, therefore, aims at a specific conclusion. It is answering the question "why" as applied to the generality. You are, in effect, saying, "My generality is true because. . . ."

For an example of this method of paragraph development we will compare a real fragment from a student paper with a full paragraph based on the same central idea. This unsubstantiated generality came from a paper entitled "Regulation or Fraud":

> It is necessary that we have government regulations in order to protect the consumer against inferior goods and fraudulent advertising. The public can't protect itself.

A reader of this paragraph naturally asks, "Why?" He wants to know the **reasoning** behind such an assertion. He is not content with the mere statement of the generality.

The writer could have developed his paragraph through a logical sequence of ideas which would lead to the conclusion that we must have government regulations to protect the consumer against fraud. The following example shows how:

> We must have governmental regulations to protect the consumer against inferior goods and fraudulent advertising, for he cannot protect himself. Everyday the average consumer uses dozens of products and is bombarded by hundreds of ads. He is so overwhelmed by the variety of material appurtenances in his life that he has only time to use them, not time to shop for them carefully in order to secure good quality. Furthermore, he seldom has the kind of education that will guide him in selecting quality even if he has sufficient shopping time. In the case of products that should last for years, the consumer can suffer badly if he has an inferior product foisted off on him. It is clear, too, that the consumer does not have the time, nor usually the education, to properly evaluate the endless ads that surround him. The scientific allusions alone now used in advertising are enough to baffle the ordinary consumer. Under such circumstances, then, must not modern society provide itself with regulatory agencies that will try to control the flow of inferior goods and false advertising?

Note that all of the paragraph after the first sentence is answering the question "why?" as applied to the opening sentence.

This method of developing a central idea through a series of logically related sentences is one of the hardest for students to learn. The chief difficulty seems to be that the human mind finds it hard to continue a series of logically related ideas without leaving a gap. A writer will think that he has put on paper what is in his mind, but the reader will find something missing. The result is that in much student writing, paragraphs of logical explanation seem faulty because one or more steps of logic have been omitted. Following is an example of such a faulty paragraph, from a student paper entitled "The New Industrial Revolution":

> In our present society, governmental action to provide jobs is necessary unless we are to have widespread unemployment and economic distress. Automation is throwing people out of work. What are they going to do? Only the government is big enough to plan for their absorption into new jobs.

This paragraph is faulty because the writer jumped steps in his logic. He undoubtedly had thought his idea through in more detail than his writing showed, but he was unable to see that what he put on paper did not represent his full thought process. He might have filled in the gaps in his logic in this manner:

> In our present society governmental action to provide jobs is necessary unless we are to have widespread unemployment and economic distress. A new industrial revolution is now taking place with the result that fewer and fewer production workers are needed. Therefore in the manufacturing industries large numbers of workers are being laid off. Even when the demand for goods picks up, these workers will not be rehired, for automated machinery will allow the factories to increase production without adding new workers. What are the millions of unemployed to do? It is a mistake to assume that the private companies will find jobs for them, for each company is relatively small and must think of its own profit. Consequently, a superorganization—namely, the federal government—must plan new ways to use these surplus workers so that all can have a chance to make a living through useful work. Only the government is big enough to do such planning and to see that in the process of transition from production to service jobs large numbers of workers do not face grave economic distress.

In planning a paragraph based on logical development of connected ideas, you must be careful not to skip steps in your logic. If your reader is forced to guess at your meaning, your writing cannot be effective. The best way to avoid this kind of paragraph fragmentation is to train yourself to reread your paragraphs as though you were not the writer. Then you can see what is on your paper instead of what is in your mind. Only then will you be able to tell if your paragraph will be clear to your readers.

When should you use a logical sequence of ideas to develop a paragraph generality? Usually this method is called for when your reader is likely to say "prove it" in reference to the generality of your paragraph. It is your duty as a writer to convince your reader by explaining the reasoning that led you to believe your generality. Following are a few generalities that call for this mode of development:

> The jury system of court trial is not as sound as most people think.
>
> A foreign ideology cannot be effectively combatted by those who do not know what it is.

> A highly trained employee is of less value to a corporation than one well educated in the humanities.

Your task as a writer of exposition is to develop your paragraph generality in some suitable fashion. With generalities like these you will need to take the reader through a logical sequence of ideas.

Development through a cause-and-result relationship

A method of paragraph development similar to the use of a logical sequence of ideas is the demonstration of a cause-and-result relationship. A logical sequence of ideas is used to prove a generality. A cause-and-result method of paragraph development is used to show how the generality came to be. Obviously, these methods are closely related. Both aim at a demonstration of the truth of the paragraph's central idea by the use of logical reasoning.

Again we will illustrate a method of paragraph development by starting with a real-life paragraph fragment, from a student paper entitled "School Conflicts":

> No doubt the chief cause of this kind of school rivalry [intense rivalry between two high schools] is a natural desire for competition. Young people love to outdo each other. When groups are involved, this drive is made stronger.

This paragraph has a suitable central idea stated as a generality; unfortunately, it was not developed. The way the generality is stated shows that paragraph development should come through logical reasoning to demonstrate the truth of the generality rather than through details to illustrate it. Indeed, the second and third sentences are an attempt to provide such proof.

The following revision shows how the writer might have developed his paragraph:

> No doubt the chief cause of this kind of school rivalry stems from a natural desire among young people to engage in competitive activities. A teen-ager feels good when it is demonstrated that he or a group he belongs to is superior to a rival. Consequently, even in an activity as innocent as a ball game the desire to win is very strong on both sides, particularly if the teams "belong" to teen-agers. This natural individual drive becomes accentuated

when large numbers of individuals are thrown together at one time with the same competitive desire. The result is apt to be an extension of the competitive feeling beyond the mere game itself. In fact, little fracases are apt to break out. After this sort of thing has happened two or three years in a row, a "tradition" of rivalry is apt to grow up between two schools. Thus there exist many established, permanent, intense school rivalries. It all goes back to the natural human desire for competition.

This example illustrates the typical cause-result method of paragraph development. The result is stated as a generality, usually at the beginning of the paragraph; then the cause or causes of that result are logically explained.

Development through steps in a process

Another method of paragraph development closely related to the use of a logical sequence of ideas is the explanation of steps used in a process. In the first method, you carry your reader through a pattern of reasoning to show why a generality is true. In the second, you carry him through a series of steps to show how a process is performed. Such paragraphs usually appear in the "how to . . ." kind of compositions and in all writing involving directions. Students often leave such paragraphs of explanation incomplete because they think that what is obvious to them is obvious to everybody, which, of course, is not true. In expository composition, you must always keep in mind that your primary job is to express your ideas fully and clearly.

Consider the following paragraph fragment, from a paper entitled "How to Train Dogs":

Dogs can also be taught to protect young children. The dog's trainer must try to make the dog understand that the child is helpless.

This paragraph has no development at all. The natural question the reader asks is "how?" And such a question usually implies that a discussion of method is needed. To develop the generality stated in the above paragraph fragment, the writer needed to describe the process (steps) involved in teaching the dog. He might have developed his paragraph in this manner:

Dogs can also be taught to protect young children. The first step the trainer takes in this part of the dog's education is to make the dog aware that the child is helpless. He does this by letting the dog see him rescue the child from various difficulties. Next he tries waiting until the last moment to rescue the child, thus giving the dog a chance to perform the rescue himself. The intelligent dog will soon catch on and will begin to take a possessive interest in the child. Then the trainer undertakes to teach the dog various dangerous situations that confront the child, such as those involving the streets, high places, stray animals, and loose objects. With such training an adaptable dog will soon become a better protector than the child's own mother.

The steps-in-a-process method of paragraph development should be one of the easiest for you to use, and you should readily spot the occasions when it is called for. The question "how?" rather than "why?" or "what?" will fit the generality of your paragraph. Then you answer the question "how?" by carrying the reader step by step through the process.

Development through extended definition

Another of the logical methods of achieving full paragraph development is the use of an extended definition of a term, principle, or concept. Essay test questions often call for paragraphs of this type. A college athelete, for example, might be asked to explain the T-formation in football or zone-defense in basketball. A drama student might be asked to define farce or tragicomedy. An art major might face an exam question calling for a full definition of expressionism or dadaism or cubism. In fact, in all phases of their work, college students are repeatedly called upon to define terms or concepts.

To write successful definition you must avoid two pitfalls: (1) defining a concept in terms of itself and (2) omitting relevant aspects of the concept so that the reader gets only a vague half-picture of your meaning. The following paragraph from a student paper on "The Principles of Outlining" illustrates both weaknesses:

Another principle of good outlining is parallelism of structure in headings. The headings should be parallel in the way they are constructed. This holds true for headings on various levels.

The first sentence of the paragraph mentions the principle to be defined—all well so far. But then the second defines the principle wholly in terms of itself. This is like a dictionary's definition of *opsonification* as "the act of opsonifying." Who knows any more than he did? Worse yet, the third sentence gives none of the details needed for a full, clear definition. Unhappily, such skimpy, circular definitions are more the rule than the exception in college writing, for no other kind of paragraph calls for so much clear thinking and attention to detail.

You can increase your ability to write good extended definition by following a set plan of four steps. First, ask yourself what larger classification your term belongs to and then give a general definition of it in relation to the larger whole. In the above faulty paragraph, for example, the term "parallelism of structure in headings" is fitted into the general classification of principles of outlining. In establishing the general classification of your term, you will find it helpful, where pertinent, to distinguish your particular term from others that fit into the same large classification. Here is an example:

> A public community junior college is a kind of institution of higher learning that offers the first two years of college only, in contrast to the four or more years offered by regular colleges and universities. . . .

Here the specific term is "public community junior college" and the general classification is "institution of higher learning."

The second step in your four-part plan of definition is to identify the special characteristics of your term and to arrange them in a logical order. For example, after establishing the general classification of your term "public community junior college," you would write sentences explaining such special characteristics as these:

> Offers both terminal and transfer courses
> Accepts any high school graduate or person over twenty-one
> Provides guidance facilities to help students pick proper major and vocation
> Operates a full line of extracurricular activities
> Operates on a philosophy of broad service to all aspects of community life
> Is financed mostly by local taxes
> Charges no tuition

As each of these special characteristics is mentioned, your extended definition grows fuller.

Your third step is not always necessary. It is to give a **limited** definition of any special term that you use. For example, when you mention that a public community junior college offers both terminal and transfer courses, you should insert a sentence of this sort:

> A terminal course is one that offers credit for junior college graduation only; a transfer course is a regular university-level course, the credit for which one can transfer to any accredited senior college.

Your fourth step is also not always necessary. It is to give a specific example to illustrate your definition. For example, in the faulty paragraph above on parallelism of structure in outline headings, the writer might have given an example of two headings in faulty parallelism, such as:

I. Destruction of large cities
II. Contaminating the atmosphere

followed by an example of proper parallelism:

I. Destruction of large cities
II. Contamination of the atmosphere

When such an example would not be of significant value in your definition, you need not put one in. For example, just the name of one public community junior college would add little to a definition of the term.

You should memorize this simple scheme of writing an extended definition: (1) give a general definition of your term as one member of a larger classification; (2) explain its pertinent special characteristics; (3) give a brief, limited definition of any special words you use; and (4) give an example if one will help clarify your definition. If you follow this plan, you can write a clear extended definition.

The length of your definition will depend on how much detail you use in listing special characteristics. In defining some terms, you might mention enough special characteristics to call for two or more paragraph divisions. Then you should follow the principle of paragraphing discussed in Chapter 3.

For practice, write an extended definition of one or more of these terms:

single-wing or T-formation	puppy love
farce	Unitarianism
jazz	sedimentary rock
isotope	intoxication
Bohr atom	brandy
one of the seven sacraments	headline
automation	impressionism
sonnet	objective test
epic	a finess
satire	dirndl
short story	counselor
exposition	Charleyhorse
paragraph	a square

Development through restatement

Some paragraphs may be made fuller in their development through the use of **restatement**—that is, through a deliberate repetition. Restatement by itself is not, of course, a method of paragraph development. Rather, it adds to the development that has been built with illustration or logical reasoning. Normally, only the generality of a paragraph is restated, for a specific detail or example hardly needs repeating.

Restatement is used for both emphasis and amplification. That is, it not only repeats the preceding idea for emphasis, but it also *clarifies* the idea with fuller statement, or amplification. *To amplify* means to increase, enlarge, or extend. Thus restatement for amplification means an enlargement or extension of an idea that has already been stated once. It re-presents the idea from a different point of view or with additional explanation. Restatement, then, is not just aimless or useless repetition, but is a means of both emphasizing and clarifying the central idea (or topic sentence) of a paragraph.

For an example of the use of restatement, study the following paragraph reproduced, with changes, from a student paper entitled "Common Themes in Cartoons":

> Another common type of cartoon, and one of the most disgusting, might be called "the tolerated brat." This is the cartoon

that shows a young child annoying his neighbors or his school teacher without being punished or reprimanded by his parents— indeed, seemingly without his parents realizing how detestably he has behaved. The tone of these cartoons is one of amused toler- ance of naughty behavior. Probably the best known of this type is the "Dennis the Menace" series. Dennis can make his neighbor- hood unbearable without drawing a stiffer sentence than a few minutes' incarceration in a corner. Cartoons of this sort perform an injustice to suburban living, for their widespread publication tends to leave the impression that parents cannot, or should not, discipline their children in the interest of pleasanter living in the suburbs. "The tolerated brat" is a despicable cartoon topic, for its confusion of cuteness and nastiness in children is chipping away at child control and discipline in the suburbs.

Restatement appears in this paragraph in the third and last sentences. The two ideas of sentence three—"tolerance" and "naughty behavior"—have both already been expressed in the sec- ond sentence in the phrases "without being reprimanded or pun- ished" and "annoying his neighbors." The third sentence, then, really adds nothing new except the idea of the "tolerance" being "amused." It is a sentence of restatement used chiefly for emphasis with a little amplification. The last sentence is similarly a sentence of restatement, for its three ideas—the despicableness of the cartoon topic, the unawareness of the parents, and the decrease in disci- pline—have already been expressed earlier in the paragraph. It is a sentence of restatement used to emphasize the central ideas of the paragraph. Note that each of these sentences of restatement is phrased so differently from the original statements that the reader is really given a different point of view even though the ideas are the same. Thus these sentences of restatement are not just repeti- tion for padding but are carefully used instruments of clarity.

When restatement comes at the end of a paragraph (as most restatement does), it serves not only to emphasize and to amplify, but also to give the paragraph a sense of completion. *Since a para- graph is a unit of composition, it should sound as though it has a begin- ning and an ending. A well-written topic sentence will sound like a beginning; a good sentence of restatement will sound like a conclusion.* For further examples of the use of restatement, reread the speci- men paragraphs found on pages 63–77. Note that the concluding sentence of restatement in each does not just add the last detail of the paragraph but rounds it off with a tone of conclusion. It serves both as an instrument of clarity and as a stylistic device to prevent an abrupt ending of the paragraph.

Restatement may also come early in a paragraph. Then it is a repetition, for emphasis and amplification, of the paragraph's topic sentence. For example, examine the following paragraph, reproduced, with changes, from a student paper entitled "Keeping Up with First Graders":

> There is a tendency for six-year-olds to seek freedom and to resent it at the same time. One impulse in them drives them to rebellion; another causes them to seek constant discipline and security. For example, one youngster that I observed thoroughly resented his teacher's trying to. . . . [The paragraph continued with an extended example.]

The second sentence of this paragraph is a restatement and amplification of the topic sentence; the specific example that develops the paragraph follows the restatement. This repetition is not useless, for it both emphasizes and amplifies the topic sentence. The restatement might, however, have come last in the paragraph. In fact, restatement might have been used in both places.

Restatement, though a very common device in exposition, should not be used in every paragraph. In general, you should not use it unless you feel a need to explain further (that is, to amplify) or to attain a sense of completion at the end of a paragraph. Repetition as mere padding is, of course, boring and obscures clarity. So be cautious in your use of restatement.

Unjustifiable restatement at the beginning of a paragraph is very easy to spot, for it will invariably give a paragraph a second beginning. For example, note the apparent restatement in the following paragraph, from a student paper entitled "The Necessity of Education":

> Schooling will help a child to develop and to learn about life. Schooling is one of the most important factors in a young person's life. . . .

Omit the first sentence and the paragraph still has a beginning; omit the second and nothing is missed. The second sentence, then, is detracting repetition rather than useful restatement. It is this sort of dual opening of a paragraph that represents the most common misuse of restatement in student writing. You should make it a habit to examine your own paragraphs for such false second starts.

Basic organization and the development of paragraphs

A paragraph is a separate unit of composition with its own self-contained structure, but all the paragraphs of a paper merge together to form a longer unified structure. Therefore a writer should not begin building an individual paragraph until he has a plan for all the paragraphs of his paper. In college exposition such a plan is usually a basic organization that establishes the main points of the proposed paper. Only after he has the whole structure of his paper in mind should a writer begin considering the modes of paragraph development that he will utilize.

Suppose, for example, that in an economics class you were asked to write an essay exam on this question: "Discuss some of the promotional gimmicks used by supermarkets to increase sales." First you would analyze your topic for clues to organization; the plural noun *gimmicks* would of course suggest that you give your paper structure by discussing from two to four different groupings of gimmicks. Your basic organization might take this form:

1. Contests, drawings, and other something-for-nothing lures
2. Displays designed to induce impulse buying
3. Various kinds of bogus sales and loss-leader promotions

Note the necessity of stating generalities to give a framework to your paper; just a catalogue of individual details would give you no design for paragraph composition.

With three paragraph topics clearly in mind, you would be ready to compose an introduction and then to undertake paragraph development. Only after getting the detailed paragraph composition underway would you decide whether or not one of the main points should receive two or more paragraph indentations for the convenience of the reader. So far as paragraph development itself is concerned, you would first plan to have three paragraphs plus a suitable introduction and conclusion.

At this point you should ask yourself whether your paragraphs will be essentially illustrative or logical in development—whether you will state a generality and then support it through details, examples, anecdotes, allusions, or comparisons or whether you will state a generality (or proposition) and then demonstrate its validity through logical analysis, cause-and-result relationship, steps in a process, or definition. Your decision will be determined by the kind of paragraph topics you have established in your basic organization. The three main points for the above essay question rather clearly call for development through illustration. For example, after your introduction you would write a topic sentence to the effect that supermarkets use various kinds of contests and drawings to lure customers. Then you would develop your paragraph topic with illustrative details and examples. Whether you used two or more indentations would depend on the extensiveness of your answer. And so with the other two points. The general points (to be stated as topic sentences) are necessary to give focus to the details that build the paragraphs.

For another example, suppose that in a psychology class you were given this essay question: "Discuss some of the reasons why human beings are so likely to rationalize their motivations." First you would look for the clue to organization contained in your topic, and the plural noun *reasons* would be your guide. Your basic organization might be this:

1. Because of a desire to conceal their selfishness and egotism
2. Because of a desire to conceal their irrationality and limited problem-solving abilities
3. Because of a desire to feel important and admired

Now you would be ready to compose an introduction and to begin paragraph development.

On inspecting these paragraph topics, you would see that a logical development seems most appropriate. Not only examples but logical explanation is called for. Thus in dealing with the first point, for example, you probably would develop the idea that there is a conflict between human selfishness and the social demand for the appearance of unselfishness and that, consequently, people rationalize when they explain why they behave as they do. A pattern of cause-and-result relationship would underlie your paragraph development.

As a final example, suppose that in a literature class you were given the question "Discuss the main influences on the growth of naturalism in American literature." In analyzing your topic, you would see that the plural noun *influences* suggests that you give your paper structure by discussing in order several major influences. Your basic organization might take this form:

1. The influence of nineteenth-century deterministic science
2. The influence of the deteriorating economic and social scene
3. The influence of the naturalistic movement in French literature

Only with such paragraph topics in mind would you be ready to compose an introduction and undertake paragraph development.

Human thought being as complex as it is, you will of course find that often both illustration and logical analysis must contribute to paragraph development. For example, in developing the first of these three paragraph topics for the above essay question, you would probably use definition to explain deterministic science, a cause-and-result relationship to show how this science influenced philosophy and thus literature, and some specific examples of authors and books which exhibit this influence. You would perhaps use more than one indentation even though according to your basic organization you would be composing one paragraph.

Summary of paragraph development

You should plan one paragraph for each main idea in the basic organization of your paper, but you should, for the convenience of your reader, arbitrarily divide a paragraph that runs more than a page in length, provided you can find a natural breaking point. You should not discuss two main ideas in one paragraph. In most cases, you should state the central idea of your paragraph in an initial topic sentence, which will take the form of a generality. It is most important for you to develop the generality of your paragraph so the paragraph will be full and well thought out. Paragraph generalities can usually be developed either through some mode of illustration (details, examples, comparisons) or through the use of logical explanation (cause-and-result relationship, definition, steps in a process). Often more than one method of development may be used in a paragraph. The essential lesson for you to learn is that you must spot your paragraph generality, which will be a main point in your basic organization, and then find a suitable means of developing it. Finally, you may use restatement to emphasize and to amplify paragraph generalities, but should avoid useless repetition.

EXERCISE 12. **Analyzing Paragraph Fragments**

DIRECTIONS: *Following are some paragraph fragments from student papers. Explain why each is a fragment and suggest a specific method whereby each might be fully developed.*

1. Federal aid should not be granted to segregated schools. It's not right for the government to help segregated schools.
2. I find that I adjust my language usage according to the kind of social situation I am in. I don't always talk the same.
3. I believe that everybody is dishonest at some time or other. Nobody is honest all the time.
4. Mr. Williams' party, I believe, has developed into the stronger party during the past few years. I think they have done a lot of good things for the United States during these years.
5. There are many dangers arising from nuclear testing that the ordinary people don't know about. They have not had enough scientific training.
6. Education and property qualifications for voting would be very wrong. No democracy should have such qualifications.
7. In a national election it is wrong to vote a straight party ticket. People who vote a straight party ticket haven't studied the qualifications of the candidates.
8. When we do not use the abilities we are given, we lose a part of the enjoyment and happiness that should be ours.
9. A book like *Catcher in the Rye* is suitable for high school seniors to read. There's no reason why they shouldn't read it.
10. Most TV ads seem to me to be deceptive. I don't think many are true.
11. It probably is not best to separate superior students from average students. It wasn't good for my brother to be put in an advanced class.
12. We should have more night-school courses for adults. They need them.
13. Participating in student government is worth as much as taking a class. It teaches you a great deal.

14. The most important characteristic of a Peace Corps worker is adaptability. He must be able to adjust to all kinds of situations.
15. The government should do more to conserve wildlife. Wild animals are an important natural resource.

EXERCISE 13. **Distinguishing between Useful Restatement and Useless Repetition**

DIRECTIONS: *In some of the following items, the second sentence is a useful sentence of restatement and amplification; in others the second sentence is just distracting repetition. Divide the items by number into two groups and be prepared to explain how the restatement amplifies and is therefore useful and how the mere repetition is distracting. Also be prepared to suggest a method of paragraph development for each of the paragraph topics.*

1. To prevent federal aid to public education from becoming a liability, we must be careful to prevent federal control of education. We can keep federal aid from being harmful only if we keep the government from running things.
2. To prevent federal aid to public education from becoming a liability, we must be careful to prevent federal control of education. Only through constant vigilance can we prevent the danger of federal interference in our school programs.
3. To maintain a steady rate of progress, we need both liberals and conservatives in politics. With a proper balance between liberalism and conservatism there will be the proper degree of stability to promote progress.
4. To maintain a steady rate of progress, we need both liberals and conservatives in politics. We must have both liberalism and conservatism if we are to progress steadily.
5. The professional military mind is usually an unimaginative mind and thus is dangerous in politics. Discipline in the military calling is so strict that it quells the imagination needed in political activity.
6. The professional military mind is usually an unimaginative mind and thus is dangerous in politics. Generals and colonels aren't very imaginative and thus may be dangerous in politics.
7. The federal government must take steps to prevent water polution if our country is not to perish for lack of pure water. Only an effort by an organization as large as the federal government can coordinate a program to combat polution.

8. The federal government must take steps to prevent water polution. if our country is not to perish for lack of pure water. If the federal government doesn't do something we will soon be without pure water.

9. To progress with the times, churches must conduct themselves more as social institutions. Churches can keep up only if they become more social.

10. To progress with the times, churches must conduct themselves more as social institutions. There is much broader awareness now of social conditions, and churches must participate in converting this awareness to progress.

11. One important source of humor is incongruity. People laugh when a turn of events reveals a sudden shift from the dignified to the ridiculous or from the urbane to the rustic.

12 A question often asked today is whether eighteen-year-olds should be allowed to vote. Many people wonder whether the voting age should be lowered three years to eighteen.

13. In crime detection, the first step is to look for a motive. Only after they understand why the crime was committed can the police begin to search for suspects.

14. The automobile affects the life of the young adult more than he realizes. Consciously or unconsciously, he is both servant and master to his car.

15. World crises have often been the result of individual whim. When the powerful act on impulse, the delicate structure of political stability trembles.

EXERCISE 14. Analyzing Paragraphs

DIRECTIONS: *Each of the following paragraphs has a clear central idea, but few of them have it stated in one topic sentence. After carefully reading each paragraph, first express its topic in a phrase that could serve as a scratch outline heading; then indicate the method by which the paragraph has been developed.*

1. "Country or suburban life demands vehicles that will serve a dual function—that of part passenger car, part cargo carrier. However, both roles are suffering at the hands of the stylists so that, in CU's opinion, the station wagon as a type has been growing less desirable yearly. Consider first the station wagon's claims of accommodations for "six" or "nine" passengers. As is the situation in sedans also, the center occupant of the front seat, as a rule, sits

on a thin cushion area atop the transmission tunnel or "dog-house." That's bad enough. But in the rear, the station-wagon seat not only is hard under the middle passenger (like the sedan rear seat), it is less wide by a matter of inches, to facilitate folding. The back-rest for a wagon's second seat also is uncomfortably low, for the same reason; and on some wagons there is a two-inch gap between seat cushion and back-rest."—*Consumer Reports.*

2. "It should be apparent, then, that a station wagon will accommodate more passengers than a sedan only rather unhospitably. On the other hand, there is no gainsaying the station wagon's distinct virtues. It affords small children an over-the-road play area; the greater freedom of movement a wagon gives them can make all the difference between a happy family excursion or a temper-taut trip. Also there is the feature which originally contributed to the wagon's popularity: quick convertibility from personnel carrier to sometime cargo vehicle. And since, as noted at the outset of this report, the wagon-like—or truck-like—characteristics have been almost entirely bred out of U.S. station wagons, the passengers in them (within the limits of comfortable seating) travel as smoothly and almost as luxuriously as in equivalent sedan models. And beyond such considerations, it must be put on record, too, that the three-seat wagons are the chief passenger cars offering *any* sort of accommodations for more than six persons."—*Consumer Reports.*

3. "Individuals appear to differ markedly in their capacity for learning to write from reading. Some children, having been taught the significance of the letters, seem able to go on and pick up the rest by themselves. When they read, they notice what is going on, and when they write, they imitate, consciously or subconsciously. They observe which words are capitalized, and they capitalize them. They notice punctuation marks and how they relate to sentence structure and use them accordingly. As their reading grows more and more mature, their writing develops with it. They pick up phraseology, sentence rhythms, tricks and style, like as not without knowing that they are doing so. Memory no doubt plays a part in it, but it isn't all memory, perhaps not largely so. It is rather an ability to observe and a bent for mimicry. Some students have it so strongly that their writing regularly reflects whatever they have been reading lately. If they have been reading Henry James, they write like Henry James; if Hemingway, Hemingway." —Roberts, *Understanding English.*

4. "For the benefit of those who have never seen a comet it should be said that there is a great difference between a comet and a meteor in nature and appearance. A comet has no evident mo-

tion; it shines in the sky all night as calmly as the moon. It is a distant and vastly large object, always larger than the earth, and sometimes as large as the sun, that is, more than 100 times the diameter of the earth. The average diameter of a comet is about ten times the diameter of the earth. A meteor, often called a shooting star, is in the earth's atmosphere, and very small, usually no larger than a tiny bit of gravel, according to estimates. A comet stays in view for hours, days or weeks. The shooting star flashes across the sky in an instant, and is gone, unless it leaves a luminous trail which may persist for a few seconds or minutes."—Skilling and Richardson, *A Brief Text in Astronomy*.

5. "In general, the primary needs are physiological, and they may also be vital in the sense that the organism dies if the needs are not supplied. Oxygen is a vital need of the organism, and so are water and food. A man can live for minutes without oxygen but not for hours, for days without water but not for weeks, and for weeks without food but not for months. Sleep is probably also a vital need, but mostly people do not die from sleeplessness; instead they go to sleep. Once an enthusiast, who thought sleep was a habit which he could break by staying awake, actually did remain awake for more than nine days, but then he went to sleep. Sexual desire is a physiological need which is not vital. Men do not die of sexual starvation. Activity is another physiological need which is not vital. It is these primary needs that drive the organism to action, and, when they are satisfied, the drive ceases until oxygen or water or food or sleep is needed again."—Boring, "Psychology."

6. "The principal contribution of anthropology to the study of *religion* has been to show that religion is not normally something apart but rather flows into all areas of life and helps to maintain the adjustment of individuals and solidarity and survival of societies. Someone has said, 'Human beings build their cultures, nervously loquacious, on the edge of an abyss.' Religious life not only affords socially approved opportunities for personal expression and prestige but also gives a sense of security in a world which, seen in naturalistic terms, appears to be full of the unpredictable, the capricious, the accidentally tragic. In the face of chance and the unexpected, of wants, death, and destruction, all humans have a fundamental sense of uneasiness. By ritualizing their words and habits, they assure themselves that "reality" too is consistent. They mask the vast role of "luck" in human life by telling each other that such and such a thing happens because of

something a supernatural being did or said long ago. In a world full of hazards, myths and rituals affirm that there is rhyme and reason after all. They give the future the appearance of safety by symbolizing the unbroken continuity of present and past."— Kluckhohn, "Anthropology."

7. "Here, to quote an actual case, is a woman canvasser who announces herself as a member of the local school committee— only she is not a member of the school committee but recites a name which induces the lady of the house to think that she is. The committee, it appears, recommends a certain book to aid the children's education. The visitor mentions the children by name, their ages, their bright looks. The lady of the house is pleased. The cost of the book is five dollars. Her face falls. She cannot afford five dollars. Haltingly, ashamedly, she confesses it. The canvasser turns on her with the sure-fire line, 'Mrs. Green, don't you care enough about the future of your children to pay five dollars?' What mother can resist such an accusation? Company statistics coldly demonstrate that seven times out of ten it consummates a sale. Yet what troubles me is not the plight of Mrs. Green with a worthless volume on the parlor table, but the utter abandonment of self-respect on the part of the lady canvasser. Had she hit Mrs. Green with a blackjack as she stood defenseless and welcoming on her own doorstep, the loss of personal integrity could hardly have been greater. Hospitality is a particularly precious custom in a civilization which drifts rapidly to cities and apartment houses. By ruthless violation the canvassers have all but killed it."—Chase, "The Luxury of Integrity."

8. "Private capital tends to become concentrated in few hands, partly because of competition among the capitalists, and partly because technological development and the increasing division of labor encourage the formation of larger units of production at the expense of the smaller ones. The result of these developments is an oligarchy of private capital the enormous power of which cannot be effectively checked even by a democratically organized political society. This is true since the members of legislative bodies are selected by political parties, largely financed or otherwise influenced by private capitalists who, for all practical purposes, separate the electorate from the legislature. The consequence is that the representatives of the people do not in fact sufficiently protect the interests of the underprivileged sections of the population. Moreover, under existing conditions, private capitalists inevitably control, directly or indirectly, the main

sources of information (press, radio, education). It is thus extremely difficult, and indeed in most cases quite impossible, for the individual citizen to come to objective conclusions and to make intelligent use of his political rights."—Einstein, "Why Socialism?"

9. "Satire is a kind of humor—a very difficult kind. In general, it is the art of the opposite approach. Swift wished to defend the Irish against English exploiters, and he wanted to make sure that everyone knew the terrible and pitiable conditions in Ireland. The result was *A Modest Proposal,* possibly the most devasting and bitter piece of satire ever written. He proposed commercialized cannibalism as the solution for all Ireland's difficulties, and the proposal is so straight-forward that a good half of his readers (college freshman level) must be persuaded that he did not mean exactly what he said. What he was doing, of course, was pushing the English attitude toward its illogical extremity. The men who had made the Irish starve were horrified at the suggestion that they themselves should eat Irish children. The French writer Voltaire, moved by the statement of a German philosopher that we live in an earthly paradise, created in *Candide* a hero who undergoes burning at the stake, earthquakes, pirates, maiming, and indiscriminate disaster, but who pops up at appropriate intervals to moan, 'Everything is for the best in the best of all possible worlds.' It is a perfect answer. In our own time Sinclair Lewis has created foolish and vicious characters to praise all that is worst in American life. Satire requires a very special genius, but it is wonderfully effective propaganda in the hands of one who knows how to use it."—Hummel and Huntress, "Propaganda in Action."

10. "Recently scientists found that skin color is determined by two special chemicals. One of these, *carotene,* gives a yellow tinge; the other, *melanin,* contributes the brown. These colors, along with the pinkish tinge that comes when the blood vessels show through, give various shades to the human skin. Every person, however light or dark his skin may appear, has some of each of these materials in his skin. The one exception is the albino, who lacks coloring substances—and albinos appear among dark- and light-skinned peoples alike. People of browner complexions simply have more *melanin* in their skin, people of yellowish color more *carotene.* It is not an all-or-nothing difference; it is a difference in proportion. Your skin color is due to the amount of these chemicals present in the skin."—Benedict and Weltfish, "The Races of Mankind."

PARAGRAPH UNITY

A successful paragraph must be not only complete in its development, but also unified in its structure. As we have seen, a paragraph is a **unit** of composition—that is, possesses oneness—because it develops just one central idea. Its unity is evident when each of its sentences pertains to its one central idea. When even one sentence in a paragraph is off its topic, the paragraph has lost its unity.

The unity of a paragraph may be violated in two ways: (1) through the inclusion of a second central idea or (2) through the inclusion of one or more sentences of detail that are not related, or are only vaguely related, to the paragraph's central idea. A paragraph may also seem to lack unity when it is underdeveloped. Such a weakness, however, is more truly the result of incompleteness rather than disunity. True violation of paragraph unity is due to inclusion of material that does not pertain to the paragraph's central idea.

A second central idea disrupts paragraph unity, for then a paragraph lacks the oneness that makes for unity. Sometimes a writer develops two complete paragraphs, each with its own clear central idea, but omits indentation for the second. The result is a run-together paragraph, the simplest and most easily remedied kind of paragraph disunity. You should never be guilty of writing a run-together paragraph if you prepare a basic organization for each of your papers and begin a new paragraph for each main point in the organization. If you find such a run-together paragraph as you revise your work, you can easily correct it by entering a new indentation between the two true paragraphs.

Sometimes a writer puts two topic sentences in a paragraph but develops only one of them. The inclusion of the second violates the unity of the paragraph by its mere presence. Following are two examples of this kind of paragraph disunity, quoted, with changes, from a student paper entitled "Building Good Will in a Small Business":

> As the owner of a small business you can best create good will by giving each customer the impression that his patronage is of special importance to you. You should observe the order of arrival of customers and not wait on one out of his turn, even if he is an especially good customer. You of course are dealing

with many customers as the day passes and you get tired, but if you concentrate on each customer as though he is the first important one you've seen that day, he will respond to your interest and will tend to think that you really do consider him special. Once he gets that idea in mind, you have acquired a steady patron. The simplest reason is that you have flattered your customer by making him think that he is important, and the person who does not respond to flattery is rare indeed.

Another way to build good will in a small business is to always keep only first-rate goods for your customers. In a small business, most of your sales will be to repeat-customers whom you know. All you have to do to lose one of them is to sell him one piece of inferior merchandise. It's true that other stores with cheaper items will draw off some of your trade, but as the buyers learn that the cheaper items are not good, they will come back to you and pay the higher prices that you have to charge for good merchandise. To encourage your customers to come back you should once in a while give them a little extra without extra cost, such as a little more than a pound of nails.

The unity of each of these paragraphs is partially destroyed by the inclusion of more than one paragraph topic. The second sentence of the first paragraph should be a topic sentence for a new paragraph and should be given detailed development of its own, for it does not help develop the idea of treating each customer as specially important. Similarly, the last sentence of the second paragraph does not relate to the idea of carrying quality merchandise. Two full, new topic sentences have been misplaced and then denied detailed development. True, they belong in the paper. But it is not enough that an idea belong in a paper; it must also belong in a paragraph. An out-of-place idea destroys paragraph unity.

The disunity of the above paragraphs might have been even worse if the writer had tried to include details for the second topic sentence as well as for the first. At best he would have had a run-together paragraph. At worst he would have had a badly mixed paragraph. A mixed paragraph—one that presents a jumble of details for two or more topic sentences—is the worst offender against paragraph unity. Following is a mixed paragraph, from a student paper entitled "How to Study When in Love":

Nothing interferes with good study habits more than being

in love. When that state of mind is on you, you must take definite steps in order to study successfully. The best thing to do is to surround yourself with distractions that will keep you from thinking of your "one and only." Play the kind of music that doesn't remind you of him. Also be sure to lock your door and to take your phone off its hook. This will keep him from calling you and also will keep out unwanted people who might remind you of him. Besides the music, you can also use food as a distraction. Constantly reaching for a bonbon or a grape will give you something to do besides think of him. You shouldn't keep his picture around either. That would be as bad as having him call you on the phone.

This paragraph suffers from disunity because the writer was not sure just which idea she was developing and consequently mixed up her details. She should have written one paragraph about providing herself with distractions that could help her forget her boy friend and another paragraph about avoiding objects that would make her think of him. She undoubtedly began with a poorly thought-out basic organization, or none at all. A well-planned basic organization would have helped her avoid such a mixed paragraph.

Paragraph incompleteness often accompanies paragraph disunity because the inclusion of a second central idea makes an indented unit longer and thus leads the writer to believe that he has written a full paragraph when he has just merged two paragraph fragments. Following is a typical example of such an incomplete-disunified paragraph, from a student paper entitled "The American Scene as Reflected in Comic Strips":

"Pogo" has a lot of political satire in it. The cowbirds represents communists and are satirized. Also it makes fun of election methods. "Li'l Abner" also has some political satire. It makes fun of other comic strips too in its "Fearless Fosdick" sequences. They imitate "Dick Tracy."

First, this paragraph is mixed. The student should either have written one paragraph about "Pogo" and another about "Li'l Abner," or he should have written one about political satire in comics and another about other kinds of satire in comics. The paragraph is also incomplete. Separate the two central ideas and you have two paragraph fragments. As an indented unit, the paragraph does look fairly full, but disunity has in fact masked paragraph incompleteness. Both weaknesses are enemies of clear exposition.

The above examples show how paragraph unity can be disrupted by the inclusion of a second paragraph topic. Careful preparation of a basic organization should help you avoid such a weakness. Another type of paragraph disunity, however, can occur even with the best of basic organizations. This is the inclusion of one or more details that do not pertain to the central idea of the paragraph. Here is an example, from a student paper entitled "How to Win at Poker":

> Being lucky helps, but you can still win at poker even if you are not lucky enough to hold good cards. You can bluff your way to good pots. If you plan to bluff regularly, you must be careful not to establish a pattern of betting. Keep your opponents off guard by varying your play widely. On the other hand, if you plan to bluff only rarely, try to establish the reputation of being a steady, conservative player. Don't let a drink too many cause you to overestimate a hand. When you are actually bluffing a hand, be sure not to give yourself away with some odd gesture, such as eye-blinking. And after you have won a bluff, never, never let your opponents know.

The detail about the "drink too many" weakens the unity of this paragraph because it is not connected with the central idea of bluffing. It belongs with some other central idea, such as the value of self-possession when playing poker. Perhaps this detail could have been related to the bluffing idea, but it wasn't and it therefore disturbed the unity of the paragraph. You can guard against this sort of violation of paragraph unity by constantly keeping your paragraph topic in mind so that you will not include details off the topic.

PARAGRAPH COHERENCE

The meaning and importance of coherence

You have now studied two important principles of paragraph development: completeness and unity. A third is **coherence.** In Chapter 2 you learned that coherence literally means a sticking together of parts and that in the whole paper coherence is achieved when there is a clear transition, or link, between its major parts, the paragraphs. Similarly, a paragraph is coherent when its major parts, the sentences, are all closely joined to each other.

Coherence in a paragraph is different from unity in that unity pertains to the **actual** relationship between the sentences, whereas coherence pertains only to the **mechanical expression** of that relationship. That is, coherence has to do with the verbal means whereby the logical relationship between sentences is made clear. Of course the real relationship must be there before coherence can be achieved, but coherence can be lacking even when the relationship is there. The following two sentences illustrate this fact of language:

> Automation can provide worldwide abundance for all people. If I were directing industrial expansion, I would reduce the rate of changeover to automated production, for unemployment is just as much a problem as a scarcity of goods.

The relationship between these sentences is real but not immediately apparent. A reader would have to pause and think about the meaning, for coherence between the sentences is lacking. The relationship becomes immediately apparent, however, when a simple means of verbal transition is used:

> Automation can provide worldwide abundance for all people. *But* if I were directing industrial expansion, I would reduce the rate of changeover to automated production, for unemployment is just as much a problem as a scarcity of goods.

Now the two sentences are coherent because a means of making them stick together has been included. Note that no new content has been added—just a mechanical way of showing the logical relationship between the two ideas that were already there. If the connective *for* had been omitted, the three ideas would have seemed even more disjointed.

This particular example did not actually appear in a student paper. Thus you might be tempted to say that it does not really represent a kind of error that a writer is likely to make. As a matter of fact, it does not seem reasonable to suppose that a college writer would leave out such an obviously needed connection between sentences. But college students do just that—and frequently. For example, here is another similar and real example, from a student paper entitled "A Dog's Life":

> I believe it is quite a privilege to be a part of the highest form of animal life. If I had to be any other animal I would be a dog.

If a simple "but" is placed between these two sentences, their logical relationship springs to life. But without that "but" the two sentences seem on first reading to be disjointed and clashing. Without the "but" they lack coherence.

Thus coherence in a paragraph is important because it helps the reader follow smoothly and rapidly the writer's train of thought. When coherence is lacking, there is an abruptness and disjointedness between sentences that hinders the reader or stops him altogether. So to write clear prose, you must give thought not only to the logical relationship between sentences but also to the **way** each sentence is linked to the previous one. There are three common methods of achieving coherence that you should be able to use consciously.

Coherence through transitional words and phrases

The simplest and most easily recognizable method of achieving coherence between sentences is the use of transitional words and phrases. There are many of these in English used solely to connect ideas. Some of these are simple conjunctions, such as *and, but,* and *for.* Others are logical connectives, such as *however, therefore, nevertheless, consequently, thus,* and *moreover.* Still others are connective phrases, such as *for example, in addition to, of course, after all, on the other hand,* and *at the same time.* There are dozens of these conjunctions and connectives. Their sole task is to show a logical relationship between ideas—sometimes between parts of a sentence, sometimes between sentences, and sometimes between paragraphs. When used between sentences, they make for coherence in a paragraph.

Though there are dozens of these transitional elements, providing both for variety and for slightly varying shades of meaning, they are used to show only six broad kinds of logical relationships: **cause-and-result, contrast, condition, manner** or

method, time, and **addition** or **accumulation.** For example, *however, but, yet, nevertheless, although, though, still,* and *on the other hand* all show the same logic of **contrast,** but they vary slightly in their suggestive meanings and in their explicitness. And so with those in the other five broad groupings.

Transitional words and phrases can be overused, with awkward and heavy-handed writing as the result. But the college student who overuses them is rare. You can safely be given the advice to use transitional elements at any time you think they will improve the clarity and coherence of your writing. In fact, the chances are high that you should make an effort to use them more frequently.

For an example of the value of this means of achieving coherence, first read the following paragraph without connective words:

> Many educators suggest that we should turn to history and philosophy in order to solve the problems of our time. Historians are in disagreement even about what happened in the past. They are hopelessly confused about why historical trends occur. Philosophers have been and still are in muddled confusion. None of them agrees with any others. Educators can't agree in their choice of philosophers whom we should listen to. In the midst of such confusion, does it not seem wise to work with new ideas?

Now read the same paragraph with connective words added:

> Many educators suggest that we should turn to history and philosophy in order to solve the problems of our time. But historians themselves are in disagreement even about what happened in the past, and they are hopelessly confused about why historical trends occur. Philosophers, too, have been and still are in muddled confusion. None of them, at any rate, agrees with any others. Furthermore, educators themselves can't agree in their choice of philosophers whom we should listen to. In the midst of such confusion, then, does it not seem wise to work with new ideas?

Note that the meaning of the passage does not change with the inclusion of connective words. What changes is the ease with which the reader can understand the passage. Also note that the second sentence begins with the conjunction *but*. If you have been taught not to start a sentence with *and* or *but*, unteach yourself, for both conjunctions can often begin sentences, or even paragraphs, with admirable effect. Finally, note that transitional elements are often placed within instead of at the beginning of a sentence.

Coherence through repetition of key words

Coherence between sentences may be effected through the repetition in the second sentence of an important word that appears in the first. The repetition of the word signals to the reader's mind that a train of thought is being continued. With such a signal, the reader is able to progress smoothly with his reading. If no signal is present, he stumbles or is made to pause uselessly.

To understand how repetition of important words can provide coherence in a paragraph, first note the disjointedness between these sentences:

> Politics is a suitable profession only for men with agile minds. Since problems shift suddenly and rapidly, one must be able to alter his mode of thinking quickly to meet new and unforeseen situations.

The absence of a signal in the second sentence to connect it with the first causes the reader to be left with a vagueness or indefiniteness in his understanding.

Now note how coherence is effected through the repetition of a key word:

> Politics is a suitable profession only for men with agile minds. Since the problems of politics shift suddenly and rapidly, a politician must be able to alter his mode of thinking quickly to suit new and unforeseen situations.

The word *politics* and *politician* in the second sentence are positive signals that help the reader's mind respond with rapid comprehension. They provide transition between the sentences and thus effect coherence.

Here is another example of coherence through repetition:

> The smallest insects are made up of a very large number of cells. An ant or a gnat, for example, is composed of hundreds of thousands of cells. Furthermore, the cells in these small creatures are widely differentiated in structure and function. Even a

mite has skeletal, digestive, and nervous organs composed of many specialized cells. The cellular structure of such small creatures cannot be seen by the naked eye, but it is nonetheless miraculously complex.

Note that the word *cell* appears in each sentence except the last; and even in that sentence the word *cellular* is virtually a continued repetition. Such repetition forms a close linkage between the sentences. Note also that the words *ant, gnat, small creatures,* and *mite* all refer directly to the key phrase *smallest insects* in the first sentence. They are so clearly related to the original phrase that they, too, serve as repetition. All of these repeated words are signals that keep the reader's mind oriented to the main idea of the paragraph. In this way they provide coherence.

Coherence through pronoun reference

In the example paragraph above, the word *cells* was repeated because the use of a pronoun would have been awkward or impossible. But quite frequently, of course, a pronoun can be used in the place of a noun. When a pronoun in one sentence refers to a noun in the preceding sentence, it serves as a signal for the reader's mind just as a repeated word does. Hence pronoun reference is a common method of achieving coherence between sentences.

To understand better the usefulness of this method of transition, first note the unclear connection between these sentences:

> The president of the school board rejected the lay committee's recommendation. Shortsightedness and prejudice were evident.

There is no specific signal in the second sentence to carry the reader's train of thought along smoothly. Coherence is lacking.

Now note how the inclusion of a specific means of transition makes for smoothness between the sentences and expresses their logic clearly:

> The president of the school board rejected the lay committee's recommendation. He recognized its shortsightedness and its prejudiced point of view.

The pronouns *he* and *its* in the second sentence are the signals that enable the reader's mind to follow the train of thought rapidly and with full comprehension. The two sentences are now coherent.

Here is a full paragraph that further illustrates the use of pronoun reference to achieve coherence:

> The novel *Elmer Gantry* by Sinclair Lewis is one of the most controversial pieces of fiction ever published in America. It is a satiric attack on hypocrisy and humbug in the American clergy. Its author maintained that he was not attacking religion, but only those who misused religion. He cited proof that some clergymen are corrupt and showed that he had respect for those who were not. But many religious groups believed he was attacking religion in general. They, in turn, were merciless in their attacks on him.

Note how each sentence is tied to the preceding one through pronoun reference. There is an invisible thread running from *Lewis* to the final *him* and holding the sentences together. The paragraph, of course, has other coherent elements, too.

Now suppose the paragraph were to be written in this way:

> The novel *Elmer Gantry* by Sinclair Lewis is one of the most controversial pieces of fiction ever published in America. Hypocrisy and humbug in the American clergy are the subject of a satiric attack. Religion was not actually attacked, but only those who misused religion. Proof has been cited that some clergymen are corrupt and that there is respect for those who are not. Many religious groups believed religion was attacked. Lewis was mercilessly attacked.

In this rewriting, the meaning of the original paragraph is not wholly obscured, but its smoothness and definiteness have certainly been drastically weakened through the absence of specific transitional signals, such as pronouns. The result is rough and indefinite—in a word, incoherent—writing.

Though there are other and more subtle aids to coherence—for example, parallelism of sentence structure—transitional elements, repeated words, and pronoun reference are the most common and most useful in college exposition. If you will learn to inspect your paragraphs for the presence of these methods of transition, you will improve the clarity of your writing. Let your ear make the test. Read the material as though you were not the author. Your ear should tell you whether you have provided a signal that links each sentence to the previous one. If your ear perceives a jolt or lack of definiteness, see if you can smooth over the rough spot by using one of these three common methods of achieving coherence.

EXERCISE 15. Improving Paragraph Coherence with Transitional Words

DIRECTIONS: *The following paragraphs lack coherence because of the absence of transitional words and phrases. Indicate transitional words and phrases that will provide coherence between sentences. Some sentences may not need additional words.*

1. (1) One of the most important qualities for a politician to possess is imagination. (2) It seems that most politicians are singularly unimaginative. (3) Some have such one-track minds that they never vary from a set line of thought and procedure. (4) Our current mayor still spends hours a week on arithmetical check-up on employees even though the city now owns a computer. (5) He seems to fail to see that the city's political problems change. (6) He is likely soon to be out of a job unless he applies more imagination to his work.
2. (1) Most people have three misconceptions about the nature of rules of grammar. (2) They feel that an arbitrary rule makes an expression correct or incorrect, whereas, it is custom only that makes correctness. (3) They think that only whole words are involved in grammatical constructions, whereas parts of words —or morphemes—play an important grammatical role. (4) The verb parts *ing, en, ed, s,* and so forth are important grammatical entities. (5) They seem to assume that all languages have similar grammatical systems, which is of course far from the truth. (6) Estonian has twelve cases, whereas Latin has only five. (7) There are innumerable differences between grammatical systems. (8) We see that the general public is much misinformed about grammar.
3. (1) My professor of Comparative Religion maintains that religious truths are relative. (2) It seems to me that many points of religious belief must be absolute. (3) How can polytheism and monotheism both be true? (4) Consider the idea of afterlife. (5) How can it both exist and not exist? (6) It seems to me that the idea of relativism can be overvalued.
4. (1) Political liberals condemn the "go slow" tactics of conservatives on the grounds that the liberal ideas of the past have

become the conservative ideas of today. (2) The liberals feel that they represent the advanced thought that leads to progress and that the conservatives represent the stagnant thought that prevents progress. (3) This line of argument oversimplifies the true nature of progress. (4) An equally important idea to remember is that not every liberal idea of the past has proved to be of value. (5) Conservatives should receive as much praise for killing unsound ideas as the liberals receive for nurturing good ideas.

5. (1) Space enthusiasts urge that billions of dollars be spent on moon travel on the assumption that valuable minerals might be mined there and transported to the earth. (2) These enthusiasts are grossly ignorant of the costs that would be involved in such mineral extraction and transportation. (3) There is not a single mineral known that could ever be profitably mined on the moon and shipped to earth. (4) Regardless of how cheaply we can learn to manufacture rocket fuel, we will always have to pay hundreds of dollars a pound (in terms of current purchasing power) to get any substance from the moon to the earth. (5) The cost of outfitting and shipping miners to work on the airless and alternately boiling and freezing surface of the moon will always be thousands of dollars an hour. (6) We can be pretty sure that no known substance—diamonds, gold, uranium, platinum—can ever be profitably brought from the moon in commercial quantities. (7) As for substances now unknown, who can say?

EXERCISE 16. Identifying Transitional Devices

DIRECTIONS: *In the following paragraphs indicate the transitional words and phrases, repeated words, and pronoun references that link each sentence with the preceding one. Be prepared to explain how each word or phrase you select helps provide coherence in the paragraph.*

1. "Ideas need the backing of institutions and firm social approval if they are to result in practical application. Yet I see pharisaic temples being built everywhere in psychiatry; pick up our journals and you will see meetings listed almost every week of the year and pages filled with abstracts of papers presented at them. These demand precious time in attendance and reading, and such time is squandered all too readily these days. Who of us, even scanting sleep, can keep up with this monthly tidal wave

of minute or repetitive studies? And who among us doesn't smile or shrug, as he skims the pages, and suddenly leap with hunger at the lonely monograph that really says something? As psychiatrists we need to be in touch not only with our patients but with the entire range of human activity. We need time to see a play or read a poem, yet daily we sit tied to our chairs, listening and talking for hours on end. While this is surely a problem for all professions, it is particularly deadening for one which deals so intimately with people and which requires that its members themselves be alive and alert."—Robert Coles, "A Young Psychiatrist Looks at His Profession."

2.   "Many students of discrimination are aware that the victim often reacts in ways as undesirable as the action of the aggressor. Less attention is paid to this because it is easier to excuse a defendent than an offender, and because they assume that once the aggression stops the victim's reactions will stop too. But I doubt if this is of real service to the persecuted. His main interest is that the persecution cease. But that is less apt to happen if he lacks a real understanding of the phenomenon of persecution, in which victim and persecutor are inseparably interlocked."—Bruno Bettelheim, "A Victim."

3.   "Grammarians have arrived at some basic principles of their science, three of which are fundamental to this discussion. The first is that a language constitutes a set of behavior patterns common to the members of a given community. It is a part of what the anthropologists call the culture of the community. Actually it has complex and intimate relationships with other phases of culture such as myth and ritual. But for purposes of study it may be dealt with as a separate set of phenomena that can be objectively described and analyzed like any other universe of facts. Specifically, its phenomena can be observed, recorded, classified, and compared; and general laws of their behavior can be made by the same inductive process that is used to produce the 'laws' of physics, chemistry, and the other sciences."—W. Nelson Francis, "Revolution in Grammar."

4.   "Memory is a word which has a variety of meanings. The kind that I am concerned with at the moment is the recollection of past occurrences. This is so notoriously fallible that every experimenter makes a record of the result of his experiment at the earliest possible moment: he considers the inference from written words to past events less likely to be mistaken than the direct beliefs which constitute memory. But some time, though perhaps only a few seconds, must elapse between the observation

and the making of the record, unless the record is so fragmentary that memory is needed to interpret it. Thus we do not escape from the need of trusting memory to some degree. Moreover, without memory we should not think of interpreting records as applying to the past because we should not know that there was any past. Now, apart from arguments as to the proved fallibility of memory, there is one awkward consideration which the skeptic may urge. Remembering, which occurs now, cannot possibly—he may say—prove that what is remembered occurred at some other time, because the world might have sprung into being five minutes ago, exactly as it then was, full of acts of remembering which were entirely misleading. Opponents of Darwin, such as Edmund Gosse's father, urged a very similar argument against evolution. The world, they said, was created in 4004 B.C., complete with fossils, which were inserted to try our faith. The world was created suddenly, but was made such as it would have been if it had evolved. There is no logical impossibility about this view. And similarly there is no logical impossibility in the view that the world was created five minutes ago, complete with memories and records. This may seem an improbable hypothesis, but it is not logically refutable."—Russell, *An Outline of Philosophy*.

5. "Since, then, it is necessary for a prince to understand how to make good use of the conduct of animals, he should select among them the fox and the lion, because the lion cannot protect himself from traps, and the fox cannot protect himself from the wolves. So the prince needs to be a fox that he may know to deal with traps, and a lion that he may frighten the wolves. Those who act like the lion alone do not understand their business. A prudent ruler, therefore, cannot and should not observe faith when such observance is to his disadvantage and the causes that made him give his promise have vanished. If men were all good, this advice would not be good, but since men are wicked and do not keep their promises to you, you likewise do not have to keep yours to them. Lawful reasons to excuse his failure to keep them will never be lacking to a prince. It would be possible to give innumerable modern examples of this and to show many treaties and promises that have been made null and void by the faithlessness of princes. And the prince who has best known how to act as a fox has come out best. But one who has this capacity must understand how to keep it covered, and be a skillful pretender and dissembler. Men are so simple and so subject to present needs that he who deceives in this way will always find those who will let themselves be deceived."—Machiavelli, *The Prince*.

EXERCISE 17. **Review**

DIRECTIONS:*Answer the following questions succinctly.*

1. What is the identifying feature of a paragraph?
2. How long should a paragraph be?
3. What is a topic sentence and where should it come in a paragraph?
4. What are the two kinds of paragraph fragments?
5. What is the difference between a generality and a specific detail?
6. How can a statement be a specific detail in one paragraph but a generality in another?
7. What are the two broad modes of paragraph development?
8. What kinds of paragraph development belong under the first broad mode?
9. What kinds of paragraph development belong under the second broad mode?
10. What is restatement in a paragraph?
11. What are the two ways in which paragraph unity can be disrupted?
12. Why is coherence in a paragraph important?
13. How is paragraph coherence different from paragraph unity?
14. What are the three most common methods of achieving coherence in a paragraph?

CHAPTER 4

Sentence Composition

CLARITY AND LOGIC IN THE SENTENCE

Expository writing is concerned primarily with meaning. Thus, above all it must be clear and logical. So far as you the writer are concerned, clarity and logic begin with the basic organization of your paper—with the over-all conception in your mind of what your material is and how you will present it to the reader. Hence we have stressed the importance of your carefully building a basic organization before beginning your actual writing. But for the **reader** clarity and logic begin with the sentence, for he does not yet have the whole in his mind. So it is also necessary for you to understand a great deal about sentence composition in order to provide your readers with clear, logical, mature sentences.

You might expect the principles of the organization of the whole paper to be more complicated than those of paragraph development, and those, in turn, to be more complicated than the principles of sentence composition. Actually, the reverse is true. The English sentence is not only "a noble thing," as Winston Churchill said, but also a vastly complicated thing. Sentence grammar alone is material enough for several courses. Even without becoming involved in grammar, we will find many important principles of sentence composition to study.

The over-all aim of the material that follows in this chapter will be to teach you to be more at home with the marvelous variety of sentence structure in English. You must learn that the first way you get a sentence on paper may not be the best way, or even a good way. You must learn to test each of your sentences with your ear to see if it is terse, vigorous, rhythmic, consistent, and logical. You must **think** about each sentence as you write it and after you write it. That is the only way to write with clarity and logic. Remember that almost no one writes an extended piece of exposition well without some revision. Also remember that until you develop the ability to choose between ways of saying something, you cannot write as a college-educated person should write.

As explained in Chapter 1, sentence structure and diction are the elements of composition that make **style.** Style has to do with terseness, rhythm, variety, smoothness, euphony, vividness, concreteness, clarity, tone, and many other complex abstractions. You should be prepared to work hard at mastering the principles explained in these chapters.

SENTENCE ECONOMY

Perhaps the most common enemy of clarity in sentence composition is wordiness. This is so because loose writing is a reflection of loose thinking. A crisp, economical sentence is usually clear; a flabby, verbose sentence, if not downright unclear, will drug its reader into inattention. When a sentence is not wordy, it is said to be **terse** and **concise.** You can achieve terseness and conciseness, and thus greater clarity, only through thoughtful revision, for the human mind seems to be naturally wordy in expressing itself. When revising their sentences, almost all writers find that they need to reduce rather than increase their wordage. The following pages discuss several methods that will help you in achieving sentence economy.

Through recasting sentences with piled-up phrases

Length and wordiness are not the same in sentence composition. A long sentence can be free of excessive wordage, while a comparatively short sentence can be clogged with useless words. But length in presenting **one** idea is a source of wordiness. Your long sentences may each contain several concisely expressed thoughts. But whenever you find yourself piling up phrases and clauses to express just one thought, you are probably being wordy. For example, consider this sentence: "A flabby, verbose sentence, if not downright unclear, will drug its reader into inattention." The first version of this sentence was this: "A flabby, verbose sentence, if not downright unclear, often has a narcotic effect on the reader so that he fails to see the clarity that is there." This sentence itself is flabby and verbose because it piles up four rather lengthy phrases to express one idea: *often has a narcotic effect/on the reader/so that he fails to see/the clarity that is there.* By the time the reader finishes this sequence of phrases, he is as limp as the sentence.

Here are some other examples of wordiness due to a piling-up of phrases. A revised version follows each example.

> Parody is a type of writing/that imitates another piece of writing/by copying some of the characteristics/of that piece of writing/and making fun of it.
>
> A parody ridicules an original piece of writing by humorously imitating some of its techniques.
>
> An unwanted guest may be encouraged to leave/when he seems reluctant to leave/by letting him know/that you have a difficult job to do/that he may be able to help you with.
>
> You may encourage an unwanted guest to leave by hinting that he may help you with some difficult work.
>
> Our age is called the age of anxiety/because of all the tensions/that everyone feels/about the possibility of a war/that might destroy us all completely.
>
> Ours is an age of anxiety because the fear of total war breeds tensions in us all.

These examples may seem extreme, but such wordy sentences are rather common in student writing. In fact, few writers can instinctively avoid wordiness. But all careful writers revise.

Through reducing uselessly long sentence elements

Another kind of wordiness is due to the choice of a uselessly long sentence element in expressing one idea. The three broad kinds of sentence elements are clauses, phrases, and single words. Clauses tend to be longer than phrases, and phrases longer than single words. If a longer element is used when a shorter one will express the same idea as well, wordiness results. Consider these two sentences.

> The professor dismissed the student in a tactful way.
> The professor tactfully dismissed the student.

The word *tactfully* and the phrase *in a tactful way* are identical in meaning, but the word is shorter than the phrase and thus makes for a more concise and pleasing sentence.

Here are some more examples of wordiness due to the choice of an unnecessarily long sentence element. A revised version follows each example.

> A student who works hard will make a favorable impression on his teacher.
> A hardworking student will favorably impress his teacher.
> The biography of Mark Twain which was written by Dixon Wecter is both accurate and definitive.
> Dixon Wecter's biography of Mark Twain is both accurate and definitive.
> A student who is earnest will set aside a specific study period for each course that he is taking.
> An earnest student will set aside a specific study period for each of his courses.
> The committee chairman acted in a selfish way when he rejected the suggestion that had been proposed by the secretary.
> The committee chairman acted selfishly when he rejected the secretary's suggestion.
> This sentence from the Bible is famous for its pessimism.
> This Biblical sentence is famous for its pessimism.

As you revise your writing, make a conscious attempt to reduce clauses to phrases and phrases to words. In this way you can make your writing more concise and thus clearer and more pleasing.

Through eliminating deadwood

Another specific kind of wordiness has the imposing names *redundancy, tautology,* and *pleonasm.* All of these words means about the same thing: the use of a word or phrase that repeats a meaning already in the sentence. Thus the use of *in a tactful way* for *tactfully* would not be called redundant or tautological or pleonastic, for even the phrase expresses the idea only once. The use of the phrase is simple wordiness. But the use of both the phrase and the word in the same simple sentence would be redundant: "The professor tactfully dismissed the student in a tactful way."

Here are some examples of redundant (or tautological or pleonastic) phrases. Note that the italicized words can be omitted without a loss of meaning.

> Repeat that *back over once again,* please.
> The President introduced a *new* innovation.
> John is *equally* as bright as Bill.
> The contest is limited *only* to juniors.
> Each *and every* coed is invited.
> A government should express the will of the people *it governs.*
> I find scientific study *more* preferable.
> I think that if I make an A *that* I will celebrate.
> We live in a fast-moving period *of time.*
> She will *continue to* remain faithful.
> You should recast that sentence *in different words.*
> Her whisperings were audible *to the ear.*
> My face was red *in color.*

Wordiness of the redundant sort is usually called *deadwood,* because the offending words and phrases can just be cut out with no loss of life in the sentence. To eliminate deadwood, you revise by omitting a part of your sentence rather than by reducing sentence elements or recasting the sentence. You cannot rely on your ear to detect deadwood as readily as other kinds of wordiness. You must consciously look at your sentences to spot useless words or phrases.

Now a word of caution against making a game of brevity. You can go too far in trying to compress your meaning into fewer words. A writer later identified as Mark Twain once wrote anonymously:

> But tautology cannot scare me, anyway. Conversation would be intolerably stiff and formal without it; and a mild form of it can limber up even printed matter without doing it serious damage. Some folks are so afraid of a little repetition that they make their meaning vague, when they could just as well make it clear, if only their ogre were out of the way.—*The Atlantic Monthly* (June 1880).

So don't write as though you are composing telegrams and will save fifteen cents for each word you can omit. Above all be full and clear in what you say. But of two full, clear ways of expressing a sentence, choose the less wordy one.

EXERCISE 18.   Eliminating Wordiness

DIRECTIONS: *Each of the following sentences is too wordy for good exposition. Eliminate the wordiness in each by either recasting to achieve terseness, reducing clauses or phrases to shorter elements, or omitting deadwood.*

1. Two characteristics which are necessary for success in salesmanship are aggressiveness and tact.
2. You must consciously look at your sentences to see if words or phrases can be left out because they are useless.
3. A car that is old is often more expensive to own than one which is new.
4. Your logic apparently seems contradictory.
5. Because I had had a disagreement with Professor McCall, I was in a state of anxiety about my grade in Political Science.
6. In order to be impartial in his judging, the judge studied both sides of the issues that were involved before he gave his verdict in the case.
7. She received my call to her on the telephone in a courteous manner.
8. The visiting minister spoke in a vague way that was not very clear to the congregation that was listening.
9. He won each and every prize that his school had to offer.

10. Many college instructors in composition classes where writing is taught teach students rules that contradict the rules that they were taught in their high school English classes.
11. In a state of nervousness, he advanced to the podium.
12. In my opinion I believe that parents who have children who are destructive should have to pay for the damage that their children do.
13. C. P. Snow, who is an Englishman, precipitated the debate about the two cultures, which are the humanistic and the scientific.
14. Two essential traits necessary for a successful politician are the ability to remember names that he hears and the knack of appearing to be interested in individuals.
15. A professor who is learned is more likely to gain his students' respect than one who takes a friendly stand but is superficial.
16. The process of developing color photos is a much less complicated process now than it was twenty years ago, when it was a very complicated process.
17. With a great deal of sadness, we left the cemetery.
18. Many students study for courses they are taking by reading notes that other students in the same course have taken from class lectures.
19. In a less conspicuous way, I followed John to the dormitory where we students lived.
20. A citizen who is conscientious will study the issues that are involved in an election before going to the polls to vote on them.

SENTENCE VIGOR

Individual sentences can be muscular and strong like brisk ale or watery and weak like cheap strawberry punch. You can test the strength of the liquids with your tongue; you can test the strength of the sentences with your ear. Wordiness, as explained above, greatly reduces sentence vigor and emphasis. There are also other flabby constructions that should be avoided for the sake of sentence strength. The following pages discuss various methods of achieving sentence vigor.

Through using the active voice

One simple method of increasing sentence vigor is to cultivate the active voice and to avoid the passive voice. The active voice is this construction: *Someone did something;* the passive voice this: *Some-*

thing was done by someone. Your ear tells you that the active voice is vigorous, the passive voice weakish. Sometimes you must use the passive voice, but you should avoid it when possible.

Here are some pairs of sentences that illustrate the increased vigor of active over passive voice:

> The food was devoured by the hungry immigrants.
> The hungry immigrants devoured the food.
> The game was played hard by the evenly matched teams.
> The evenly matched teams played the game hard.
> The little republic of Erewhon was bailed out again by our government.
> Our government again bailed out the little republic of Erewhon.
> Many requests for dates were turned down by the beauty queen.
> The beauty queen turned down many requests for dates.

The sentences in the active voice in these examples are more emphatic for two reasons. First, each requires two fewer words—and this economy itself adds strength. Second, each has as its subject a more important word than the related sentence in the passive voice—and this emphatic placement of important words also adds strength. In the last sentence, for example, *queen* is a more important word than *requests* and for emphasis it should be placed in a dominant position. In your own writing, you must watch your sentences carefully to avoid a weak use of the passive voice. You cannot hope to avoid this construction instinctively, for it is so common that our minds accept it without question.

Through effective word order

Other aspects of word order also affect sentence vigor. Usually, for example, a subordinate construction should be placed at the beginning or in the middle of a sentence, where it will be strong, rather than at the end, where it may be weak. Note the difference in vigor between these pairs of sentences:

> We might have lost the Revolutionary War if France had not come to our aid.
> If France had not come to our aid, we might have lost the Revolutionary War.

Grant allowed corruption to enter his administration, not being a strong president.

Not being a strong president, Grant allowed corruption to enter his administration.

In the 1920s too many people bought stocks on margin. The stock market collapsed in October 1929, as a result.

In the 1920s too many people bought stocks on margin. As a result, the stock market collapsed in October 1929.

President Truman was wise to implement the Marshall Plan, in my opinion.

In my opinion, President Truman was wise to implement the Marshall Plan.

Usually your ear will tell you when a sentence ends with a weak subordinate construction. You may often increase the vigor of such a sentence by shifting the construction.

Through proper subordination of ideas

Two sentence ideas are said to be *coordinate* when they are given equal rank. Coordinate ideas are usually joined either by a coordinating conjunction (*and, but, or*) or by a logical connective (*however, therefore, nevertheless, so,* and so on). One sentence idea is said to be *subordinate* to another when it is placed in a position of lesser importance. Most subordinate elements are introduced by connective words called subordinating conjunctions (*when, after, since, so that,* and so on) and relative pronouns (*who, which, that*); some are attached to sentences without the use of connective words.[1]

Sentence vigor is weakened by *faulty coordination*. Note the primer-style flabbiness of the following examples and the increased vigor that proper subordination brings:

Faulty coordination: Dean Collins prepared a new school calendar, and it calls for longer final exam periods.

Effective subordination: Dean Collins prepared a new school calendar that calls for longer final exam periods.

Faulty coordination: I read an article by Paul Pundit in *The Reporter,* and it said that by 1975 the United States and Russia would form an alliance against China.

---

[1] The section "Some Problems in Sentence Clarity" (below) gives a fuller discussion of coordination and subordination and of the functions of coordinating and subordinating connectives.

Effective subordination: I read an article by Paul Pundit in *The Reporter* which said that by 1975 the United States and Russia would form an alliance against China.

Weak coordination: The Floor Leader knew the bill would not pass at that time, so he postponed the vote.

Effective subordination: Since he knew the bill would not pass at that time, the Floor Leader postponed the vote.

Weak coordination: Earnings on school bonds are not taxable, so I invested my money in our local bond issue.

Effective subordination: Since earnings on school bonds are not taxable, I invested my money in our local bond issue.

Weak coordination: I had been warned about the vicious dog, but I carelessly entered the gate.

Effective subordination: Though I had been warned about the vicious dog, I carelessly entered the gate.

The commonest source of weak coordination is an excessive use of the connective *so.* Though fully acceptable in ordinary conversation, *so* tends to weaken sentence vigor in exposition. You can strengthen your writing by consciously replacing the coordination expressed by *so* with the subordination expressed by *since* or *because.* In other cases you must depend on your ear to warn you of weak coordination, though you must also have an intellectual understanding of weak coordination so that you can interpret the flaw that your ear detects.

Through proper placement of modifiers

Another aspect of sentence order that affects vigor and emphasis is the placement of modifiers. Generally, a word or phrase modifier should, for sentence strength and clarity, be placed near the word it modifies. Otherwise sentence structure is likely to be loose and weak.

Here are some examples of sentence improvement through shifting of modifiers:

This simple operation can be learned by anyone who has had high school algebra in eight hours.

This simple operation can be learned in eight hours by anyone who has had high school algebra.

A mother wants to know what her daughter's plans are for her own satisfaction.

For her own satisfaction, a mother wants to know what her daughter's plans are.

People worry from the time they get up until they go to bed about many things.

People worry about many things from the time they get up until they go to bed.

I learned that my father was sick in a letter.

I learned in a letter that my father was sick.

Faulty modifier placement, which can greatly reduce sentence vigor, is one of the most common weaknesses in composition because sentence structure is so complex. Most sentences in exposition have a half dozen or more clauses, phrases, and single-word modifiers that require exact placement for clarity and vigor. It is not surprising, then, that a sentence element frequently gets misplaced. You can eliminate such weaknesses in your own sentences only through careful revision, for since your mind thinks you have said all you wanted to say, it does not easily detect a misplaced sentence element.

Through recasting chopped-up sentences

A sentence broken into many short phrases and clauses usually lacks vigor. The following example appeared verbatim in a student paper: "For many years, since the birth of our country, the schools of the South, and some in the North also, have welcomed, heartily, any American (except those in black skin) into their doors." This sentence, aside from being senseless, has no strength at all, for its chopped-up construction never allows the reader to get properly launched in his reading. Now suppose the writer had composed this sentence: "For many years the schools of the South have welcomed any American (except those in black skin) into their doors." With only one parenthetic element, this sentence has strength and also a fine irony in its meaning.

Here is another chopped-up sentence from a student paper: "In this period of our lives, as the United States stands, almost alone, defending itself against communism, we feel the urge, in our anxiety, to be conservative." The reader himself feels chopped to pieces as he reads such a sentence. The writer could have strengthened his sentence with only minor revision: "In this period of our lives, as the United States stands almost alone in resisting communism, we feel the anxious urge to be conservative." If the writer of the faulty sentence had tested his work with his ear, he could doubtless have made such an improvement himself. He should have remembered that in writing there is no substitute for careful revision, and that successful revision calls for testing with his ear as well as with his mind.

Through recasting overloaded sentences

Another enemy of vigor is the overloaded sentence. This is the kind of sentence into which a writer crams too many ideas without giving due consideration to the relationship between them. A long sentence is not necessarily limp and weak if all of its parts are closely related and logically fitted to each other. But a long sentence without these qualities is invariably overloaded and weak. Here is an example:

> College entrance tests seem to be holy writ to counsellors, for they take the scores to be immutable evidence of a student's ability, and they aren't always, and so when some other data might give the counsellor a better understanding of the student's capacity, he'll only say, "But your score was so and so," whereas I know that a student can make an entirely different score on a different day, which I did once.

This sentence has no sustained vigor, for there is too much looseness between its parts. It rambles too much.

Here is a revision:

> Counsellors seem to think of college entrance tests as holy writ, for they take the scores to be immutable evidence of a student's ability. Thus when some other data might give the counsellor a better understanding of a student's capacity, he'll only say, "But your score was so and so." But I know from experience that an individual's score on a test one day may vary widely from his score on the same test on another day. Thus I believe that test scores should not be thought of as iron-clad evidence of one's ability.

Now the rambling, loose quality has been eliminated with the separation of the ideas into four sentences. The resulting tightness greatly improves the vigor of the writing.

These comments about sentence vigor have all related to sentence structure. You have been advised to prefer the active over the passive voice, to avoid placing weak subordinate constructions at the end of a sentence, to avoid weak coordination, to place modifiers in a clear position, to avoid chopping up a sentence into a series of small units, and to beware of the rambling, overloaded sentence. Choice of words is also important in composing strong sentences. This aspect of composition will be dealt with in Chapter 5: Diction.

EXERCISE 19. Improving Sentence Vigor

DIRECTIONS: *Write a more vigorous and concise version of each of the following sentences.*

1. Some unfavorable criticism is beginning to be written about Hemingway by the critics.
2. My sociology professor has just published a new book, and it is about the effects of divorce on children.
3. Secretary Burrows made a policy speech about Sikkim though he had been warned by the President to avoid commenting on the Sikkim-China fracas.
4. A new industrial revolution is coming. Its new machinery is not mechanical. It is electronic. The principle of the gear and cam is still valid. But the electronic impulse does new and more wonderful things. The giant electronic brains are the basis of the new revolution. They seem to become more marvelous every month.
5. Our professor brought in a guest lecturer and he talked about the religious beliefs of the Australian aborigines.
6. Today's new highways are much superior to those of twenty years ago chiefly because the development of huge earth-moving machines, which were pioneered by a man named Le Tourneau, who had his plant in Toccoa, Georgia, has allowed engineers to plan roads with no short or sharp curves or steep grades because they can simply cut huge gaps through mountains and make small hills level so that the road bed can be straight with only a small degree of rise or fall.
7. When they are potted, my grandparents like African violets.
8. I was chatting with my girlfriend when my father came home on the telephone.
9. In these modern times, when crises develop daily, the political authorities, who are often uneducated, make many decisions, and also appointments, that intensify rather than relieve pressures, much to our unrest.

10. Is a mentally ill person of today treated better than one of the past by society?
11. We had to walk about twelve blocks to our appointment in the rain.
12. Many experimental books were written by William Faulkner, and the general reading public has been puzzled by most of them.
13. Our relations with Russia could be improved if more tourists from each country would visit the other, which would give everybody better understanding, in my opinion.
14. To vote right, or at least intelligently, in national elections, and some local ones, too, you must not only know the candidates, that is, how they stand on issues, but also the views of the two parties, for the parties, being strong organizations, often dominate the candidates.
15. We had been warned that a storm was brewing, so we took the large boat which would be able to weather high gales.

SENTENCE RHYTHM

All language has rhythm, the source of which lies in the varying stresses which we give to individual syllables. Stress in language is the degree of loudness in pronouncing syllables. Even when we are reading, the stress of syllables is silently recorded in our minds, and we thereby feel the rhythm of the phrases. There are four degrees of stress, but for the sake of simplicity we usually speak only of accented (stressed) and unaccented (unstressed) syllables. When studying poetry, students are often asked to mark off the pattern of accented and unaccented syllables, as in these lines[2]:

> "Tér/ence, this/ is stu/pid stuff:
> You eat/ your vic/tuals fast/ enough;
> There can't/ be much/ amiss,/ 'tis clear,
> To see/ the rate/ you drink/ your beer.
> But, oh,/ good Lord,/ the verse/ you make,
> It gives/ a chap/ the bel/lyache."

The rhythm of this poetry is due to the poet's special arrangement of accented and unaccented syllables.

Obviously, there can be enormous variety in the sequence of accented and unaccented syllables, especially since there are really four degrees of stress. Poets consciously manipulate this variety to produce their poetic rhythm, but prose writers generally let the accents fall where they will. Nevertheless, the mere presence of various degrees of stress creates rhythm of some sort in all writing. And while a pleasing rhythm is perhaps more important in imaginative writing, good writers of exposition make it a practice to listen to their sentences to avoid harsh, awkward, or limp rhythm and to achieve some degree of smoothness.

Following are a few well known prose quotations that illustrate the power of strong rhythm:

> The race is not to the swift, nor the battle to the strong, . . . but time and chance happeneth to them all.—Ecclesiastes.
>
> The sun never shone on a cause of greater worth. 'Tis not the affair of a city, a county, a province, or a kingdom, but of a continent.—Tom Paine, *Common Sense.*
>
> A foolish consistency is the hobgoblin of little minds.— Emerson, *Self-Reliance.*
>
> Under a government which imprisons any unjustly, the true place for a just man is also a prison.—Thoreau, *Civil Disobedience.*

As an exercise in understanding the value of powerful rhythm in prose, try writing new versions of these sentences. You will find that much of their effectiveness will vanish. For example, suppose the quotation from Ecclesiastes to be rewritten in this manner: "In a race, the swiftest person does not always win, and a strong person does not always win a battle; both of them are affected by time and chance." The limpness of the rhythm in this rephrasing has killed the stirring quality of the original.

You need not—in fact, should not—try to give your exposition poetic rhythm, but you should use your ear to avoid awkwardness and limpness. Rhythm and smoothness are very closely allied to sentence terseness and vigor, as discussed in the preceding sections. When you revise to achieve economy and strength, you also necessarily improve sentence rhythm.

SENTENCE VARIETY

A concise, vigorous, rhythmic sentence is a creation you can be proud of. But unfortunately you cannot learn just one sentence pattern embodying these qualities and then use it over and over. In the first place, a wide variety of sentences is necessary to express different kinds of meaning. Furthermore, a sequence of unvarying sentences becomes monotonous and destroys vigor. Though repetition of sentence structure can often be used effectively, each sentence is, nevertheless, a separate challenge and must develop its own vigor without aimlessly imitating that of the preceding sentence.

To achieve smooth qualities in writing, you must effect some variation in your sentences both in kind and length. Wholly unvarying structure in the sentences of a paragraph produces dull writing even if each separate sentence is vigorous and smooth. Here is an example:

> When you travel in a foreign country, you should imitate the customs and habits of the natives. When you see a native use strange table manners, you should observe closely so you can learn them. If you find that all the gentlemen of the street are dressed formally, you should dress in that fashion. If, on the other hand, the natives dress in sport clothes, you should also wear them. Even if a custom seems repugnant to you, you should still practice it. For example, if in rural France you find men and women using the same rest room together, you should use it too unabashed.

Such unrelieved repetition of one sentence pattern eventually becomes monotonous, regardless of the quality of the individual sentences.

Now note the improvement to be gained through varying sentence structure:

> When you travel in a foreign country, you should imitate the customs and habits of the natives. On your day of arrival, you might begin by closely observing table manners, which are sure to differ from yours. By the second or third day, you should be eating like a native. You may also quickly learn to imitate the habits of dress in your host country, and soon you should not be so gauche as to be seen in the wrong kind of clothes. Even if a

custom seems repugnant to you, you should still be courteous and brave enough to practice it. For example, in rural France you might find men and women using the same rest room together. With a little will power you can behave as though intimate bathrooms are the rage in your own country.

Even the most unperceptive reader will respond more readily to this paragraph than to the monotonous one above, for his sense of rhythm receives more satisfaction from it. You may often want to repeat sentence structure for special effects, but you should avoid having four or five similar sentences in sequence.

When used in sequence, sentences of the same length also become monotonous and lose vigor. In the faulty paragraph above, the sentences are not only similar in construction but also in length. This is usually the case in a paragraph without sentence variety, for sentences of similar patterns are often of about the same length. The most common and offensive kind of repetition of sentence length, however, is the use of a sequence of short, choppy sentences. Here is an example:

> Most of modern man's illnesses are psychosomatic. This means that the mind makes the body sick. These illnesses affect all parts of the body. The most common of them occur in the digestive system. But the circulatory organs are also affected. Liver and diabetic troubles can also be psychosomatic. According to some doctors even obesity has a similar origin. And of course most headaches are psychosomatic.

A short, compact sentence has many uses in expository writing. But seldom can more than two of them appear in sequence without sounding childishly monotonous.

Now note the improved vigor gained through injecting sentence variety into the above paragraph:

> Most of modern man's illnesses are psychosomatic, which means that the mind makes the body sick. These illnesses affect all parts of the body. The most common of them occur in the digestive system, but diseases of the circulatory organs, the liver, and the pancreas can also be psychosomatic. Even obesity, according to some doctors, can be caused by the mind's effect on the body. And of course most headaches are psychosomatic.

Two short sentences are effectively used in this revised paragraph. But they are separated and thus do not set up a monotonous pattern of rhythm.

SENTENCE PATTERNS

The grammar of the English language is awesomely complex. To study it completely would be the work of more than one college course. In fact, at the present time it would not be possible to study English grammar completely, for the expert grammarians themselves are by no means in full agreement about how to describe what goes on grammatically in all aspects of English sentences. Indeed, a revolution in English grammar is at present underway, and the old traditional grammar based on the eight parts of speech, though partially sound, is now seen to be inadequate in its attempt to describe grammatical functions. But the new grammar is still incomplete and is as yet being taught only in a very few schools. In fact, there are several new grammars competing with each other. It is likely that the year 2000 will have arrived before a new, truer grammar is firmly ensconced in the curriculum of all American schools. In the meantime school children are somewhat victimized as they struggle to understand a partially illogical system of grammar.

Fortunately, however, you do not need a full knowledge of grammar in order to write well. Many excellent writers have only the foggiest understanding of grammar. In fact, if one had to know grammar fully in order to write well, we would have very few good writers. But a knowledge of certain large elements of sentence structure and their logical relationship to each other will help you write better. This section will explain these large elements and the logic they embody, but it will not explain a system of grammar.

The pattern of the simple sentence

The core of all writing is the simple sentence (also called independent clause), not the individual word. Except for such sentences as "Go out and play!" and a few miscellaneous constructions, all simple sentences have a fundamental two-part pattern called the subject and the predicate. The first part, the subject, is usually defined as what the sentence is talking about (this is the same meaning as the *subject* of an essay). But this definition is true only in a limited sense. Consider these sentences:

> The President sent the Speaker a list of recalcitrant representatives.
> The Speaker was sent a list of recalcitrant representatives by the President.
> A list of recalcitrant representatives was sent to the Speaker by the President.
> What the President sent to the Speaker was a list of recalcitrant representatives.

Each of these sentences has a different subject, but each says the same thing. Therefore the above definition of a subject must be qualified.

A sentence subject bears a special relationship to the verb and can only be identified in relation to the verb. If the verb is an action verb, the subject performs the action, as in the first sentence above. If the verb is in the passive voice, the subject receives the action, as in the second and third sentences above. (The verb *send* has two meanings in the passive voice: it can be used to say that an object *is sent* by someone and it can be used to say that someone *is sent* an object by someone else. Thus *was sent* can take the two different subjects illustrated.) If the verb performs a defining or descriptive function or expresses a state of existence (*is, looks, seems, appears, becomes,* and so forth), the subject is the thing defined or described or the thing that exists, as in the last sentence above.

But since identifying a subject is easier than defining one, we will use the simple definition that the subject is what the sentence is talking about. With this definition, the predicate can be defined as what is said about the subject. That is, the predicate tells what the subject does or what is done to the subject or what the subject is. The following examples show how most simple sentences have this natural two-part structure:

> Most simple sentences (subject) / naturally fall into two parts (predicate).
> The study of grammar (subject) / deserves to be a subject field of its own (predicate).
> A knowledge of the large elements of sentence structure

(subject) / can be helpful in learning to write good sentences (predicate).

The old traditional English grammar (subject) / is a partially illogical imitation of Latin grammar (predicate).

Into the classroom strode (predicate) / the professor (subject).

From these examples you can see that a subject establishes what a sentence is talking about and that a predicate says something about the subject. What, for example, is being talked about in the last example? "The professor." And what is being said about him? "That he strode into the classroom."

Traditional grammar has much to say about the structure of subjects and predicates. But that need be only of small concern to us here, partly because it is not really relevant to the process of writing and partly because much of it is not true. The grammatical construction of the predicate is much more complex than that of the subject and traditional grammar uses many terms to explain the various aspects of the predicate. For our study, we need only know that every predicate has a verb and that most have in addition a complement—that is, a word or group of words that completes the sense of the predicate. The following sentences illustrate this:

The human body // can tolerate (verb) / only a certain amount of radiation (complement).

The study of grammar for its own sake // is (verb) / a profitable academic pursuit (complement).

A poorly trained English teacher // may confuse (verb) / his students (complement).

The culprit // should have remained (verb) / quiet (complement).

There are various kinds of complements. In the study of grammar, they are of interest; but in the study of writing they are of small significance.

For the purpose of learning to write better, the foregoing simple analysis of subjects and predicates is all you need. In learning how to compose a variety of mature, logical, clear sentences, you must start with the subject-predicate pattern, which, as a simple sentence, is the core of all writing. From this core you can build a wide variety of more complex sentence patterns. And you can best learn to do so by understanding the logical function of large sentence elements rather than the grammatical function of individual words.

The following four sentence patterns involve **coordination** of ideas. The verb *to coordinate* literally means to arrange together. Thus when ideas (or sentence elements) are coordinated, they are given equal rank. Usually when two or more elements are coordinated, a connecting word is put between them to show that they are linked together equally. The coordinating conjunctions *and, but,* and *or (nor)* may be used to coordinate any kind of sentence elements. A group of words called logical connectives (*however, therefore, otherwise,* and so on) can be used to coordinate only independent clauses. When independent clauses or lesser sentence elements are coordinated, the writer is indicating that the ideas they contain are of equal importance.

The pattern of simple sentences with compound elements

The least complicated expansion of the simple sentence is the use of compound elements within the sentence. By doubling or tripling either the subject or the predicate or either part of the predicate, we can add a second full idea to a simple sentence without composing a separate sentence:

> Intellectual curiosity is necessary for successful college work. Industrial application is also necessary. (two simple sentences)
>
> Intellectual curiosity and industrious application are necessary for successful college work. (compound subject)
>
> The detective interviewed all the principals in the crime. He examined the scene of the crime. He scrutinized the claims of the supposed victim. (three simple sentences)
>
> The detective interviewed all the principals in the crime, examined the scene of the crime, and scrutinized the claims of the supposed victim. (triple predicate)
>
> The murderer dismembered the body. Then he hid it. (two sentences)
>
> The murderer dismembered and then hid the body. (compound verb)
>
> The Governor ordered the Highway Patrol to blockade

Stine Road. He also ordered the National Guard to send out helicopters. (two sentences)

The Governor ordered the Highway Patrol to blockade
Stine Road and the National Guard to send out helicopters.
(compound complement)

The use of compound elements in these examples has improved
sentence economy, vigor, and rhythm. The separate sentences, on
the other hand, sound wordy, flabby, and awkward.

EXERCISE 20. Building Sentences with Compound Elements

DIRECTIONS: *Combine each of the following pairs
of sentences into one sentence with compound elements. Any part of a
sentence may be compounded.*

1. While at home, the Senator usually drank beer on an equal footing
   with his budding lawmaker.
   While at home, the Senator usually exchanged ideas on an equal
   footing with his budding lawmaker.
2. The future of the United States depends on our avoiding nuclear
   war.
   The future of the free world depends on our avoiding nuclear war.
3. The Senator's assistant scrambled for the file bearing upon the
   conversation.
   The assistant placed it in front of his boss's eye.
   The assistant offered up key information in urgent whispers.
4. We must use every means short of surrender to avoid armed conflict with Russia.
   We must use every means short of aggression to keep free nations
   on our side.
5. Blinded by ambition, the Senator accepted my offer.
   Not questioning my authority, the Senator accepted my offer.
6. The professor was angered by my tardiness.
   The professor was angered by my failure to turn in an assignment.
   The professor was angered by my inattention in class.
7. Political tensions oblige us to negotiate with Russia.
   Political tensions oblige us to continue the foreign aid program.
8. The public man is usually an extrovert.
   His assistant is usually an extrovert.
9. In a bitter campaign, Smathers ran against Pepper.
   Smathers defeated Pepper.

10. The Congressman's time must be shared with party leaders.
It must be shared with lobbyists.
It must be shared with reporters.
It must be shared with constituents.

The pattern of compound sentences
with coordinating conjunctions

Whole simple sentences, as well as their subjects and predicates, can be compounded, with the so-called compound sentence resulting. Simple sentences (or independent clauses) are compounded not to avoid composing separate sentences, but in order to show a close logical relationship between the two (or more) independent clauses. There are various kinds of logic that can be expressed between the clauses of a compound sentence and various methods of expressing the logic.

The most common method of expressing the logic between the two clauses in a compound sentence is the use of one of the **coordinating conjunctions:** *and, but, for,* and *or (nor).* The conjunction *and* expresses the logic of addition; it is used to connect ideas that are just being added to each other. For example: "The Governor sought votes among the country club set, and the Lieutenant Governor campaigned in the factories." The conjunction *and* shows how these two statements are closely related. To express the two ideas in separate sentences would sound childish.

Sometimes the word *and* expresses the logic of cause-and-result as well as of addition. For example: "The reviewers panned Broadway's newest musical, and theatergoers stayed away in droves." Again, the two closely related statements are added together, but with an additional suggestion that the first statement was the cause of the second. This is a subtle and sophisticated use of *and,* and one that you might imitate.

Though *and* seems the simplest of words, it is subject to misuse even among college students. Some misuse it by childishly adding together clauses not very closely related. For example: "The meter of this line is iambic, and it has multiple alliteration to heighten its musical effect, and it means that the athlete was honored while still quite young." These three statements are closely enough related to be in the same paragraph, but not in the same sentence. Since they refer to three separate areas of poetic discussion, the clauses should have been given independent status. Some writers also fail to use *and* when it is needed. For example: "The metaphor 'house of dust' is contrasted to 'house of flesh.' It means death or the grave." These two statements are closely enough related to be added together. In this case, sentence smoothness as well as logic will be improved by making one sentence with a compound predicate: "The metaphor 'house of dust' is contrasted to 'house of flesh' and means death or the grave."

The conjunction *but* expresses the logic of contrast. When used between independent clauses, it shows that one of the statements contradicts or opposes the other. For example:

> The Army promised to send me to electronics school, but I was actually sent to Germany as a truck driver.
> The weather department predicted warm, cloudy weather, but a clear cold spell suddenly developed.

Like *and, but* is subject to misuse even by college students. Sometimes, for example, a writer uses *but* when there is not a clear logic of contrast between his two statements: "Most of the time in Fairbanks we played cards, but every soldier finds duty in remote places boring." The logic in this sentence is not clear because the first statement does not seem to be in opposition to the second. Sometimes a writer will also lose control of his logic by omitting a needed *but:* "While stationed in Fairbanks, we were often sent pretty little reminders of home. No one sent us what we really needed." The logic of these two statements springs alive with the conjunction *but:* "While stationed in Fairbanks, we were often sent pretty little reminders of home, but no one sent us what we really needed."

In spite of their apparent simplicity, the conjunctions *and* and *but* can work logical wonders. You should pay closer attention to their use. And incidentally, you should know that, contrary to a common belief, both *and* and *but* can effectively be used to begin sentences and paragraphs.

The connective *for* is usually called a coordinating conjunction, but it is not of the same class of words as *and* and *but*. As a connective, it can be used only between independent clauses and not between single words, phrases, or subordinate clauses. It does not, on the other hand, appear to be in the same class as the logical connectives discussed below. Perhaps some future grammarian can decide just what class of words it belongs to.

Whatever it may be called grammatically, *for* is a very useful connective but one rarely used to advantage in student writing. It can express the logic of cause-and-result in the same way that *because* does, but it should be so used only when the clauses it joins are of equal or coordinate value. For example:

> My father insisted that I stay in college, for he knew the economic and social value of an education.
>
> The President called a special session of Congress, for he was afraid that war was about to break out.

In each of these sentences the first statement is the result of the second—or, of course, the second may be called the cause of the first. And in each case the two statements appear to be of equal value. If the word *because* were substituted for *for,* the sense of the sentences would remain perfect, but the first statement in each would then appear to be more important than the second. You should practice using *for* instead of *because* in sentences like these, for such practice will help you be somewhat more precise in expressing yourself.

The conjunctions *or* and *nor* are used to join *alternative* ideas. These conjunctions, not especially common in compound sentences, give student writers very little trouble. Both *so* and *yet* are sometimes called coordinating conjunctions; they more properly belong, however, in the group of words called logical connectives.

Compound sentences are usually punctuated with a comma preceding the conjunction. Only when the clauses are short and clear should the comma be omitted, as in this sentence: "The lightning flashed and the thunder rumbled." A comma should always precede *for* when it is used as a conjunction, for otherwise ambiguity would result. For example: "I bought several boxes of candy for the salesgirl was very pretty." If a comma is not used in such a sentence, *for* will be mistaken for a preposition, and the reader will stumble in his reading. Semicolons may be used to separate clauses in a compound sentence when the clauses are very long or have several other commas of their own.

EXERCISE 21. Building Compound Sentences

DIRECTIONS: *Combine each of the following pairs of sentences into one compound sentence with a coordinating conjunction.*

1. The political battle between the Governor and his Attorney General has become more bitter of late.
   Both factions of the party in power have hopes of a reconciliation.
2. The war may last many more years.
   The enemy shows no sign of weakening.
3. The sergeant called for volunteers.
   Fourteen of the squad's members promptly raised their hands.
4. The party leaders are very apprehensive.
   They know that intraparty fighting can lose them their present position of power.
5. The Senator appealed to the labor unions for votes.
   The union leaders ignored him.
6. W. H. Auden hasn't the pleasantest voice in the world.
   He knows what he means.
   He reads illuminatingly.
7. Radio will continue to flourish.
   The teen-age market will continue to grow.
8. Robert Frost was constantly reading his poetry aloud.
   He read it as it should be read.
9. He devoted twenty hours a day to his campaign.
   He received only 38 percent of the votes cast.
10. A political candidate usually belongs to a church.
    The voting public is afraid of agnostics and tepid believers.

The pattern of compound sentences
with logical connectives

Simple sentences may also be compounded through the use of **logical connectives** (also called **conjunctive adverbs**), a rather large group of similar words that express various logical relationships between ideas. These are coordinating words in that they join elements of equal rank—that is, independent clauses. They are different from coordinating conjunctions, however, in that they cannot be used to join single words and phrases.

Several of these words express the logic of cause-and-result: *so, accordingly, consequently, hence, therefore,* and *thus.* Examples:

Words that express logical relationships are important in the thinking process; therefore you can improve your thinking and writing by learning to use logical connectives more effectively.

My philosophy teacher told us to be original in our thinking; accordingly, I sold my text and thought for myself.

I received a ten-dollar raise; thus I was able to keep up my car payments.

In each of these cases the first statement is a cause and the second a result. Note that the connective *for* could be used in each example if the clauses were reversed. Note also that any one of the connectives in the above list could be used in any one of the three examples. These connectives, however, differ slightly in their suggestive meanings, and so there is usually a best choice for any one sentence.

Some of the logical connectives express the logic of contrast: *however, nevertheless, still,* and *yet.* The logic inherent in these words is substantially the same as that in *but.* Slightly different shades of meaning are involved, however, and so usually there is a best choice for any one sentence. Examples:

The Student Council voted to ban liquor at football games; some of the rooters, however, continued to bring vodka-filled oranges.

My philosophy instructor says that all philosophic problems are relative; still, I believe there must be some absolute truths.

Note that any of the four connectives given in this paragraph as well as *but,* will express the logic between these statements.

The logic of condition is expressed by *otherwise.* This means that the truth of one of the statements is dependent on the truth of the other. Example: "We must avoid nuclear war; otherwise civilization will end." The condition in this example can be seen when an *if* clause is substituted: "If we do not avoid nuclear war, civilization will end." The use of the compound sentence instead of the *if* clause shows that each statement is receiving equal emphasis.

These logical connectives express the logic of time: *afterwards, earlier, later,* and *then.* And these express a simple logic of addition: *besides, furthermore, moreover,* and *also.* Examples:

The President vetoed the omnibus farm bill; then he asked Congress to reconsider the Tanner Plan.

The President vetoed the omnibus farm bill; he vowed, moreover, that he would use all the power of his office to prevent its passage over his veto.

Compound sentences with logical connectives are usually punctuated with a semicolon at the end of the first clause. If the connective word comes immediately after the semicolon and before the second clause, it may or may not have a comma after it, depending on whether the writer wants a distinct pause after the connective. When the connective is shifted to the interior of the second clause, as it often is for stylistic variation, it is set off by commas on both sides. The short logical connectives—*so, yet,* and *then*—are sometimes used with only a comma instead of a semicolon between the clauses. The above examples illustrate these methods of punctuation.

All of the logical connectives are very useful words. In any coherent piece of writing there is always a logical relationship between successive statements, and good writers use conjunctions and connectives generously to make their logic clear. Most students can improve their writing by consciously increasing their use of logical connectives in general.

EXERCISE 22.   Building Compound Sentences

DIRECTIONS: *Combine each of the following pairs of sentences into one compound sentence with a logical connective joining the clauses. How many different connectives could be used in each sentence?*

1. Almost everyone agrees that college students should write mechanically correct English.
   No one has found a satisfactory method of teaching this aspect of writing.
2. A poet gives an insight into his intentions.
   I like to hear a poet read his own poetry.
3. Edith Sitwell had a strong, rich voice.
   She read with a kind of showmanship suited to her poetry.
4. Today we face a new kind of poverty.
   The struggle against poverty has taken on a different aspect.
5. We must eliminate hard-core poverty from our land.
   We will face continuing political crises and upheavals.

    6. The camel may be "the ship of the desert."
      The Sahara remains today a greater obstacle to travel than the Mediterranean Sea.
    7. The Congo must reduce its tribal rivalries.
      It will not make democratic progress.
    8. In theory the immigrants had been absorbed into the country.
      They were discriminated against by the older inhabitants.
    9. The court dismissed his appeal.
      He seemed doomed to spend the rest of his life in prison.
  10. Billwiller made a straight A average in his senior year.
      He was awarded a University Fellowship.

The pattern of compound sentences without connectives

Frequently the logical relationship between two independent clauses is clearly implied without the use of a conjunction or connective. For example, everyone will unconsciously understand the logic of result-followed-by-cause between these two sentences: "Professor Lippman refused the salesman's offer of a free set of encyclopedias. He knew that excessive hidden costs would be revealed to him later." The words *because, since,* and *for* will express the logic between the two ideas, but that logic is already so clear that such a connective is not needed.

    Closely related, rather short independent clauses are often made into compound sentences without connective words; then a semicolon must separate the two clauses. A comma alone, unless the clauses are short and very closely related, creates a comma splice. Usually the logic implied between the clauses in a compound sentence without a connective is either addition or result-followed-by-cause. Here is a sentence from George Bernard Shaw's writing that shows how ideas can just be added together with semicolons separating the independent clauses: "Be a teetotaler; don't gamble; don't lend; don't borrow; don't for your life get married; never take anybody's advice." Here are more examples of this kind of compound sentence:

> Senator Gorman voted against reduction of the oil depletion allowance; he knew that most of his campaign funds would come from his state's oilmen.
> Scientists can already synthesize many organic compounds; they will eventually create life that can reproduce itself.

Love can make a person happy; love and money can make him even happier.

Even the most learned professor consults the dictionary frequently; no one can know all about all English words.

The next six sentence patterns involve **subordination** of ideas. The verb *to subordinate* literally means to arrange under. Thus when an idea (or sentence element) is subordinated, it is placed in a position of lesser importance than the idea to which it is subordinated.[3] Just as there are connective words that show a coordinate relationship between sentence elements (*and, but, therefore,* and so on), so there are connectives that show a subordinated relationship. They will be discussed below.

The subordinated constructions discussed in the following sections, commonly called clauses and phrases in traditional grammar, have sometimes been given different names in more recent grammatical descriptions. Though in each case we shall have to settle upon a term by which to identify the construction for convenience, we shall always be most concerned with the way they work in sentences rather than with terminology.

The pattern of sentences
with appositive phrases

One simple method of expanding a subject-predicate construction into a more complex sentence, and thus avoiding the composition of a second, unnecessary sentence, is the use of an **appositive phrase.** An appositive is usually a noun or noun phrase that makes a full, separate statement about some other noun in the sentence. It is said to be **in apposition** to the noun it identifies. Here are some examples that show how separate full statements can be converted into appositives:

Ecology is the study of the mutual relation between organ-

---

[3] Actually, in many sentences the idea in a subordinated construction is more important than that in the main clause of the sentence. For example, the italicized subordinate clause is *the* important idea in the following sentence: "He is a politician *who tries to be all things to all voters.*" This linguistic phenomenon, however, is too subtle and complex to warrant a place in our elementary discussion of sentence structure. An understanding of it is not necessary for a mastery of the principles that are given a detailed treatment here.

isms and their environment. It is required for a degree in forestry.

Ecology, the study of the mutual relation between organisms and their environment, is required for a degree in forestry.

Tartuffe is Moliére's best known play. It is about a religious hypocrite who tries to make love to his patron's wife.

Tartuffe, Moliére's best known play, is about a religious hypocrite who tries to make love to his patron's wife.

The nation's mightiest "affair of honor" is, of course, the Civil War. It accounts for an average of ten romantic novels a year.

The nation's mightiest "affair of honor"—the Civil War, of course—accounts for an average of ten romantic novels a year.

One of the most acute political satirists today is Walt Kelley. He is the creator of "Pogo."

One of the most acute poltical satirists today is Walt Kelley, the creator of "Pogo."

The logic of the appositive phrase is that of identification or definition—that is, the appositive identifies or defines a noun by making a direct statement about what the noun is. Thus the verb *is (are)* or *was (were)* will always fit between an appositive and the noun it is in apposition to. The value of the construction is that it lets you write a mature, complex sentence with clear logic rather than two separated, choppy sentences. A sentence pattern with an appositive is more economical, vigorous, and rhythmic than two simple sentences saying the same thing.

An appositive may identify any noun in any sentence position. It usually comes after the noun it is in apposition to and is usually separated from the rest of the sentence by commas. An appositive may be separated by dashes when it is long or when there is a sharp break between it and the rest of the sentence. The examples just shown illustrate the proper punctuation of appositives.

Sometimes the appositive construction is in apposition to an entire sentence rather than to just one noun. In such cases, it comes at the end of a sentence and makes a statement about the whole idea of the sentence. Again, it permits a writer to avoid writing two separate sentences. Examples:

The theory of relativity maintains that space is curved. This is a concept that most of us have a hard time understanding.

The theory of relativity maintains that space is curved, a concept that most of us have a hard time understanding.

He was known to have supported the subversive Committee for Democratic Principles. This fact hurt his political career.

He was known to have supported the subversive Committee for Democratic Principles, a fact that hurt his political career.

The version with the appositive is more economical, vigorous, and rhythmic than the two-sentence version.

EXERCISE 23. Building Sentences with Appositive Phrases

DIRECTIONS: *Combine each of the following pairs of sentences into one sentence with an appositive. Be sure to punctuate properly.*

1. Traditional English grammar has been taught in schools since the eighteenth century.
   It is a system somewhat illogically based on Latin grammar.
2. William Faulkner is considered by many to be America's greatest author.
   He is a writer of prose fiction.
3. Man is in many ways built like his furrier relatives.
   They are the gorilla, the orangutan, and the chimpanzee.
4. Programmed learning is the newest educational technique.
   It seems most successful when adapted to machine teaching.
5. William Burroughs is one of the "black humorists."
   He writes always as though he is in a total rage at the universe.
6. The follicle widens into a bulb at its deep end.
   The bulb is the hair root.
7. Mrs. X is in jail on a morals charge.
   She is the mother of three teen-agers.
8. Morphemes are composed of one or more phonemes.
   Morphemes are the smallest meaningful units in language.
9. The pupils gave very creditable performances in the play.
   The pupils were mostly fifth graders.
10. The eccrine glands secrete water.
    The eccrine glands are the source of most of man's sweat.

The pattern of sentences
with adjective-clause modifiers

The **adjective clause** is one of three types of constructions called dependent or subordinate clauses in traditional grammar. It is called dependent or subordinate because, although it contains a subject and predicate, it is incorporated within another sentence and is connected to (dependent on) some word or words in the main sentence. Usually when taken out of the main sentence, it does not make a complete statement by itself. It is called an adjective clause because the kind of word it is usually connected to is a noun. It is said to modify that noun. In some cases it modifies the entire main sentence rather than just one noun in it.

An adjective clause is a subordinated construction rather than a simple sentence because it begins with a word (usually *who, which, that, whom,* or *whose*) that keeps it from being a self-contained sentence. These words may be called relative pronouns or subordinators. But regardless of its grammatical complexities, an adjective clause is important in the study of composition because it provides a means of writing one logical, mature sentence rather than two choppy simple sentences.

The logic of the adjective clause is somewhat like that of the appositive in that it makes a statement of identification, definition, or description about a noun or about the whole idea of a sentence. Here are some examples that show how a separate simple sentence can be converted into an adjective clause by substituting pronouns and linking the two together:

> In the vanguard there were some soldiers. They had already spent three months at the front without relief.
> In the vanguard were some soldiers who had already spent three months at the front without relief.

> The President proposed a compromise. It would have perpetuated the unsettled conditions.
> The President proposed a compromise that would have perpetuated the unsettled conditions.

> The President was a certain kind of politician. This was the kind whose sense of compromise never deserted him.
> The President was a kind of politician whose sense of compromise never deserted him.

> One proposal won favor. It was to impeach the mayor.
> The proposal that won favor was to impeach the mayor.

It is clear that in each example the sentence pattern with the adjective clause is more economical, vigorous, and rhythmical than the two-sentence pattern saying the same thing.

Like the appositive construction, the adjective clause can modify the whole idea of a sentence as well as a single noun in it. Here are some examples that show how a separate simple sentence can be converted into such a clause:

> The Governor often signs minor bills that he opposes in order to get legislative support for major bills. This is thought to be good political strategy.
>
> The Governor often signs minor bills that he opposes in order to get legislative support for major bills, which is thought to be good political strategy.

> The Mayor wanted to employ additional policemen. This seemed like a good idea.
>
> The Mayor wanted to employ additional policemen, which seemed like a good idea.

> It is hard to carry nineteen units and maintain a B+ average. Any student who can do this is sure to receive a scholarship.
>
> Any student who can carry nineteen units and maintain a B+ average, which is hard to do, is sure to receive a scholarship.

Some authorities have objected to such sentences on the grounds that the adjective clauses do not modify specific nouns. But such an objection is not wholly valid, for such sentences are surely clear and occur in the best writing. It is true, however, that when we use such constructions we must be especially careful not to confuse the reader. For example, note the lack of clarity in this sentence: "The President visited the military installations at Point Barrow, which pleased newsmen." Did the installations or the President's visit please newsmen?

Sometimes an adjective clause is separated from the rest of the sentence by commas, and sometimes it is not. When the clause is necessary to identify the noun it modifies, it is not separated by commas. Examples:

> The bill that was most likely to stir up controversy was quietly dropped.

The player who maintains the highest batting average will receive a trophy.

In these sentences neither *the bill* nor *the player* is clearly identified without the adjective clause. Thus no commas are used.

When an adjective clause modifies a noun already fully identified, it is set off from the rest of the sentence with commas. Examples:

The Robinson-Hawley proposal to increase depletion allowances, which antagonized many Congressmen, was quietly dropped.

Sinclair Lewis' novel *Babbitt,* which satirized American materialism, won him the Nobel Prize for Literature.

In each of these sentences the noun that the adjective clause modifies is fully identified without the clause. Therefore the clause, which simply gives extra information about the noun, is set off by commas.

When an adjective clause is not set off by commas, it is called a *restrictive* or *essential* clause, because it is needed to identify its noun. When such a clause is set off by commas, it is called *nonrestrictive* or *nonessential,* because it is not needed to identify its noun. Adjective clauses that modify the idea of a whole sentence are always nonrestrictive. To a degree your ear will tell you how to punctuate such clauses. There will be distinct pauses at both ends of a nonrestrictive clause but little if any pause at either end of a restrictive clause. An adjective clause beginning with *that* is always restrictive and thus not set off by commas.

EXERCISE 24.   Building Sentences with Adjective Clauses

DIRECTIONS: *Combine each of the following pairs of sentences into one sentence with an adjective clause. Be sure to punctuate correctly.*

1. Psychic phenomena are human experiences.
   These experiences seem contrary to the known laws of science.
2. The Board was composed of citizens.
   Their selfless dedication to duty was evident.
3. The Vietcong troops melted into the jungle.
   This further frustrated the American troops.

4. We encountered a company of returning infantrymen. Many of them were wounded.
5. The surrounding villages were being methodically searched. Some of the villages were known to harbor guerrillas.
6. The greatest growth will be in the two-year community college. This college is usually run by a local school board.
7. The President of the Board was Mr. Heyns. The local press opposed him.
8. The Senator planted an article. It suggested that he would be a good candidate for President.
9. We were scouting a line of villages. The Vietcong had been using the villages as its main line of communication.
10. One of the retired officers in my class was Mr. Nickleby. He had taken up the study of literature.

The pattern of sentences with adverbial-clause modifiers

The **adverbial clause** is another of the dependent clauses of traditional grammar. Such clauses are frequently said to—and in some cases do—modify the verb in the main sentence. But more often, adverbial clauses seem to modify the whole sentence rather than just the verb. Sometimes they are called sentence modifiers rather than adverbial clauses. Most important in composition, however, is the fact that this construction adds a full, separate statement to a main sentence and shows a logical relationship between that statement and the main statement of the sentence.

Like the adjective clause, the adverbial clause is introduced by a word (*when, if, because, though,* and so on) that keeps it from standing by itself as a simple sentence. This word incorporates the clause into the main sentence, making the clause subordinate or dependent in much the same way that words like *who* and *that* make adjective clauses dependent. There are many of these words and they express various kinds of logic. As a group they may be called subordinating conjunctions or subordinators.

Several of these subordinating conjunctions express the logic of cause-and-result: *because, since, in that, now that, in order that,* and *inasmuch as.* Here are some examples that show how a separate simple sentence can be converted into an adverbial clause:

No one else would undertake the hazardous patrol. Sergeant Coombs bravely volunteered.

Since no one else would undertake the hazardous patrol, Sergeant Coombs bravely volunteered.

Mr. Jones performed a great service for the Owls Club. He devised a scheme to pay off their deficit.

Mr. Jones performed a great service for the Owls Club in that he devised a scheme to pay off their deficit.

The United Nations is weakened. We must seek other methods of working for peace.

Now that the United Nations is weakened, we must seek other methods of working for peace.

The President refused to endorse the Tanner proposal. He thought it would increase the power of his opponents.

The President refused to endorse the Tanner proposal because he thought it would increase the power of his opponents.

In each of these examples one of the statements is a cause and the other its result. Not only does your ear tell you that the sentence pattern with the adverbial clause is more vigorous and rhythmic than the two-sentence pattern, but your mind tells you that its logic is clearer. It is the use of the subordinating conjunction that makes the logic clear.

Some of the subordinating conjunctions express the logic of contrast: *although, though, whereas,* and sometimes *while*. Examples:

The President expressed a desire to have the Tanner proposal enacted into law. In reality he opposed it.

The President expressed a desire to have the Tanner proposal enacted into law, while in reality he opposed it.

Mr. Appleton lost the national election. He remained the leader of his own party.

Although Mr. Appleton lost the national election, he remained the leader of his own party.

The results of the experiment will not be known conclusively for two weeks. It seems likely that the new serum will be effective.

Though the results of the experiment will not be known conclusively for two weeks, it seems likely that the new serum will be effective.

By early afternoon Hurricane Sally had veered toward the Atlantic Ocean. It had been expected to hit the coast cities full blast.

By early afternoon Hurricane Sally had veered toward the Atlantic Ocean, whereas it had been expected to hit the coast cities full blast.

In each of these examples the subordinating conjunction shows that there is a contrast of some sort between the two statements. The logic of the contrast is made much clearer in the sentence pattern with an adverbial clause, and that pattern is also more vigorous and rhythmical than the two-sentence pattern.

The logic of condition is expressed by the subordinating conjunctions *if* and *unless*. Examples:

If sewer bonds are not voted for in the West Knolls District, real estate sales will continue to be slow there.

Real estate sales will continue to be slow in the West Knolls District unless sewer bonds are voted in.

In each of these cases the truth of one statement depends on (is conditional on) the truth of the other.

The logic of manner or method is expressed by the subordinating conjunctions *as, as . . . as, as if,* and *as though*. Examples:

The Berliners continued to live as if war did not threaten.

The Teamsters' President used his powers as extensively as the law would allow.

In each of these cases the subordinating conjunction tells how something was done.

The logic of a time relationship is expressed by the subordinating conjunctions *after, as, as soon as, before, since, until, when,* and *while*. Also the logic of cause-and-result is sometimes combined with the time relationship. Examples:

When the President saw that his bill was in danger of being defeated, he quickly called conferences with his Senate leaders.

Before the Mayor was put on trial, several contractors left town.

After it was certain that the Tanner proposal had no chance of passing the Senate, the President decided to adjourn the special session of Congress.

Though in these examples *when*, *before*, and *after* seem to express only a time relationship between the two statements, the reader understands in each case that the second statement is the result of the first.

No simple rule can be stated governing the punctuation of all adverbial clauses. However, when the clause comes first in a sentence, it is usually separated from the rest of the sentence by a comma unless it is short. When the clause comes within or at the end of the sentence, it will usually need to be separated by a comma or commas if, when you read it aloud, you hear a distinct pause before the clause.

EXERCISE 25. Building Sentences with Adverbial Clauses

DIRECTIONS: *Combine each of the following pairs of sentences into one sentence with an adverbial clause.*

1. It is not likely that the present confusion in the teaching of grammar will be cleared up soon.
   Most of our English teachers have been taught only traditional grammar and know little about the new.
2. The excise tax on cars was reduced.
   Car sales increased.
3. We had done all we could.
   We were forced to leave A Company's wounded behind.
4. Urban renewal projects have been undertaken in most cities.
   Slums still abound.
5. Clinics might be available for all mentally disturbed children.
   Then delinquency would be reduced tenfold.
6. The radar was inoperative.
   Our pilot made a perfect landing.
7. The heat became too oppressive.
   Then our tempers became frayed.
8. Their foreign straw bosses turned their backs.
   At the same time the natives slowed down their work.
9. Kennedy might have lived longer and had time to do more.
   Then he would have sought more outside advice.
10. Patton was invariably successful in the field.
    He received honor after honor from the High Command.

The pattern of sentences
with verb-cluster modifiers

In traditional terms, the grammar involving verbals and verb phrases is so complex that once you start explaining or defining you find yourself in bottomless quicksand. For example, even without trying to explain their various uses in sentences, many students find it difficult to distinguish between the present, past, perfect, and past perfect participles, not to mention gerunds. But since we are interested in composition rather than grammar, we need not name and define all the different kinds of verbals. We will just use the names **verbals** or **verb clusters** to apply to all kinds.

A cluster is one kind of phrase, and a phrase is a group of words (without a subject and predicate, which form a clause) acting as a unit. In the kind of phrase called a cluster there is always a headword—the dominant word of the phrase about which other words cluster. In a verb cluster the headword is a verb—any form of a verb: *to explain, explained, to be explained, explaining, had explained, had been explained, had been explaining, having explained, having been explained, being explained.* A verb cluster is formed when modifiers or complements or both are joined to such verbs or verb phrases to form a unit. Here are some examples:

> <u>Telling</u> the inspector off
> Loudly <u>insisting</u> that he was right
> <u>Having been entitled</u> to a share of the estate
> Not <u>having known</u> her prior to her marriage
> By <u>repeating</u> the big lie incessantly
> <u>Raised</u> above its former position
> <u>To be informed</u> about world affairs
> <u>Spread</u> out evenly and <u>moving</u> slowly
> <u>To spend</u> money without getting fair value
> After <u>spending</u> the night alone
> <u>Being eaten</u> by a tribe of cannibals

Though it has various functions, a verb cluster can act as a sentence modifier or as the modifier of a noun within a main sentence. Because the cluster usually appears to modify a specific noun, it is often called an adjective phrase or an adjectival. But whatever it is called, it can add a full, separate statement to a main sentence. It is this function of a verb cluster that is most important in the study of composition. By learning to use verb clusters more effectively, you can increase your ability to write sentences that are mature and logical. Here are some examples of how simple sentences can be converted into verb-cluster modifiers:

> The lawyer chose his words carefully. He was trying hard to control his temper.
> The lawyer chose his words carefully, trying hard to control his temper.

> The 39th Regiment fought savagely. It broke out of the German trap.
> The 39th Regiment, fighting savagely, broke out of the German trap.

> The Indians did not have a chance to build up immunities. They were devastated by the white man's diseases.
> Not having had a chance to build up immunities, the Indians were devastated by the white man's diseases.

> The President had the purpose of keeping the public well informed. He ordered much top-secret material declassified.
> To achieve his purpose of keeping the public well informed, the President ordered much top-secret material declassified.

> The old man was withered and broken by a lifetime of heavy toil. He was content to die peacefully.
> The old man, withered and broken by a lifetime of heavy toil, was content to die peacefully.

> The company president carefully manipulated the price of his stock. He cheated investors out of millions.
> By carefully manipulating the price of his stock, the company president cheated investors out of millions.

> The coach piloted his team to a perfect season. He endeared himself to his school's alumni.
> The coach piloted his team to a perfect season, thereby endearing himself to his school's alumni.

The sentence pattern with the verb-cluster modifier is surely more economical, vigorous, and rhythmical than the two-sentence pattern. Note also that its logic is more clearly expressed. Most sentence patterns with verb-cluster modifiers express a logic of cause-and-result.

EXERCISE 26. **Building Sentences with Verb–Cluster Modifiers**

DIRECTIONS: *Combine each of the following pairs of sentences into one sentence with a verb-cluster modifier.*

1. The Governor had not been informed about the move to block his tax-reform bill.
   He planned to make a campaigning tour while the Legislature debated the bill.
2. He left the capital.
   Shortly thereafter he received a telegram from the Speaker of the House.
3. These housing developments are usually sponsored by churches on a nonprofit basis.
   These housing developments are given low-cost financing.
4. We were assailed by profanity.
   We walked nervously through the crowd.
5. These films are often precariously financed.
   These films have to earn their money back as fast as possible.
6. Nine conservative congressmen spoke before two hundred businessmen. They charged that the Urban Renewal Act is "taxing the needy to benefit the greedy."
7. Urban Renewal originated as a simple real-estate venture.
   Urban Renewal brought into public view the extent of poverty in the city slums.
8. Confusion surrounded the issues.
   It caused a light voter turnout.
9. Slums were rapidly devouring the nation's cities.
   This was sending into the suburbs everyone who could afford to move.
10. A juvenile judge deals day in and day out with delinquents.
    He has an excellent opportunity to spot mentally disturbed youngsters.

The pattern of sentences
with prepositional-phrase modifiers

Prepositional phrases often combine with modifiers to form large elements that can act as sentence modifiers. For example, consider this unit: "in the book just mentioned." In traditional grammar only *in the book* would be called a prepositional phrase; *mentioned* would be called an adjective modifying *book,* and *just* an adverb modifying *mentioned.* But whatever the grammar of these words, all five form a large element that can act as a sentence modifier, as in this example: "In the book just mentioned, there are sixteen full-color plates." Most traditional grammarians would call the first element not a sentence modifier but an adverbial phrase modifying the verb *are.* Some of the new grammarians call such large elements *P-groups,* on the grounds that they are more than (but are governed by) prepositional phrases. But that name is not in widespread use. For want of a better name, we will simply call them **prepositional-phrase sentence modifiers.**

Like the other constructions discussed above, these large elements can add full, separate ideas to simple sentences. Here are some examples that show how simple sentences can be converted into prepositional-phrase modifiers:

> Prepositional-phrase modifiers are like the other constructions discussed above. They can add full, separate ideas to simple sentences.
> Prepositional-phrase modifiers, like the other constructions discussed above, can add full, separate ideas to simple sentences.

> The Governor had nothing but a reputation for honesty and a firm handshake. He began his campaign for re-election.
> With nothing but a reputation for honesty and a firm handshake, the Governor began his campaign for re-election.

> Mr. Jones was under pressure to resign as Circuit Judge. He investigated his opportunities to return to law practice.
> Under pressure to resign as Circuit Judge, Mr. Jones investigated his opportunities to return to law practice.

> Mr. Smith was in a state of shock over the accidental death of his wife. He entered the hospital for a rest and complete check-up.
> In a state of shock over the accidental death of his wife, Mr. Smith entered the hospital for a rest and complete check-up.

The pattern with the prepositional-phrase modifier is more economical, vigorous, and rhythmical than the two-sentence pattern.

The pattern of sentences
with adjective-phrase modifiers.

An adjective phrase is an adjective headword with its modifiers. Here are some examples with the adjective headword italicized:

Intensely *happy* with her new kitchen
Oblivious of the political implications of the new tax bill
Generous beyond his means

Such adjective phrases as these contain statements that could appear in separate simple sentences. Here are examples that show how a full sentence can be converted into an adjective phrase:

Mary was intensely happy with her new kitchen. She delighted her husband with various culinary experiments.

Intensely happy with her new kitchen, Mary delighted her husband with various culinary experiments.

The Governor was oblivious of the political implications of the new tax bill. He praised it in routine political announcements.

Oblivious of the political implications of the new tax bill, the Governor praised it in routine political announcements.

He was generous beyond his means. He quickly became bankrupt.

Generous beyond his means, he quickly became bankrupt.

Again it is clear that the pattern with the adjective-phrase modifier is more economical, vigorous, and rhythmical than the two-sentence pattern.

Complex sentences of various patterns

In this section on sentence patterns you have studied the patterns of simple sentences; simple sentences with compound elements; compound sentences with coordinating conjunctions and with logical connectives; and sentences with various kinds of sentence modifiers: appositive phrases, adjective clauses, adverbial clauses, verb clusters, prepositional-phrase modifiers, and adjective phrases. These latter patterns can be called complex sentences, because each contains a full statement in a subordinate position as well as one in an independent position.

These patterns can be used in a great variety of ways with three, four, five, or more separate statements being included in one complex, or compound-complex, sentence. Examples:

> With the Ambassador's written promise in his pocket,/ the Secretary of State rushed to the President,/ hoping that the new crisis could be ended/ before military orders were issued.

> Although the evidence pointed to his guilt,/ the accused,/ a notorious member of the Dollo gang,/ expected to be found not guilty,/ for he had hired a very expensive criminal lawyer/ who had a record of pleading successful cases before this particular judge.

In the first example there are four statements, in this order: prepositional-phrase modifier, simple sentence, verb cluster, and adverbial clause. In the second there are five statements, in this order: adverbial clause, simple sentence, appositive phrase within the simple sentence (continuation of the first simple sentence), another simple sentence, and an adjective clause.

Though long sentences are not especially common in college exposition, you certainly should learn to write moderately complex sentences like the two illustrated here. The following exercises will give you some practice.

EXERCISE 27.   Building Complex Sentences

DIRECTIONS: *Each of the following items is composed of three or more separate statements. Combine the statements in each item into one sentence, converting all but one of the separate statements into either appositive phrases, adjective clauses, adverbial clauses, verb clusters, prepositional-phrase modifiers, or adjective phrases. The statement you do not convert should remain the core independent clause of your full sentence.*

1. The urban renewal proponents often have had no experience with slum life. Most of the urban renewal proponents are well-meaning people. Slum life has its own peculiar set of mores.
2. Not all slum children become delinquent. The proportion who do

is high. This fact leads sociologists to attribute much delinquency to slum conditions.

3. The evidences of maladjustment in Oswald might have led to his being given early treatment. He might have overcome his instabilities. He might have overcome them at least sufficiently to lead a nearly normal life.

4. It was on that day in April 1963. The 21st Recon Company was with us. The 21st Recon Company was a particularly good company. It was largely made up of certain troops. These were troops who had fought with the Vietminh during the Indo-China war.

5. Racial discrimination is not virulent in New Mexico. There exists some prejudice against citizens of Spanish descent. Many of these citizens of Spanish descent consider themselves the elite of the state. They rightly consider themselves the elite.

6. We were making our advance on the tree line. We were making our advance almost an inch at a time. At that time we saw one man in a black suit. The man was desperately running across the open field.

7. The Whig candidate wanted to appeal to the upper-class voters. He was Major Frumpton of World War II fame. He promised to enact tax reforms. They would eliminate discriminating levies.

8. I read *Frown No More*. It received good reviews. I found the book disgusting. It had a low moral tone.

9. I offered my assistance. I offered it with reluctance. I soon found that I had good cause to be reluctant. I was spattered with mud from head to toe.

10. Governor Horton gave only a passing gesture to some independents. They were the independents who supported him. He was the dark-horse winner of the election. He presented to the Legislature a partisan program. It consisted of proposals. These proposals would benefit the Whigs only.

EXERCISE 28.   Building Compound and Complex Sentences

DIRECTIONS: *The following passage is composed of a series of short sentences. Write an improved version by using a variety of the sentence patterns discussed above. Keep in mind that you may use compound elements, compound sentences with either conjunctions or logical connectives, or sentence modifiers such as appositive phrases, adjective clauses, adverbial clauses, verb clusters, prepositional-phrase modifiers, and adjective clusters. You should keep only one simple sentence in your revision of the two paragraphs.*

One of the finest short stories ever written in America is William Faulkner's "Two Soldiers." It is the story of an eight-year-old Mississippi farm boy. He tries to follow his older brother to enlist in the Army. On the night after his brother leaves for Memphis to enlist the little boy leaves. He walks to Jefferson. Jefferson is the county seat of Yoknapatawpha County. Then he manages to get a bus ride to Memphis. He gets to the Induction Center. His brother Pete is brought to see him. Pete tells him he must go home. Some officers of the Center are impressed with the boy's devotion. Their being impressed causes them to treat him well. It also causes them to give him a ride home in a chauffeur-driven Army car.

The story is not sad or tragic. It brings tears to the eyes of every sensitive reader. It so poignantly expresses the great human virtues of devotion, loyalty, love, and kindness. The little boy is magnificent in his love for his brother. The big brother is memorable for his devotion to his small brother. He is also memorable for his devotion to his country. The understanding shown by the soldiers at the Induction Center also makes the reader feel proud of the goodness of human beings. The Colonel himself, and his wife, treat the little fellow royally. They do this because they realize what a testimony to human faithfulness his journey has been. The story is written in prose. The story is truly a poetic expression of the most admirable qualities of man.

EXERCISE 29. Building Compound and Complex Sentences

DIRECTIONS: *The following passage is composed of a series of short sentences. Write an improved version by using a variety of the sentence patterns described above. You should keep only one simple sentence in your revised version.*

"Advertising copywriters might be less skillful masters of word connotation. Then we should spend far less money than we do on certain products. These are the products they recommend. They know how to cultivate our responses. In doing so they always evoke pleasant pictures. And they make us yearn for what we lack. And they do all this without our being aware of it. They also have a formidable list of taboos. These are words which must never be mentioned. They must not be mentioned because they have negative connotations of one sort or another. They advocate the purchase of a product because it doesn't cost much. When they do this they never use the word *cheap*. Cheap connotes shoddiness. It also connotes penny pinching. And so they appeal to our sense of *thrift*. This is more fashionable perhaps because it has the approval of Ben Franklin. He was an American folk-hero. They promote a large-size package of their product. They call it the *economy size. Fat* is never used except in reducing-course ads. You can never induce a woman to buy a dress or corset by calling her fat. Instead there are dresses for the *larger figure* or the *mature woman*. And sometimes it is a matter of selling pipe tobacco, perfume, coffee, or even Air-Wicks. Then *smell* is absolutely forbidden."—Altick, *Preface to Critical Reading,* 5th ed.

SOME PROBLEMS IN SENTENCE CLARITY

The source of sentence clarity

Above all, expository writing must be clear, for its chief purpose is to inform. Though all the principles of composition are involved in achieving clarity, one of the most common sources of unclear writing is faulty sentence structure. Since a sentence is a complex arrangement of several parts (the subjects, predicates, appositives, subordinate clauses, verb clusters, adjective phrases, and prepositional-phrase modifiers discussed), it is easy for its structure to become misshapen and thus for its clarity to be marred. You can make sure that all of your sentences are clear only by carefully reviewing each of them separately to see that all parts fit together properly and make good sense.

Almost all errors in sentence structure involve some improper change of structure after the sentence is underway. The first part of a sentence conditions a reader's mind to expect a certain structure to follow, for language is made up of an immensely complex set of signals that we follow unconsciously. If a sentence is properly constructed, all of its signals are in place and the reader's mind follows the sentence smoothly. But if an improper change of structure occurs, the reader's mind stumbles because it comes to a pattern to which it is not accustomed.

As an example, consider the following portion of a sentence: "I was waiting for a _____." Your knowledge of English has conditioned your mind to expect a noun to fulfill the pattern: "I was waiting for a lady." Your mind is also conditioned so that it will accept an adjective as a continuation, though not a fulfillment, of the pattern: "I was waiting for a lovely _____." Now your mind expects a noun to fulfill the pattern. Your mind will also accept an adverb in the pattern: "I was waiting for a spectacularly _____." Now your mind expects an adjective plus a noun to fulfill the pattern; a noun or adjective alone will not suffice.

But suppose that a verb is suddenly put into the pattern: "I was waiting for a to begin." Or suppose that the adverb-adjective pattern is reversed: "I was waiting for a lovely spectacularly lady." Your mind will immediately become confused and reject these patterns, for it has never been conditioned to accept signals like these.

Thus when you shift signals somewhere within a sentence, you confuse your reader's mind and leave him with an unclear sentence. Though the kind of faulty shifts in grammar just illustrated do not appear in anybody's writing, there are several less obviously faulty sentence patterns that recur frequently in careless writing. Some of these are so serious that they obscure clarity almost completely. Others are relatively minor and only annoy educated readers. Most involve some sort of improper change of structure that confuses the system of signals that the reader's mind is following. Six of these common types of errors are analyzed below.

Mixed sentence structure

Mixed or confused sentence structure occurs when a writer starts out with one standard pattern of sentence grammar and shifts to another somewhere in midsentence. He literally forgets what kind of construction he is using and unconsciously undertakes another. Here is an example from a student paper: "The older generation knows that in their younger days. . . ." At this point the sentence has signaled to the reader's mind to expect a subject, probably *they,* followed by a predicate. But this was the full sentence: "The older generation knows that in their younger days how irresponsible and immoral they were." Instead of an expected subject and predicate to follow the subordinating conjunction *that,* the reader found a second subordinating conjunction (*how*) followed by a subject and predicate. The result was momentary confusion in his mind because of the mixed grammatical constructions. The writer confused his grammatical signals. He could have written either of these sentences:

> The older generation knows that in their younger days they were irresponsible and immoral.
>
> The older generation knows how irresponsible and immoral they were in their younger days.

Each of these sentences contains familiar signals following one grammatical pattern, and thus each is clear. But it was the writer's carelessness rather than his ignorance of grammar that led him to write the faulty sentence. One does not need to understand consciously the complexities of grammar to write sentences with proper grammatical signals; he just needs carefully to follow his unconscious knowledge of the structure of his language. (Correct conventional usage is another matter.)

Here is another example of mixed structure from a student paper: "Today it is increasingly hard to stay out of trouble in which our parents never came in contact with." After the word *trouble* the sentence is so jumbled that no clear signals are present. The writer's difficulty began when he thoughtlessly made present and future trouble the same as past trouble. Notice how clear the signals are with this beginning: "Today it is increasingly hard to stay out of a kind of trouble. . . ." Now the reader's mind is fully conditioned to expect a subordinate clause beginning with *that:* ". . . that our parents never came in contact with." The grammatical signals in this revision are clear.

Here is one more example of mixed structure from a student paper: "In furthering my education here at the college by attending adult classes has been very interesting." In this sentence the signals get crossed after *classes*. At that point the reader's mind is conditioned to expect a subject (I) followed by a predicate. But instead it gets only a predicate, and at that one that can't go with the subject I. If the sentence had continued after *classes* with ". . . I have taken several interesting courses," the signals would have been in order and the sentence clear. How did the writer go wrong? He carelessly forgot that he had begun his sentence with *in*. If he had omitted the word *in*, all the rest of the signals in the sentence would have been clear. It is understandable that a writer should make such a mistake, but it is inexcusable that he should fail to revise the sentence.

EXERCISE 30. Revising Mixed Sentences

DIRECTIONS: *The following sentences are mixed in their construction. Rewrite a proper version of each and be prepared to tell how the writer lost control of his sentence signals.*

1. The secret of political success is a good memory for names and willingness to compromise make it easy to achieve.
2. The speaker insisted that the only way to avoid world war, the United Nations must have an independent military force larger than that of any one country.
3. The more I tried to explain my absence, the teacher was not willing to listen to me.
4. By encouraging more and more common people to buy corporation stocks can strengthen the capitalist system.
5. Because his secretary forgot to make a note of the appointment was why Mr. Jones did not appear at the conference.
6. I think the world can only have peace is when disarmament is a completed fact.
7. If the accused was insane at the time of the crime, his punishment is enough by being put into a mental institution.
8. Suburbanites want houses that are reasonably priced, attractively designed, and upkeep should be inexpensive.
9. Freedom must forever be guarded with vigilance is a fact demonstrated by human history.
10. Christmas comes during the yuletide season which many people interpret it as being the yuletide season.
11. By forcing a student to take a science class, the purpose of the class is not fully realized.
12. The fact that the professor had traveled in Europe, this added interest to his course.
13. The unexpectedly large number of students voting in the election took a great deal of time for the tellers to count them.
14. Every letter that we got seemed to be a different person writing it.
15. The opening paragraph is kind of hard to tell what he is driving at.
16. The number of advantages lost by both the strikers and the employers took a matter of years in order to regain them.
17. In establishing a new method of cost accounting has resulted in important savings for the company.
18. Many scientists have admitted that in some of their experiments how they did not understand what they were doing.
19. Every time one world crisis is solved seems to bring a new one.
20. Swimming is a form of exercise that if you do it regularly you will have better health.

Faulty predication

The basic structure of a simple English sentence is a subject-predicate combination. The predicate completes a meaning initiated in the subject by telling what the subject is, or what the subject does, or what is done to the subject. Thus in grammar **predication** means the addition of a predicate to a subject. When a predicate does not fit its subject, faulty predication occurs.

There is a difference between grammatical and logical predication. Predication is grammatical when the predicate establishes a signal pattern[4] that, to native speakers of English, fits the subject. For example, saying that one noun is another noun is a common kind of grammatical predication: "Education / is a valuable asset." No question about the grammatical (or logical) predication here. The same pattern is also grammatical even when the sentence is nonsense: "Education / is a green frog." All native speakers of English will recognize a familar signal pattern in such a sentence in spite of its nonsense. There is no shift of grammatical patterns as explained in the section on mixed sentence structure above. But saying that a noun is an adverb is not a pattern of English predication: "Education / is advantageously." Even though this sentence is more meaningful than the preceding example, its predication is ungrammatical, as any native speaker of English would instantly perceive.

Now observe a grammatical pattern of predication built with nonsense words: "Education / is a morgy blution of pregunt kluppers." Of course no real meaning is delivered here, but most literate speakers of English would recognize that the predication is grammatical since *education* is obviously being called *something,* as in the first example above. The signal pattern (a noun is another noun) is grammatical. Now observe this same pattern as actually used by a college writer: "Education / is a major problem of migrant workers." The predication here is grammatical; but it is not logical because education is not what the sentence says it is. Not education but lack of education or lack of the opportunity to get an education is a major problem of migrant workers. Thus predication is illogical when a subject and predicate don't fit together sensibly. Illogical predication, which is due to muddy thinking

---

4 —a grammatical construction which establishes proper syntax.

rather than to a false sense of grammar, is a frequent source of bad sentences in student writing.

Most errors in predication involve an illogical **something-is-something-else** construction—that is, a sentence with a form of *to be* as the verb of the predicate, but with the subject and complement not being equivalent to each other. Here are a few examples from student themes:

> The arguments presented in favor of parent-arranged marriages / are financial security and social standing. (Are financial security and social standing arguments?)
> The first step in writing / is spelling and sentence structure. (Are spelling and sentence structure a step in writing?)
> One example of the courage of a Peace Corps member / is the tractor. (Can a tractor be an example of courage?)
> Water / is one of America's most pressing problems. (Is just water itself a problem?)

These sentences are grammatical, for each says that one noun is another noun, but their predication is illogical because each says that one thing is something else that it cannot be. They represent one of the most serious errors in sentence structure.

A related kind of faulty predication involves the commonly used *is when* . . . and *is where* . . . predicate constructions. The *is when* . . . predicate should not be used with a subject that does not denote time, and *is where* . . . should not be used with a subject that does not denote a place. Examples of faulty predication:

> The Dean's List / is when you have a grade-point average of 3.5 or above.
> Courage / is when you act brave even though you are scared.
> Sluice mining / is where you use water to wash out the ore-bearing gravel and sand.

The predication in such sentences is illogical (as well as awkward) because the subjects denote neither a time of occurrence nor a place.

Faulty predication occasionally occurs in sentences with verbs other than *to be*. To understand an example, first note the grammatical and logical predication in this sentence: "Unemployed men / constitute the smallest percentage of welfare recipients." Now note a similar pattern of predication built with nonsense words: "Unemployed men / constitute the flunktion of flersible octives." The sentence is meaningless, but it fulfills a recognizable grammatical pattern. Now observe this same pattern as actually used by a college writer: "Unemployed men / constitute the lack of available jobs." Though grammatical, the predication of this sentence is illogical because the predicate does not sensibly complete a meaning initiated in the subject. Here are a few more live examples of such illogical predication:

> The mass destruction of human life and property / would take a terrible toll. (It would be the cause of the destruction that would take a toll.)
> My first reaction to being in a large English class / seemed a little strange and different. (It was the class, not the reaction, that seemed strange and different.)
> The price of his election / cost him the respect of his close friends. (Apparently the tactics he used in getting elected cost him the respect of his friends, or the price of his election was the loss of the respect of his friends.)

You will note that usually such faulty sentences can best be corrected through a change in subject rather than predicate. Thus the error might be called faulty "subjectivation" rather than faulty predication. But since the illogicality does not become apparent until the predicate is read, faulty predication is the most convenient label for the error.

Faulty predication, like the similar mixed sentence structure discussed earlier, is a serious and inexcusable error in college writing. It is a symptom of muddy thinking. Of course even an experienced writer will occasionally compose such a sentence, for since its grammar is sound its meaning may at first glance seem clear. But a careful writer will detect his error as he rereads his work and will revise for logic and clarity.

EXERCISE 31. Revising Faulty Predication

DIRECTIONS: *The following sentences have illogical predication. Rewrite a proper version of each and be prepared to explain why the predication is not logical. The subject rather than the predicate of a sentence may be rewritten to achieve proper predication.*

1. Too many people working on a good thing may prove faulty.
2. Cheating in school is another area in which I must disagree with my parents.

3. Teaching their children would be another prevention of delinquency.
4. The white lie is not living up to what one believes.
5. For people to break all social and financial relations and move to another part of the world takes a very dedicated person.
6. Twenty-five years ago was quite different from what it is now.
7. An understanding of our country's standing in the world is one of leadership.
8. The best method of deception is the advertisments for a sale.
9. Another way to help preserve wildlife is during the winter months.
10. Sex is another serious controversy.
11. Another example of how people are dishonest is in the schools.
12. One of the reasons restricting the fulfillment of goals may be conformity.
13. Another argument that one may use is the Bill of Rights.
14. Another well-known advertisement is hair oil.
15. An example of not rotating crops is during the time of the great cotton plantations.
16. Franklin's *Autobiography* was written as an old man giving advice to his son.
17. My opinion about the age of drafting young men into the service should stay as it is today.
18. Flagrant infractions of discipline by students, particularly those involving drinking and relations between the sexes, usually demand the participation of the President of the College.
19. Children playing with matches could be prevented if parents were more cautious.
20. Onomatopoeia is when the sound of a word is the same as its meaning.
21. Another undesirable trait of sports is where money is involved.
22. Some misconceptions of the Negro race are intelligence, responsibilities, and their standard of living.
23. My first reaction to being placed in a large class frightened me.
24. His first trick was a deck of cards.
25. The price of the components for modifying the engine cost me $259.

Faulty parallelism

In writing, parallelism means the use of any kind of sentence element in a series of two or more, usually with a coordinating conjunction between the last two elements of the series. Here are some examples:

English and history are required subjects. (two nouns in parallel structure)

The General ranted, raved, and pounded his desk. (three verbs)

That is a story which I have heard before, which I expect to hear again, but which I wish I had never heard the first time. (three adjective clauses)

Expecting his aunt to drop in but not relishing the idea of talking to her, Henry became increasingly nervous. (two verb clusters)

Henry dropped the coins in the slot machine and his aunt pulled the handle. (two simple sentences)

In each of these cases the two or more elements are said to be in parallel structure because they are of the same grammatical construction and are joined by a conjunction. Indeed, the sole use of coordinating conjunctions is to join elements that are similar in structure and function.

Faulty parallelism occurs when the elements joined by a conjunction are not similar in structure. A conjunction (*and, but, or*) signals that a construction similar to the preceding one is to follow, and the reader's mind unconsciously expects the pattern to continue. Note these examples:

beautiful and proud (adjectives)
men and boys (nouns)
talking and smiling (verbs)
easily and cleverly (adverbs)

Now mix these constructions and see how your mind rejects the patterns:

beautiful and boys (adjective and noun)
men and smiling (noun and verb)
talking and cleverly (verb and adverb)
easily and proud (adverb and adjective)

Thus when unlike elements in a sentence are joined by a conjunction, the sentence signals get confused and the particular kind of sentence error called **faulty parallelism** occurs.

Here are some typical examples of faulty parallelism, with revised sentences:

Several committee members were at the secret meeting but

not agreeing to change their votes. (sentence predicate in faulty parallelism with a verb cluster)

Several committee members were at the secret meeting but did not agree to change their votes.

I believe that the United Nations has been fairly effective but we can improve it. (subordinate clause in faulty parallelism with a simple sentence)

I believe that the United Nations has been fairly effective but that we can improve it.

To listen to classical music and reading great novels are pastimes too few students enjoy. (two different kinds of verbals—infinitive and gerundive—in faulty parallelism)

Listening to classical music and reading great novels are pastimes too few students enjoy.

Mullins of the White Sox had a near-perfect day on the mound, striking out twelve batters and he allowed only two hits. (verb cluster and simple sentence in faulty parallelism)

Mullins of the White Sox had a near-perfect day on the mound, striking out twelve batters and allowing only two hits.

The best way to avoid faulty parallelism is to have a thorough understanding of the mechanics of sentence structure. But an error in parallelism usually disrupts sentence rhythm and vigor, and so you can often detect the error by listening carefully as you reread your sentences to yourself.

EXERCISE 32. Revising Faulty Parallelism

DIRECTIONS: *Each of the following sentences has an error in parallelism. Write a correct version of each by placing all elements in a series in parallel structure.*

1. A person may be brilliant in a specific field but he does not have general knowledge.
2. When we turn on our TV sets, radios, or read magazines, we are usually seeking entertainment.
3. A citizen of this country is assured freedom of many things and one of these being freedom of speech.
4. Americans want peace, a high standard of living, to be the best, and they want to be liked.
5. Agricultural areas use water not only for everyday use and crop use, but the wildlife also use it.

6. He would leave his farm idle and may cause erosion.
7. The poem starts out with an ant running into a moth and is so busy that he doesn't notice.
8. Disinfect diapers with boiling, sunshine, or, best of all, use special antiseptic diaper rinse granules.
9. He was like the king who ate and drank poison and he finally became immune to it.
10. These three things can be decided by the young people and do not need any interference from the adults.
11. The flowers are smaller, many having holes in the petals and some petals are discolored.
12. The armed forces offer financial security, opportunity for travel, and to learn of people from different cultures.
13. There are two ways to preserve wildlife: One is be careful with fire, and second have laws to control the hunter.
14. Franklin set up his own code of ethics, not to please God but he thought his ethical system would increase his prosperity.
15. He is the kind of man who is honest but he makes careless mistakes.

Dangling modifiers

We have already discussed verb clusters as sentence modifiers and pointed out that, though these constructions may be called sentence modifiers, they often more specifically modify one particular noun or pronoun in the main part of the sentence. When a construction of this sort is so placed in a sentence that it has no apparent word to modify, or when it seems to modify the wrong word, it is said to dangle. Thus a dangling modifier is one that hangs on to a sentence without having a clear place in the sentence. Here is a typical kind of amusing example: "Being well fried, we enjoyed the chicken."

The error in a faulty sentence of this sort is due to an improper change of structure that confuses the sentence signals that the reader's mind is following. A verb cluster such as *being well fried,* having a verb in it, expresses an action or condition, and obviously if there is to be an action or condition, there must be someone or something to perform the action or be in the stated condition. But the verb cluster itself does not name that someone or something; he or it is named somewhere else in the sentence. The verb cluster does, however, signal to the reader's mind that the doer of the action will be immediately named. Thus the reader's mind expects the verb to be followed directly by the name of the doer. When it isn't so followed, the cluster dangles.

To understand how this specific sentence signal works, examine the following verb clusters, each of which could easily be a sentence modifier (or adjective or participial phrase, according to some grammarians):

> Having expressed his opinion that the proposal would not work, . . .
> Being the daughter of a millionaire, . . .
> Known as a persistent social climber, . . .
> Not daring to vote against the majority, . . .
> Whimpering and whining at the door, . . .

Each of these clusters quite clearly signals to your mind to expect the doer of the action (or possessor of the condition) to be named immediately. Your mind is just poised to find out who expressed his opinion, who is the daughter of a millionaire, and so forth. Thus when a sentence contains a construction of this sort, a pattern is set up that supposedly guarantees the immediate naming of a doer for the verb in the cluster.

What happens when that sentence pattern is improperly shifted? The signals become confused, and the whole verb cluster is left dangling. For example:

> Having expressed his opinion that the proposal would not work, a quick vote was taken. (Who expressed his opinion? The quick vote?)
> Being the daughter of a millionaire, the boys pretended great romantic interest. (Who was the daughter of a millionaire? The boys?)
> Known as a persistent social climber, few worthwhile invitations were received. (Who was known as a persistent social climber?)

In each of the above sentences the pattern of signals is broken by the omission of the name of a doer for the verb cluster. The faulty dangling effect can be eliminated if the doer is named:

> Having expressed his opinion that the proposal would not work, the committee chairman called for a quick vote.
> Being the daughter of a millionaire, Cora was pestered by boys who pretended great romantic interest.

> Known as a persistent social climber, Rory received few worthwhile invitations.

Now the signals are in order and the sentences clear.

Most dangling modifiers are verb clusters of the above type, but prepositional-phrase modifiers and adjective phrases can also dangle. Examples:

> As an experienced grifter, many were cheated out of their money.
>
> Without a penny to his name, things were looking hopeless.
>
> Happy over her approaching wedding day, the years of waiting now seemed worthwhile.

These constructions also signal the reader's mind to expect a name to follow. When the name does follow, there is no dangling:

> As an experienced grifter, Carney cheated many out of their money.
>
> Without a penny to his name, Murdock felt that things were hopeless.
>
> Happy over her approaching wedding day, Miss Bildt felt that the years of waiting were now worthwhile.

Sometimes danglers are best eliminated by recasting the whole sentence rather than by just naming a doer. Examples:

> When dejected, a prayer often helps to regain one's sense of proportion.
>
> A prayer often helps a dejected person to regain his sense of proportion.
>
> Having arrived late, the train had already departed.
>
> Since I was late in arriving at the station, the train had already departed.

Certain set introductory phrases are quite acceptable even though technically they seem to dangle. Examples:

> Considering the scarcity of experienced mechanics, it's easy to understand why so few used cars are in good condition.
>
> In dealing with the public, the first lesson to learn is that almost everyone is dominated by self-interest.

Whenever an introductory phrase seems perfectly clear and not absurd, you should not consider it a dangler regardless of the technical construction.

A kind of sentence weakness closely related to but not identical with the dangler is the illogical sentence modifier. In this kind of absurd sentence, a verb or adjective phrase, though used with technical accuracy, is forced to function illogically or nonlogically. Here is a live example taken from a college football program: "Bothered by minor injuries, Manski is rugged on both offense and defense." You will remember that a logical relationship exists between a sentence modifier of this sort and the main clause of a sentence. In the case of verb or adjective phrases, this logical relationship is usually one of cause-and-result. For example: "Afraid to speak up again, Billy did not get an answer to his question." Here the adjective phrase gives the cause and the main sentence gives the result.

Now look again at the sentence from the football program. The logic implied in the sentence is that Manski is rugged on both offense and defense *because* he is bothered by minor injuries— rather clearly a foolish piece of logic. The sentence would be more logical in this version: "Although bothered by minor injuries, Manski is rugged on both offense and defense." But it is likely that the writer did not mean to express any logic between the two statements. He probably just wanted to make two separate statements and constructed this rather absurd sentence because he had been taught not to write too many short simple sentences in a row. But certainly it is less effective to write an illogical sentence than to write separate simple sentences.

Illogically used verb or adjective clusters of this sort are not common in the writing of college students. Paradoxically, they are quite common in the writing of semiprofessionals (generally journalists). The reason is that suggested above: these writers know that they should get two or three separate ideas into most of their sentences in order to avoid sequences of monotonous simple sentences. Thus they become infatuated with the initial verb or adjective cluster and use it without thought of logic. You will not have to search far in journalistic writing to find sentences like these:

> Born in Austria, Schildkraut became famous as the youngest scientist ever to receive a Nobel Prize.
>
> Five feet three inches tall and weighing 126 pounds, he relaxes by tinkering with hi-fi sets and reading murder mysteries.
>
> Married to an actress, he visits the old country whenever he has a few weeks off between experiments.

These modifiers all seem to express a logic of cause-and-result, but that logic is clearly lacking in the sentences. It is very unlikely that the author of the first example wants us to believe that Schildkraut became the youngest scientist ever to receive a Nobel Prize *because* he was born in Austria. But that is what the sentence implies, just as the third sentence would seem to suggest that he conducts experiments with his actress-wife.

Should you ever reach a state of semiprofessionalism in your writing, beware of the illogical or nonlogical modifier.

EXERCISE 33. Revising Dangling Modifiers

DIRECTIONS: *Each of the following sentences contains a dangler of some sort. Write a corrected version of each.*

1. By doing right all the time, your conscience will feel at ease.
2. Most accidents take place when angry.
3. While investigating the burglary, another house was robbed.
4. Being unused to such attention, the hotel service delighted me.
5. Coming at an inconvenient time, I rather resented my parents-in-law's visit.
6. Although suave and sophisticated, anyone could see that he was an intellectual fraud.
7. Besides offering a great deal of entertainment, people can sometimes improve their educational status by watching TV.
8. By teaching the dangers of communism, our citizens can learn to protect our freedoms better.
9. When in a state of despair, a visit to the church is helpful.
10. The game between the Rams and the 49ers was quite exciting, not having seen a professional football game before.
11. Having numerous dangerous curves, she drove very carefully over that stretch of road.
12. Not having been refilled after the last draining, we just sunbathed around the pool's edge.
13. The rescue team could hardly be seen, having been nearly blinded by the flash of the explosion.
14. Although sometimes exaggerated a bit, anybody can see through most advertisements.
15. Intently searching his underside for parasites, the zoo attendant showed us a rare South American species of monkey.

Miscellaneous shifted constructions

We have shown above that the most common kinds of sentence errors are due to an improper shift from one kind of construction to another. The errors described thus far are quite serious, for they can wreck sentence clarity. There are several other kinds of shifts in sentence structure that do not seriously disturb clarity but that do annoy educated readers. You should learn to eliminate these shifts from your own writing so that it will be on an educated level.

Perhaps the most common of these minor shifts is a **shift in number.** The two numbers in grammar are the singular (one) and the plural (more than one). Shifts in number can occur because our language allows us to refer to people in general either in the singular or in the plural. Examples:

> A person may be a celebrity even when he is notorious rather than famous.
>
> People may be celebrities even when they are notorious rather than famous.
>
> A teacher must respect the beliefs of her pupils even when she disagrees with those beliefs.
>
> Teachers must respect the beliefs of their pupils even when they disagree with those beliefs.
>
> Everyone stated his opinion.
> All stated their opinions.

There is no difference in meaning between the two sentences in these examples. In each case a general reference is made.

Since our language allows either the singular or the plural for general reference, careless writers often mix the two, or shift from one to the other. By far the most common shift of this sort is from a singular noun or indefinite pronoun to a plural pronoun, as in these examples:

> If a person is ignorant of the law, *they* can still be prosecuted for breaking it.
>
> A musician is probably the most envied of professionals because *they* enjoy their work so much.
>
> Anyone who thinks *they* are being cheated should complain to the manager.
>
> A football player deserves pay, for *they* work hard.

In each of these cases the pronoun *they* should be *he*. (And of course in the last three examples the verbs would also have to be changed to the singular.)

Errors of this type are sometimes called faulty agreement in number between pronoun and antecedent, and it is certainly true that the above pronouns do not agree in number with their antecedents. But the cause of the error is a shift in number, due to the confusion of the two ways in which we can make a reference to people in general. And, for the purpose of learning to revise, it is more important to know the cause of an error than just a name for it.

An improper shift in number also occurs when a singular noun is used when only a plural noun will make sense. Examples:

> People may be a *celebrity* when . . .
> Football players can show they are a good *sport* when . . .
> All the members raised their *hand.*

The italicized nouns in these examples clearly should be plural, for the nouns they refer to are plural. This kind of error is the equivalent of saying "several are one." Several people cannot be one celebrity or one sport, nor can several members own one hand among themselves.

You can avoid a shift in number only by being intellectually aware that the error exists and by consciously reviewing each of your sentences. The error is so common that our minds tend to accept it as logical. The error does not actually obscure clarity, but it does annoy educated readers.

Less common but more awkward is a **shift in person.** The three persons in grammar are the first (*I, me, we, us*), the second (*you*), and the third (*he, him, they, them, one, anyone, person, people*). The English language allows us to refer to people in general either in the third person or in the indefinite second. Example:

> A person should not depend on a crutch if he doesn't need one.
> You should not depend on a crutch if you don't need one.

There is no difference in meaning between these two sentences when each is referring to people in general.

Since English allows either the third or the indefinite second person for general reference, careless writers often mix the two, or shift from one to the other. Examples:

A person should not depend on a crutch if he doesn't need one, for if you do you will soon find yourself unable to be independent.

When someone finds a piece of money, he usually keeps it; but sometimes you are honest enough to look for its owner.

For consistency, these sentences should use *he* and *himself* instead of *you* and *yourself*. Again, the error can be called faulty agreement between pronoun and antecedent, but its true cause is a shift in person, due to a mixture of the two ways in which we can refer to people in general.

An improper **shift in tense** is quite common in material that summarizes a novel, short story, or book of history. The reason for this shift is that English allows us to tell about the past both in the past tense and in the so-called historical present tense. An essay test answer might, for example, open with either of these two tenses:

At the beginning of his reign, King John *was* very suspicious of his nobles and *decided* that he would put them to a test before he *trusted* them with policy-making.

At the beginning of his reign, King John *is* very suspicious of his nobles and *decides* that he will put them to a test before he *trusts* them with policy-making.

There is no difference in meaning between these two versions, for the historical present tense can tell about the past.

Since English provides for either the past or the present tense to be used in narrating the past, careless writers often mix the two. As a matter of fact, even the best and most experienced writers have trouble controlling their tenses when describing events of the past or summarizing a piece of fiction. Here is an example of a typical shift of this sort:

The setting of the story *is* Padua in pre-Renaissance Italy. Giovanni *has come* to the city to study at the Universty. He *rents* a suite that *overlooks* the botannical garden of a scientist. Giovanni *had* not *been* there long when he *saw* a beautiful girl in the garden.

Such a shift does little to obscure clarity, but it does annoy educated readers. Careful writers do not allow such slips to go unrevised.

A **shift in voice** does not obscure clarity, but it does weaken sentence vigor. If the subject of a sentence performs an action, its verb is said to be in the active voice. If the subject is acted upon, its verb is said to be in the passive voice. Thus many statements can be made in either of two ways. Examples:

> The Governor vetoed House Bill 3467.
> House Bill 3467 was vetoed by the Governor.
>
> The Bijou Theater raised its admission prices 20 percent.
> Admission prices were raised 20 percent by the Bijou Theater.

There is no difference in meaning between the two versions of each example. The two first versions are in the active voice and the second ones in the passive.

Since English permits these two methods of making a statement, careless writers often mix the two. Examples:

> When I study hard for a test, it is usually passed with a high grade.
> We refused to admit defeat, and the game was won by us in the last few seconds.
> The Governor called in his lieutenants, and they were lectured by him on the necessity of getting House Bill 5943 passed quickly.

Each of these sentences would be more vigorous and economical if both clauses were kept in the active voice:

> When I study hard for a test, I usually pass it with a high grade.
> We refused to admit defeat and won the game in the last few seconds.
> The Governor called in his lieutenants and lectured them on the necessity of getting House Bill 5943 passed quickly.

If you will keep your ear tuned for sentence economy and vigor, you can revise awkward shifts in voice, provided you have an intellectual understanding of the nature of the shift.

The least common kind of shift, but one of the most annoying, is a **shift in mood.** The grammatical term *mood* has to do with the attitude of the writer or speaker. A sentence in the indicative mood expresses a statement; one in the imperative mood expresses a request; one in the subjunctive mood expresses a supposition, possibility, or obligation. Here are examples of the three moods:

> Baldwin Day is running for Governor. (indicative—a statement)
> Run for Governor, Baldwin. (imperative—a request)
> Baldwin Day should run for Governor. (subjunctive—an obligation)

Sometimes a careless writer will shift moods when all of his sentences should be written in the same mood. Here is a typical example:

> Benjamin Franklin felt that learning was as good as earning. Spend some time everyday with books. Try to progress as the times progress.

The shift here is from the indicative to the imperative. Who is issuing the requests in the second and third sentences?—Franklin or the writer? To maintain consistency in mood, the writer should have composed a passage like this:

> Benjamin Franklin felt that learning was as good as earning. He advised his readers to spend some time everyday with books and to try to progress as the times progressed.

Now the sentences are both indicative, and Franklin is responsible for all the ideas.

Sometimes a careless writer will also shift from the imperative to the subjunctive mood. Example:

> Your success in college will depend on your establishing good habits. First, set aside a definite period of study time. Then develop study habits that are suitable for the kind of courses you are taking. Next you *should* work on your attitude toward learning so that you can do your work with pleasure rather than as a task.

The second and third sentences of this passage are in the imperative mood, but the fourth shifts to the subjunctive. The fourth should, of course, have been kept in the imperative. Note, incidentally, that there are legitimate shifts in mood, as from the indicative to the imperative between the first two sentences of the last paragraph.

Improper shifts in mood are quite annoying to good readers because their minds are suddenly made to adjust to an unexpected pattern of thought. Such errors almost never appear in a careful writer's work. Only the writer who is unwilling to think about his composition falls into the mire of improper shifts in mood.

Even when there is no shift in mood, an annoying **shift in point of view** can occur. A writer can express an idea from his own point of view or from that of someone about whom he is writing. Above we saw how a writer shifted his point of view by shifting mood. Here is an example of shifted point of view with all the sentences kept in the indicative mood:

> (1) Those who argue that social and moral reform is impossible on the ground that the Old Adam of human nature remains forever the same attribute to native activities the permanence and inertia that in truth belong only to acquired customs. (2) To Aristotle slavery was rooted in aboriginal human nature. (3) Native distinctions of quality exist such that some persons are by nature gifted with power to plan, command, and supervise, and others possess merely capacity to obey and execute. (4) Hence slavery is natural and inevitable. (5) There is error in supposing that, because domestic and chattel slavery has been legally abolished, slavery as conceived by Aristotle has disappeared. (6) But matters have at least progressed to a point where it is clear that slavery is a social state, not a psychological necessity.—John Dewey, *Human Nature and Conduct.*

Sentence (1) of this passage represents the point of view of the author about an idea held by "Those who argue. . . ." Sentence (2) represents the point of view of Aristotle. Sentences (5) and (6) again represent the point of view of the author. But whose point of view is involved in sentences (3) and (4)? It seems to be the author's, but close inspection shows that these sentences continue to express Aristotle's thought. The passage is not immediately clear because of the muddy shifting of point of view.

The author should have made it crystal clear that sentences (3) and (4) were still Aristotle's ideas. He might have done so in this way:

> Those who argue that social and moral reform is impossible on the ground that the Old Adam of human nature remains forever the same attribute to native activities the permanence and inertia that in truth belong only to acquired customs. To Aristotle slavery was rooted in aboriginal human nature. He thought that native distinctions of quality exist such that some persons are by

nature gifted with power to plan, command, and supervise, and that others possess merely capacity to obey and execute. Hence to him slavery was natural and inevitable.

With the use of proper transition for coherence, the various points of view of the passage become clear rather than discernible only through a pause for rereading.

EXERCISE 34. Eliminating Faulty Shifts

DIRECTIONS: *Each of the following sentences or passages contains a faulty shift of some sort. Identify the kind of shift involved in each and compose a revised version. In some cases you will need to recast the sentences completely to achieve clarity.*

1. Aristotelian scholars are all a professor in some philosophy department.
2. Aristotle believed in spontaneous generation. Small creatures just come into being in stagnant water.
3. Aristotle taught the golden mean. Always avoid excess. Don't drink too much or too little. Don't be too high tempered or too phlegmatic.
4. Aristotle says that the good life calls for moderation; he suggested ways in which we can avoid the extremes that cause us pain.
5. An epicurean is one who thinks that the good life consists in avoiding pain and cultivating pleasure. But they mean the kind of pleasure that does not cause pain later on.
6. A stoic is one who believes in facing life's harsh realities with fortitude and determination. Don't whimper and complain and don't try to run away.
7. After about A.D. 300 many of the old Greek and Roman philosophies begin to wane, and the Christian philosophy became dominant.
8. In the early 1840s Henry David Thoreau lived in the woods by himself for two years and two months, and the book *Walden* was written by him about his experiences there.
9. In *Walden* Thoreau says that his sojourn in the woods was an experiment in simple living; he did not say that he was trying to escape from civilization.
10. According to Thoreau, one should keep his life as simple as possi-

ble, for only in simple living can you realize your full spiritual and intellectual powers.

11. A farmer, says Thoreau, is not the keeper of his herd; instead, it is their keeper.

12. "Superfluous wealth will buy superfluities only," said Thoreau, which means that he thought that a person should pay more attention to their mind than to their material possessions.

13. In the chapter in *Walden* entitled "Economy," Thoreau tells how he built his own cabin and raised his own food; he claimed that his food cost him only about one dollar a month.

14. From reading *Walden,* one can learn a great deal about what is wrong with modern life; but chances are you won't be moved enough to change your own mode of living.

15. All of the professors at Westend College have a doctorate.

16. A student of American literature may not fully agree with all that Thoreau says, but they most certainly should be acquainted with his work.

17. Thoreau was a close associate of Ralph Waldo Emerson's; in fact, for a while Emerson's household chores were done for him by Thoreau.

18. At first a reader does not see much similarity between the writings of Thoreau and Emerson, but after some close reading you realize that they thought alike to a considerable degree.

19. Students can become a member of the CQ Club by dating one of the campus queens.

20. A college student should try to learn about the philosophies of the Ancients as well as the Moderns, for you need a wide range of ideas in order to function in the complex modern world.

21. You should not be quick to accept one philosophy of life and to reject all others; be openminded and form your opinions carefully.

22. A determinist believes that every occurrence is determined by a rigid sequence of cause-and-result and that therefore man does not have any free will. If they are right, then you can't help being quick or slow to make up your mind.

23. The modern physicist, however, does not believe in scientific determinism; they believe in something called Heisenberg's Principle of Uncertainty.

24. College students are often confused by all the conflicting opinions of the experts. Don't be dismayed, however, for you will soon learn that it is mostly a world of gray rather than of black and white.

25. The last three chairmen of the Ways and Means Committee have all been a conservative.

Unclear reference

In writing, *reference* is a general term used to indicate that the meaning of one word depends on another. By far the most common kind of reference word is the pronoun, for a pronoun cannot deliver meaning unless it has a specific reference (antecedent). Hence the use of a pronoun without specific reference will spoil sentence clarity.

Our language can make frequent use of reference words because our minds have been conditioned to accept many signal patterns involving reference. For instance, our minds learn to store nouns in specific signal positions so that their meanings can be reissued to our understanding when pronouns refer to them. For example: "The Governor will veto House Bill 3267 as soon as he understands its partisan purpose." As your mind reads this sentence it instantaneously and unconsciously stores the nouns *Governor* and *House Bill 3267* for reuse, because it long ago learned that words like these are frequently referred to later in pronouns and it knows that it must keep them ready for reference. Thus when your mind comes to the pronouns *he* and *its*, it calls forth the nouns from their stored positions in order to give meaning to the pronouns. These signals work with lightning speed, of course, and you do not consciously pause to think about the reference of the pronouns. That is, you don't pause unless the writer has used a pronoun in a faulty signal position. If he has, you pause in confusion.

Pronouns can refer not only to single nouns but also to whole ideas. Thus our minds have also learned to keep whole units of thought in a stored position, just in case a pronoun reference is later made to a whole idea. For example: "I had an uncanny feeling that a surprising piece of world news would soon flash on my television screen, and that is exactly what happened." The pronoun *that* in the second part of the sentence refers to the whole subordinate "that . . ." clause of the first part. While reading the first half of the sentence, your mind stored the subordinate clause in a signal position just in case such a reference might be made to it. When the reference was made in the form of the pronoun *that,* your mind was ready to reissue the whole idea so that the pronoun *that* would be immediately clear with perfect reference.

The signal system involving reference is so complex that it is subject to frequent breakdown. Often a signal will be clear to a speaker or writer when it is not clear to his listener or reader. Everyone has had the common experience of hearing his girl friend or wife say, apparently out of the blue, "That would be a nice thing to do," and finding out, only after some exploration, that the *that* referred to a statement some minutes in the past. The speaker's mind had kept the stored signal, but the hearer's mind had not kept it that long. It is this sort of descrepancy between the signal stored in the writer's mind and that stored in the reader's that makes for unclear reference and much faulty composition. You should remember that a reader's mind keeps a noun or statement in a stored signal position for only a very short time.

Reference is said to be *ambiguous* when there are two possible signal words (antecedents) to which a reference word (pronoun) may refer. Example:

> The Governor and the Attorney General are currently engaged in a bitter political dispute. He claims that he deceitfully betrayed him for political gain.

As you read the first sentence your mind stores the nouns as possible reference signals. But when you get to the second sentence you find that *he, he,* and *him* are confusing because your mind can't tell which stored signal to reissue. The writer was not similarly confused, for he knew which signal went with which pronoun, but he carelessly ignored the reader's problem. You can avoid such ambiguity only by thinking carefully about your sentences so that you can avoid false or confusing signals. In revising the above passage, for example, you would have to abandon the reference words to avoid ambiguity:

> The Governor and the Attorney General are currently engaged in a bitter political dispute. The Governor claims that the Attorney General betrayed him for political gain.

Note that the pronoun *him* can still be retained, for the reader's mind can clearly attach the reference word *him* to the signal word *Governor*.

The ambiguity in the above example occurred because the same reference word (*he*) could refer to two different signal words. When different reference words can be used, such ambiguity vanishes. For example:

> The Governor and his wife are currently engaged in a bitter dispute. She claims that he deceitfully betrayed her.

There is no ambiguity here, for your mind has learned to associate different reference words with male and female nouns.

Sometimes ambiguous reference occurs when the pronoun *this* can refer to either of two full statements. Example from a student paper:

> Parents are asking themselves if they should force their children to go to college. In most cases *this* is wrong.

Ambiguity arises here because it is not clear whether the writer considers it wrong for the parents to ask the question or wrong for them to force their children to go to college.

Here are some more examples from student papers:

> It was once thought that the atom was indivisible, but today this theory has been discarded. The atomic bomb has proved *this*.
>
> Our era has been called the Age of Anxiety, and perhaps *this* is true.
>
> There are many people today who feel that the human conscience is a reliable guide to moral conduct. *This statement* is fallacious.

Reference errors involving such ambiguous use of the pronoun *this* are especially annoying to good readers. You should watch your own use of *this* so that you can guarantee your readers clarity when you use this reference word.

Faulty reference is called *broad* or *vague reference* when there is no specific signal word or idea for the pronoun to refer to. Usually, broad reference occurs when a pronoun is forced to refer to an adjective. Examples:

> Maury was quite amorous, but he kept *it* under control.
>
> If our teenagers are irresponsible, a great deal of *this* is due to their parents.

Since our minds do not normally store adjectives in signal positions, such sentences become vague. Understanding is managed only because our minds will subconsciously manufacture the signal nouns *amorousness* for the first sentence and *irresponsibility* for the second so that the reference words will have meaning. Only careless or ignorant writers will force this task on their readers.

Sometimes broad reference occurs when a pronoun refers only to an implied noun. Example: "I was surprised when I visited Hawaii to find that almost all of them speak English." The pronoun *them* is intended to refer to *Hawaiians*, but since that word does not appear in the sentence, the reference is broad or vague.

Most problems of reference involve pronouns, but occasionally verbs are involved. Example from an old movie announcement: "Those that have seen the entire show will please pass out so others may do so." The verb *do* in this sentence is a reference word, for the reader wants to know what the others may do. Ambiguity arises here because *do* may refer to *have seen* or to *pass out*. Here is another example from a book on bridge:

> How many people would fail to play the king in this position? Well, Sam Fry, Jr. didn't.

Didn't is a reference word in this sentence, but its reference is ambiguous because the reader can't tell whether it refers to the verb *fail* or the verb *play*.

EXERCISE 35. Eliminating Unclear Reference

DIRECTIONS: *Each of the following sentences or passages contains one or more errors in reference. Write a clear version of each and be prepared to explain why the reference is faulty.*

1. The automobile has become in the space of a few years one of the largest industries in the United States today. This was not done overnight.
2. Although the car struck the palm tree with considerable force, it was not damaged.
3. He was discharged from the Army because of his father's death, but it did not help him improve his financial status.
4. This man was very intelligent, but it did not help him in the kind of work he entered.
5. Unfortunately, our party ignored the warnings of the independents, which turned out to be the right policy.
6. Our chairman told us to ignore the attacks of the extremists. This was difficult.
7. Professor Obon testified that the student had maliciously disrupted his class. That was a despicable thing to do.

8. Will those who have looked at the exhibit please leave so others may do so too?

9. If I can be a volunteer, I hope it will be possible to do so.

10. It is time the country developed some new industry, like the helicopter, for example.

11. The use of *ain't* is considered an error in usage because cultured people do not do so.

12. The conservative position has a lot of merit. Senator Taft was a good example of this.

13. I believe all Christians will be saved because my pastor explains it so clearly.

14. The speaker spent too much time on the introduction to his talk on sex education, which was boring.

15. The professors don't understand the young students' need to rebel. They are really just like they have always been.

16. The audience requested a repetition of his earlier talk, which he did.

17. The Rules Committee objected to the antidiscrimination section of the bill. This was unnecessary.

18. A student who doesn't know how to study properly will probably not pass, which this booklet is designed to prevent.

19. The Dean of Students was informed about our infraction of the rules. This was all too true.

20. Belief in one God meant a rejection of the Trinity, which Tom Paine did.

CHAPTER 5

Diction

So far, we have studied the larger elements of composition: organization of the whole paper, paragraph development, and mature sentence structure. Now we will study some principles of individual word choice—the aspect of composition covered by the term *diction*.

A study of diction properly begins with the use of the dictionary and proceeds from that to vocabularly building. Both of these areas of study are important in any composition course. The best material for the study of the dictionary is that provided by the makers of the three or four excellent collegiate dictionaries, one of which is usually a required text in freshman English classes. The pamphlets of dictionary study furnished free by these dictionary makers cover all aspects of dictionary use.

Vocabulary building is probably most effectively accomplished by close reading in which new words are examined in their context. The chief duty of a composition text such as this is to focus upon problems of word choice, explaining and illustrating the principles that students can apply both in using words long established in their vocabularies and in using new ones they acquire through their reading. It is to this task that Chapter V of this text is devoted.

LEVELS OF DICTION

The categories of language usage

A person reveals his social and educational level most clearly through his language usage. True, we judge a stranger initially on the basis of his personal appearance, for our first knowledge of him is by sight; but we also judge him on the basis of his language usage as soon as he speaks. What kind of judgment we pass depends upon circumstances. We are quick to pass unfavorable judgment on anyone whose language usage is on a lower level than ours if he asserts himself as our educational equal; but we are usually tolerant of the language usage of those we consider our educational inferiors. For example, an encyclopedia salesman using an uneducated level of language can seldom make a sale to a well-educated person. But the same well-educated person may repeatedly and happily use the services of a plumber who speaks the worst sort of English.

The level of our oral language usage, then, is a social matter. We expect our social equals to use our kind of language, though we are tolerant of the language of those we tacitly consider our social inferiors. It follows that if we want to be accepted as the social equals of educated people—or if we want to engage successfully in work that educated people think should be done by other educated people—we must use an educated level of language.

Though the level of written language is also a social matter, we are not judged on the basis of our writing as frequently as on our speaking. This is so because we don't often write to people not on our own level, and in any event we talk to many more people than we write to or for. But you as a college student do have to produce written materials for your instructors to judge. And after your graduation, judgment may be passed on your letters of application, business reports, office memos, and other personal or business communication. In these writing situations, your language usage will always evoke an unfavorable judgment if it is not on an educated level.

Before we try to answer the obvious question we have raised—what is an educated level of language usage?—let us first understand just what the term *language usage* means. It is not a simple term referring to just one aspect of language. Instead, it can refer to any one of four different aspects: *pronunciation, spelling, grammar,* and *diction* (or word choice). Grammar and diction apply to both oral and written language. Pronunciation, of course, applies only to oral, and spelling only to written language. All four of these aspects are involved in the social acceptability of your oral and written language usage; incorrectness in any one of them can prejudice your standing as an educated person. For example, the following sentence, as written, is fully acceptable in its spelling, grammar, and diction: "The state guarantees the support of this widow's children." But educated people will snicker if you (without jesting) speak the sentence with this pronunciation: "The state garn-tees the support of this widder's chillun." Thus one of your spoken sentences may be improper only in pronunciation, or in grammar, or in diction, and one of your written sentences only in spelling, or in grammar, or in diction. Your total language usage must be acceptable in all four respects to satisfy the social requirements of educated society.

Traditional classifications of language usage

Language usage is commonly classified according to situational levels of acceptability—that is, students of language say (with validity) that a certain level of language usage may be acceptable in one situation but not in another. A commonly used scheme of classification identifies three levels: *vulgate, informal,* and *formal* (sometimes called *vulgate, general,* and *formal*). The term *vulgate* (from the Latin *vulgus,* meaning the common people) is applied to the language usage of people with little or no formal education. The following sentences are rather extreme, but certainly possible, examples of vulgate:

> They ain't nobody to home.
> I come as soon as I heerd you was sick.
> Him and me should of went with you'uns.

Such language usage is acceptable when one vulgate user is speaking to another, but it is not considered suitable for educated usage.

Informal (or general) usage, according to this classification, is used by educated people in casual conversation, workaday business writing, much journalism, friendly letters, and all kinds of personal writing. These sentences are typical of informal usage:

> The Mayor looked into the charge that his cops had taken payoffs.
> The Mayor paid no attention to their begging for mercy.

No educated person could reasonably object to such language for informal situations, but many might feel that it is not entirely proper for formal situations.

Formal language is supposedly reserved for scholarly, professional, religious, and diplomatic writing, for high-level speeches, or for any occasion when the speaker or writer wants his utterances to be considered especially important. The following sentences are more formal versions of the above informal sentences:

> The Mayor investigated the accusation that his policemen had accepted bribes.
> The Mayor ignored their entreaties for clemency.

Some people would think this language too pompous for informal use.

Though this three-way classification—vulgate, informal, formal—sounds valid, it is not wholly logical. In the first place the terms *informal* and *formal* apply to situations, such as barbershop talk, sermons, and Congressional debate, whereas *vulgate* applies to the kind of language used in all situations by the grossly uneducated. In other words, the three terms are not divisions of one whole. Furthermore, none of the three terms applies to all four aspects of language usage. The term *vulgate* identifies language with certain grammatical forms and pronunciations that do not occur in the speech of educated people. It implies a limited range of diction, but not necessarily diction lacking in respectability. The terms *informal* and *formal,* on the other hand, identify only levels of word choice. Though they both do imply correct grammatical usage, they are not thought of as pertaining to grammar. And certainly there is little if any distinction between informal and formal pronunciation or spelling. Thus the three terms do not identify three levels of diction, pronunciation, spelling, and grammar as a group, nor three levels of any one of the four. Instead, one term, *vulgate,* chiefly refers to the grammar and pronunciation of one class of speakers and the other two, *informal* and *formal,* to the diction of all classes of speakers.

The weakness of the vulgate-informal-formal classification is demonstrated when we try to fit slang into the system. Slang is not generally considered a part of informal or formal usage. Therefore, if the three-range classification covers all usage, slang should be vulgate (or else all slang would belong to the top two categories). But slang is not to be equated with vulgate, both because it has to do with vocabulary rather than with grammar and pronunciation and also because it is widely used by sophisticated people who would laugh at vulgate usage. In fact, rural people who speak vulgate probably use less slang than any other broad group, less, even, than highly educated people use. Thus the terms *vulgate, informal,* and *formal* do not allow for a full range of levels of diction, since slang is not represented in the classification.

Language usage is sometimes just classified as *standard* and *nonstandard.* This is a useful classification, for both terms can refer to all four aspects of usage. And so far as pronunciation, spelling, and grammar are concerned, it is a valid classification, for almost all pronunciations, spellings, and grammatical constructions are either standard or nonstandard. But if we are to talk usefully about levels of diction, we have to talk about more than two, and so this two-range classification is not entirely adequate for a discussion of diction.

A study of language usage will be more meaningful to you if you remember to distinguish between the four aspects of usage—pronunciation, spelling, grammar, and diction. Though standard pronunciation is an especially important aspect of the social acceptability of oral language, we will disregard it in this composition text. We will, however, make a distinction between diction and grammar and will consider diction in this chapter and grammar and spelling in Chapter 6.

Grammar does not have to do with word choice at all but with word form and word order. For example, the following pairs of short sentences do not vary in word choice; only the inflectional forms of the words are different.

> Him and me is cousins.
> He and I are cousins.
>
> Them beans was stole by he and I.
> Those beans were stolen by him and me.
>
> You has growed rapid.
> You have grown rapidly.

The first sentence of each of these pairs does not represent faulty word choice, but faulty grammatical form. *Him* and *he*, for example, are just different inflectional forms of the same word, as are *I* and *me*, *stole* and *stolen*, and so on. Choosing the proper word form is a matter of grammar but not of diction.

Diction, on the other hand, has to do with word choice, not with grammatical form. For example, the following pairs of sentences are grammatically correct but they vary in word choice.

> I will look into the matter.
> I will investigate the theft.
>
> Jane is a swell gal.
> Jane is an agreeable young lady.
>
> I feel lousy.
> I have a headache and slight fever.

These pairs of sentences are similar in meaning. In each case, however, the second sentence is more precise because of better word choice. Also each second sentence is on a higher level than the first and therefore suitable for use in a more formal or important situation. But the grammar of all six of the sentences is correct.

The term *level of diction*, then, refers to the appropriateness of a particular word for a particular situation. For example, when you are talking casually to close friends you are likely to say that someone is "stuck-up." In a conversation with your English teacher or in college writing you would more likely use the word "conceited." In a more formal piece of writing you might want to use "egotistic." Your meaning would not have varied significantly —just your word choice, according to the situation. You, as everyone else, tend to choose high-level words for important occasions and lower-level words for casual conversation. In your study of composition you need to learn something about levels of word choice and how to select an appropriate level for your college writing. Our next task, then, is to learn whether or not levels of diction can be identified, and if so, how.

Whatever conclusion we reach as to whether or not levels of diction can be truly identified, we must first understand that many or most words in a piece of English writing are not subject to choice and therefore cannot be assigned to one particular level. This is so because much of the basic language usage of English is common to all levels. Many of the pronunciations and grammatical constructions in vulgate speech are standard for all usage. Similarly, many of the words in the most formal kind of writing are also standard for all other levels, even vulgate. Thus when we discuss levels of diction, we understand that articles, prepositions, conjunctions, connectives, auxiliary verbs, and many common nouns, verbs, and modifiers are used on all levels and thus are not classifiable according to level. But many of the important words in a piece of writing are subject to choice and thus may, perhaps, be assigned to certain levels. For example, would you consider these two sentences to be on the same level?

> The rest of the money was all gravy.
> The rest of the money was unearned profit.

Don't answer the question too hastily!

Usage labels

Most good dictionaries employ **usage labels** to identify words that are, in some way, outside the bounds of standard, fully acceptable usage. The most important of these labels (usually abbreviated in the dictionary) are *obsolete, archaic, dialectal, slang,* and *colloquial.* Sometimes the first three of these terms are applied to spelling or pronunciation rather than to meaning and sometimes all five are variously applied to just one particular definition of a word whose other definitions are in good usage. We will discuss these labels only as they apply to definitions.

The label *obsolete* means that a word (or one of its definitions) is no longer in use. For example, *prester* at one time was a commonly used word meaning priest; *rubious* once meant ruby-red. Now they are obsolete.

The label *archaic* is applied to words that are obsolete except for special uses, such as in poetry or church ritual. For example, *silvern* is an archaic adjective meaning silvery; *thou* is an archaic form of *you* in the singular; *silly* can be archaically used to mean feeble or infirm. So far as your college writing is concerned, obsolete and archaic words are no problem at all. If you use a word naturally, you can be sure it is not obsolete or archaic. You may, of course, encounter such words in your reading.

The label *dialectal* is used to denote words in good usage only in one restricted locality—that is, a dialectal word belongs to an English dialect, not to the standard English language. The term can refer either to spelling or pronunciation or definition. We will consider it only in this latter sense. Dialectal words are often called *localisms* or *regionalisms*. English regionalisms now exist in America chiefly in rather remote mountain or rural regions, where language change has been at a less rapid pace than in urban areas. Such words are associated with vulgate usage because only people without much formal education continue to use them. This is so because a person from the backwoods who becomes educated learns to avoid those words that mark his place of origin. Though regionalisms are considered nonstandard, they are not to be equated with slang, which is an entirely different linguistic phenomenon, as will be explained. Since modern methods of mass communication are rapidly reducing the number of regionalisms in use, such words present few problems for English students. As a matter of fact, an English teacher who takes the generous view may be pleased to find regionalisms in his students' papers.

Here are a few regionalisms with their standard English meanings:

    to angle—to walk slowly without purpose
    barick—hill
    to bapsouse—to baptize
    bonnyclabber—thick curdled milk
    clomper—heavy boot
    diddle—a young duck
    to faunch—to be angry, to rage
    larruping—good; very
    to mind out—to take care
    oddments—sundry items
    pukish—nauseated

to shammick—to lounge about idly

Though some of these words may strike you as slang, they are not.

The usage label *colloquial* is often misunderstood. It has nothing to do with *local;* instead it comes from the Latin *colloquium,* meaning conversation. A colloquialism, then, in its original definition, is a word or phrase in good usage in spoken language (in **any** locality) but not in written language. The word is losing its original meaning, however, and now signifies language suitable for informal usage, both spoken and written. At the present time, the word seems to apply to an area between slang and high-informal, say low-informal.

Here are a few colloquialisms, with a more formal counterpart for each:

join up—enlist
give up—relinquish
give in—acquiesce
put up with—tolerate
split up—separate
full up—filled to capacity
peaked—pale
know-how—technical skill
the law—a policeman
a natural—one who is naturally expert
needle—to goad or provoke
patter—meaningless talk
outside of—except
ride—to torment or tease
fleece—to cheat or swindle

No stigma should be attached to the use of such colloquial words as these, but most educated people would feel a little uneasy about using them in important writing. Furthermore, sticklers for propriety (especially among English teachers) would look down their noses at such usage.

The status of colloquial terms has been upgraded recently because of a decision made by one of America's most important dictionary makers. The Merriam-Webster Company, publisher of the third edition of the *New International Dictionary,* the finest of unabridged American dictionaries, decided to abandon *colloquial* as a usage label. This decision was made because too many people tended to believe that the label *colloquial* meant that a word did not have full respectability. Since colloquialisms are not at all disreputable, it seems reasonable for dictionary makers to abandon the misunderstood label.

The Third International has, however, added two new usage labels: *substandard* and *nonstandard*. Its *substandard* label is applied to rather widely used vulgate forms, such as *drownded* for *drowned;* its *nonstandard* label is applied to a few words that have no reason for existing, but that nevertheless are rather widely used, such as *irregardless* for *regardless*. The *substandard* and *nonstandard* labels do not appear frequently in the Third International and by no means should be thought of as replacing the *colloquial* label.

In America's most respected dictionary, then, words not labeled *obsolete, archaic, dialectal, slang, substandard,* and *nonstandard* are considered to be on one level of full respectability. Other good dictionaries, however, continue to use the label *colloquial*. But regardless of what dictionaries say, educated people do in practice distinguish levels of diction and choose words according to the importance of speaking or writing situations. But more about that problem later.

Our one remaining common usage label is *slang*, also a somewhat misunderstood term. Originally, slang meant the specialized vocabulary of various criminal types who wanted to conceal their meanings from outsiders. That definition of the word long ago became obsolete, but many people still think the word refers only to low-level, disreputable language resorted to only by the uneducated. But slang is not just one narrow band of socially unacceptable language, and its use is certainly not restricted to the uneducated classes. It is, indeed, quite a complex linguistic phenomenon.

One way to explain the nature of slang is to tell what it is not. Hence we will define various terms (they are, in effect, usage labels) that are sometimes confused with slang. *Argot* is primarily used to define the specialized language of thieves and tramps who want to conceal their meaning; sometimes the word is applied to the specialized vocabulary of the members of any one vocation or group (for example, legal argot). *Cant* also once was applied to the specialized vocabularies of the disreputable; but currently it means the insincere or parrot-like appeal to religious, moral, or political principles that the speaker himself does not believe in or act upon or does not understand. Many sermons and political speeches are full of cant phrases. *Gibberish* is the name for unintelligible language—not necessarily slang. The word *idiom* in a restricted sense means a fully respectable expression that does not exactly fit the normal grammatical pattern of a language and cannot be translated exactly into another language. In more general usage it means the natural, native expressions of a language. An idiomatic expression is by no means to be equated with slang. *Jargon* has several definitions: (1) the specialized technical vocabulary of a particular trade (for example, educational jargon); (2) a hybrid speech of different languages or dialects; (3) incoherent speech or gibberish; and (4) long words, circumlocutions, and generally pompous and hard-to-comprehend language. Number (4) is the meaning most commonly applied to jargon. *Lingo* is just a contemptuous name for any foreign language or specialized vocabulary. *Shoptalk* refers to the specialized or technical vocabulary of those engaged in the same kind of work. *Regionalisms* have been discussed above; they are not to be equated with slang. *Vernacular* means the common language of the ordinary people of any nationality. *Vulgate* has also been discussed above. *Slang* should not be confused with any of these terms.

For the most part, slang is the result of linguistic inventiveness, especially of young and lively persons who want fresh, original, pungent, or racy terms with which they can rename ideas, actions, and objects that they feel strongly about. In effect, slang is the result of a combination of linguistic irreverence and a reaction against staid, stuffy, pompous, pretentious, or colorless diction.

There are two broad kinds of slang words. One kind is derived from, or gives a new meaning to, a standard word. For example, *heller* (a noisy, wild person), *kisser* (mouth or face), and *ripsnorter* (a noisy or violent thing or person) are not completely original creations, but are coinages from common words. Similarly, *dirt* (slanderous gossip), *pass* (an amorous overture), *off* (somewhat unbalanced mentally), and *railroad* (to rush through quickly) are slang only when used for nonstandard meanings.

Other slang words are new creations or at least have only a vague connection with established words. For example, *whoopee, blurb, goop, zorch,* and *floozy* do not appear to have etymologies (traceable origins). Thus some slang terms are entirely new creations and some are new applications of old words. The latter are by far the more common.

Slang terms originate as nonstandard diction because, as new applications, they run counter to established, traditional usage or because, as new creations, they have no root in established usage. For example, a new word coined out of a Greek root to name a newly discovered chemical would not be considered slang, because it would be derived from a respectable tradition and used to fill a definite need. But the coinage of a word like *pooped* to mean fully exhausted does not follow a tradition of "respectable" language change or inventiveness, and it fulfills a demand only for a racy or pungent word to replace an established one, not a demand for a new word to name an entirely new concept.

Though their etymologies are often generally clear, few slang words can be traced precisely to their origin. They just seem to pop up, and if they catch on, they spread quickly. Undoubtedly, however, there is an exact point of origin for most slang terms, and, presumably, one person was originally responsible for each slang term. For example, H. L. Mencken, who was a well-known student of language and devotee of slang, said that some unknown college boy must have consciously created the term *handcuff* for engagement or wedding ring because he wanted a fresh expression for an old situation. But who that boy was, no one can say.

The lifetime of most true slang words is less than a generation. They either drop from use or else rise on the scale of respectability to a standard level. Only a few hang on in subrespectability for many decades. Many of the words now labeled *colloquial* in dictionaries were originally considered slang, and the dictionaries of the 1970s, if they continue to use the label *colloquial,* will apply that term to many words that, in the 1960s, they call slang. The ever-changing face of language usage presents many problems in the classification of levels of diction. But more about that presently, too.

Much slang is regional; many terms in common use in New York, for example, are unknown in Los Angeles. Radio, TV, and comic books, however, tend to spread slang from coast to coast. To a greater extent slang is class structured. For example, much of the slang of factory workers is different from that of café society; and that of high school students is noticeably different from that of college students. Even college professors enjoy a small amount of private slang. From one point of view slang itself has various levels.

Experts in the study of language are much more tolerant of slang now than they were a few decades ago, for they recognize that our language has been enriched by many strong, pungent, racy slang words. Mencken, for example, wrote at length and learnedly of the value of such slang creations as *rubberneck, lame-duck, cow-catcher, to gum-shoe,* and *poppycock.* Most linguists think such words enliven the language and keep it growing. In fact, they think that most of our language growth (except for scientific terms) comes through slang and its gradual rise on the scale of respectability.

A current tendency among students of language and followers of Mencken (he died in 1956) is to refuse to prescribe levels of diction. The dropping of the label *colloquial* from the third edition of the *New International Dictionary* is a part of this trend. Experts who follow this line of thought say that no one word is intrinsically any better than another and that "good" English is any English that accomplishes the speaker's or writer's purpose without causing the hearer or reader to pay more attention to the words themselves than to their meaning. In other words, they say that natural language that accomplishes its purpose is good language, regardless of the "level" of diction.

There is much merit in this attitude toward language. Much linguistic harm is probably caused by stuffy English teachers who frighten students out of using their natural language. However, regardless of the theory behind the proposed junking of usage labels in dictionaries, educated people still choose their level of diction according to the importance of the situation that prompts their speaking or writing. This is an undeniable fact that can be verified by comparing the casual conversation, friendly letters, business letters, and professional writing of any one educated person.

Though you should maintain a liberal attitude toward the choice of words, you should not assume that all words have equal status. Both H. L. Mencken and other sensible experts have recognized that much slang owes its existence and continued use to a lack of linguistic ability rather than to commendable linguistic inventiveness. For example, many terms such as *peachy keen, real cool, guys and gals, the greatest,* and *zorch* can hardly be considered the result of an inspired search for fresh and vigorous expressions, and those who depend on such terms cannot be praised for their pungent and racy vocabulary. Much ineffective slang is used by those who take a lazy, inattentive, and unimaginative attitude toward language. A distinction, then, must be made between strong and useful slang terms and weak, ineffective ones.

New slang terms are like new ideas—some are good and some aren't. And just as human beings can be slow to reject unsound ideas, so they can form an undue attachment for feeble slang terms. And therefore much limp slang remains in use. A racy, vigorous, expressive slang term, however, deserves the same fate as a good idea—permanence and respectability. How can you tell whether a slang term is vigorous and expressive? By realizing that you prefer it to a more conventional word that you do know and could use. When you are limited to a slang word because you cannot choose another in its place, your language usage cannot be wholly on an educated level.

In view of this discussion of usage labels and of the modern trend among students of language not to prescribe "good" usage in narrow terms, how shall we answer our question about whether or not levels of diction can be identified? First we should remember that we are now speaking only of diction; for educated people, spelling, pronunciation, and grammar may suitably be classified as either standard or nonstandard. Diction, however, cannot be so classified. Perhaps the best answer to our question is that within certain limits levels of diction can be identified, but that, because of the changing nature of language and the varying proclivities of educated individuals, no hard and fast boundaries can be assigned to various levels. In actual practice, the terms *slang, colloquial, informal,* and *formal* are useful in discussing the relative status of individual words and expressions. But we must remember that not even English teachers will always agree on the status of any one particular word; and, more important, we must remember that even slang words are not necessarily disreputable.

There are many words that almost everyone will agree are slang. For example: *broad* (woman), *skirt* (woman), *icky* (distasteful), *the Joe Blakes* (nervous agitation), *sawbones* (a medical doctor), *headshrinker* (a psychiatrist), and *stonkered* (incapacitated). But there are many other words that some educated people will call slang and some will call standard or colloquial. For example: *middling* (moderately), *duds* (clothing), *kid* (child), *jinx* (cause of bad luck), *jittery* (nervous), *ham* (pretentious or egotistic actor), *down in the mouth* (depressed), *rave notice* (enthusiastic review), *well-heeled* (prosperous or rich), *go places* (make a quick and easy success), *chew the rag* (engage in a general discussion), and *dig* (a calculated insult). Regardless of what the best dictionaries may say, words like these will strike knowledgeable people in different ways, and there will be no consensus as to their exact status. As an exercise, you might first decide which of the above words you think are slang and which colloquial and then check your opinion with that of a good dictionary. Also you might see if different dictionaries have different usage labels for any of the words. Do not be afraid to disagree with a dictionary's usage label.

Proper level of diction in college writing

In view of the partially indeterminate state of language classification, how can an educated level of diction be identified for you as a college student and what sound advice can be given to guide you in your choice of words? First, you should understand that *level of diction is a consideration secondary to those principles discussed in the following sections of Chapter 5.* Regardless of level, try to choose precise, vigorous, concrete, and idiomatic diction. Also regardless of level, try to avoid trite and pretentious diction and be wary of abstract diction. For example, on many semiformal or even highly formal occasions pungent slang (for example, *corn*) is to be favored over dull respectable diction (for example, *sentimental drama*). Keep in mind that this discussion of levels is only one aspect of the whole area of diction. *Other aspects are more important.*

Probably the solution to any problem you may have with level of diction lies in your developing a capacity to choose among two or more words. Many of the words in any expository paragraph are hardly subject to choice: articles, prepositions, conjunctions, auxiliary verbs, and many common verbs, nouns, and modifiers used in all writing. But many of the most important words in your writing will be subject to choice. If you find yourself unable to think of alternative words so that you can choose the most appropriate, you probably will find yourself limited to an unsatisfactory level of diction. For example, if you can think of no word but *swell* to describe a girl's personality, your instructor will charge you with slang usage and will remind you of specific and respectable words like *vivacious, charming, pert* and *agreeable*. On the other hand, if you can think only of *bad* to describe the behavior of an insincere person, your instructor is likely to accuse you of colorless diction and to suggest the useful slang word *phony*. You will find that when you can choose the better of even two alternatives you will have little trouble with level of diction. The problem is not only one of developing your vocabulary, but also of fully utilizing the vocabulary you already have. You must learn to **think** about your word choice.

Although you may have been taught that your writing should be like your talking, you should know that *almost any kind of writing, and especially exposition, calls for a higher level of diction than casual conversation does.* Writing is really not like talking. Think of sentence structure. Even your highest level of conversation utilizes mostly rather simple sentence structure. But good expository writing calls for a variety of complex sentences. Educated readers simply expect carefully composed sentences of a nonconversational type. They also expect a level of diction above that of casual conversation. If you think writing is like talking, try secretly tape-recording a casual conversation and then reproduce it as writing. You will find it much different from any writing you have ever read.

But high-quality exposition should have the natural quality of conversation. It should not sound strained or stilted, and it should not give the impression that it caused its author great labor. It should sound like high-level conversation even though it isn't conversation. *Therefore in your college writing you should use the highest level of diction you have at your command, provided it sounds natural and unaffected.* For example, avoid a generally low level of diction like this:

> The frontman and his sidekick divvied up their loot.
> Freddie turned chicken when his bluff was called.

Also avoid a stilted diction like this:

> The sales-potential analyst and the direct-contact representative bifurcated their monetary accumulation.
> Freddie exhibited pusillanimous behavior when his pugilistic artistry was questioned.

Instead, use a respectable but natural diction of this sort:

> The canvasser and the salesman divided their earnings.
> Freddie turned coward when he was challenged to prove his
> fighting skill.

Naturalness in writing is to be highly valued, but the casual quality of ordinary conversation should be avoided.

The advice to use the highest level of natural diction at your command is a general precept and does not necessarily apply to each individual word choice. Remember the precept that a vigorous piece of slang is better than a lack-luster formal term. An examination of good magazines shows that a smattering of well-chosen, racy slang words can add color to expository writing. For example, articles in a magazine like *Harper's* sometimes use such slang terms as *gift of gab, kickback,* and *snitching.* An overuse of slang, however, will surely wreck expository writing. So will the use of limp slang. For example, the term *guys and gals* will invariably kill the effectiveness of any sentence, whereas the term *hot number* could be effectively used in writing with an otherwise high level of diction. *The secret is to use only vigorous slang and to use it sparingly.* Or you might express the truth in this paradox: sometimes slang, because of its vigor and color, is on a higher level of diction than an equivalent colloquialism or formal term.

You should be conscious enough of your level of diction *not to shift levels within a piece of writing,* unless you make a momentary shift for a calculated effect. For example, you should not, in a paper on your college's dramatic performances, start off with such phrases as "carefully coached stage business," "precise and distinct delivery of lines," "gifted mimicry," and "exotic props" and then suddenly use such phrases as "cut it sharp," "a honey of an entrance," "wowed 'em with his ad-lib cracks at the college brass," and "jazzed-up gimmicks." Such incongruity of phrasing is quite distracting to perceptive readers.

An occasional brief drop in level of diction, however, can be effective. For example: "His carefully measured delivery of the Queen Mab speech was exquisitely lyrical until he *cracked his jaw* on 'Her whip, of cricket's bone; the lash, of film.' " The incongruity of a momentary shift of this sort can be engaging rather than distracting. But such an effect must be planned; it will seldom occur accidentally. *Remember that slang terms should be used only sparingly and only when they are vigorously effective.*

As stated above, the modern fashion in choice of diction is to keep a liberal attitude, and that is a good attitude to keep. Contrary to old-fashioned attitudes, most writing, even by the highly educated, is not formal. *College writing, for example, is on a semiformal level at its highest.* Even college textbooks should avoid a stilted formalism and should cultivate a natural, clear, informal-to-semiformal style.

An example of an unwise stressing of formalism is the advice not to use contractions in college exposition. Long ago some precise grammarian arbitrarily decided that contractions, being colloquial, should never appear in serious writing. The precept has been perpetuated and even today some students are uselessly warned to avoid contractions. In fact, such advice is often harmful rather than just useless in that it causes many students to be afraid to write naturally.

Now it is true that the higher the level of writing, the less likely it is to have contractions. A legislative bill, for example, is usually written without contractions. However, there is no logical reason why contractions should be avoided in any college writing. Naturalness in most writing situations is to be desired above stilted formalism, and contractions can add naturalness without reducing writing to the level ef casual conversation. You should not deliberately avoid *don't, won't, can't* and so forth when the two full words would sound less natural. But you should not deliberately use a contraction when the two full words would sound natural. The advice not to overuse contractions is sound.

A similar illogical precept sometimes given is that the indefinite *you* should be avoided. For example, sometimes this mode of reference is insisted upon: "When one is preparing a term paper, he should recheck his direct quotations for accuracy." And this mode of reference is sometimes thought to be inappropriate: "When you are preparing a term paper, you should recheck your direct quotations for accuracy." The truth of the matter is that in most writing situations the use of the indefinite *you* is preferable to the indefinite *one*. It is a more natural and a warmer usage. The objection that the reader will not be able to tell who is meant—he personally or people in general—is not valid. Many students become afraid to write naturally because they are hounded with such insignificant, or downright false, precepts.

In general, then, you not only can but should use an informal to semiformal level of diction in your college writing. You should avoid a stilted formalism, but you should use your highest level of diction if it sounds easy and natural. You need not avoid colloquialisms, but you should avoid slang[1] except for the occasional use of a sharp, expressive slang term that appeals to you more than a conventional term that you could use.

You should not try to write as you talk, but you should try to make your writing sound as natural as conversation. A natural quality can be achieved with a high level of diction. In fact, in exposition a low level of diction usually does not sound natural. For example, a paper with these words might sound awkward and unnatural: *smart, two cents' worth, high-faluting,* and *real useful.* Whereas one with these words might sound natural and unaffected: *precocious, contribution, prestigious,* and *invaluable.* The expert writers who use slang and colloquialisms do not use **only** diction of that level. For the most part they use a semiformal level of diction with only a scattering of rich and pungent slang and colloquial terms. Remember the precept stated above: *level of diction is not as important as vigor and precision of diction.*

Finally, it should be pointed out that *a natural quality in expository writing will not come to you naturally.* You learn an educated level of diction from reading good books and from conversing with educated people. You should make a conscious and sustained effort to learn new words and to use them in your writing. And though you should strive for natural diction, it will be better for you to fail occasionally in your attempts to use new words than for you to avoid them for fear of making a mistake.

---

[1] When using a slang word, it is not necessary for a writer to put it in quotation marks just to show that he knows it is slang. If a word is worth using, it should just be used; a writer should not try to save face by distinguishing it from other words. For example, don't signal a slang expression in this way: "The president of the corporation implied that he wanted his junior executives to 'butter him up.' " Just use the phrase. Quotation marks, however, should be used to signal words that do not really mean what they say. For example:

The Mayor put through many "reforms."
Henry belongs to the "literary" set.

Here the writer indicates that he does not think the Mayor's "reforms" were legitimate reforms or that Henry's set really had literary abilities.

EXERCISE 36. Discriminating between Strong and Limp Slang

DIRECTIONS: *Many of the following slang terms are of the sort that weaken rather than strengthen expository writing. A few, however, have enough strength or raciness to warrant their occasional use in good writing. On the basis of your own linguistic preference decide which of these terms should be avoided altogether and which you might use on occasion in your college writing. Also see how many equivalent expressions you can think of for each of these terms and then decide what level of diction you think each equivalent expression is on.*

1. kidding around
2. oat burner
3. jalopy
4. lousy
5. dough
6. the whole shebang
7. smack on the dot
8. heebie-jeebies
9. screwy
10. burned up
11. clothes-horse
12. crummy
13. corset stretcher
14. stacked
15. hot stuff
16. some dish
17. creep
18. clammed up
19. weak sister
20. bag
21. tomato
22. tommyrot
23. all that jazz
24. hit the sack
25. daffy
26. looney-bin
27. sharpie
28. cream puff
29. chicken
30. hogwash
31. passion pit
32. gam
33. jag
34. booze
35. bean
36. fuzz
37. snafu
38. plastered
39. eyeful
40. good joe

EXERCISE 37. Distinguishing Levels of Diction

DIRECTIONS: *Following are groups of words that are approximately equivalent in meaning. Assign a level of diction—slang, colloquial, semiformal, and formal—to each word or phrase and decide which of each group you think would be preferable in a semiformal piece of college writing.*

1. balmy, off, crazy, in left field, insane, nutty, goofy, not normal, psychotic
2. stinko, drunk, lubricated, intoxicated, high, inebriated, tipsy, plastered
3. smart, brainy, brilliant, razor-witted, highly intelligent, bright, all gray matter
4. a real dish, a beauty, an eye catcher, a lovely girl, a looker, a comely lass
5. cut up, misbehave, be obstreperous, clown, play practical jokes
6. smooching, intimate affection, petting, necking, amorous diversion
7. guzzle, imbibe, drink rapidly, chug-a-lug, down it
8. chatter, gabble, talk rapidly and inanely, yak, run on, yammer
9. fizzled, shot its wad, died out, flopped, pooped out, ended weakly, failed after a successful beginning
10. deadbeat, bum, a lazy and idle person, spiv, sponge, moocher

EXERCISE 38. Slang in High-Level Writing

DIRECTIONS: *The following sentences are from articles in either* Harper's *or* The Atlantic, *two of America's highest-level general magazines. Point out the slang or low-colloquial term in each and pass judgment on its use in writing of the quality that appears in these magazines.*

1. Bartók himself would have no truck with it.
2. He may have an English girlfriend stashed away in one of the nearby villages.
3. This modest report is offered as an antidote for election-year stomach-ache.
4. Probably most people who remember it at all think of it as a fiasco: a harebrained, hastily conceived make-work scheme that flopped, after wasting a potful of the taxpayers' money.
5. The *Globe* dishes up the fattest menu of canned goods.
6. The shabbiest heritage of Boston reporting is the pay-off.
7. Nobody suspected him of hanky panky.
8. Nikita Krushchev once again emerged as top dog in the Communist orbit.
9. It takes some doing for a lad just out of Harvard Business School to act the part of a restaurant bus boy without spilling the beans.
10. They come up with viruses, which eventually, and predictably, become old hat when the professional men get going on some new and fascinating diversion like the current cholesterol kick.

PRECISE AND VIGOROUS DICTION

The vocabulary of the English language is so extensive that only the most learned can know more than a small fraction of the total. But even the small fraction that most of us know gives us many alternatives in individual word choice. All of us have in our vocabularies various levels of diction, and most of us choose from these levels according to the circumstances confronting us. If you want the truth of this assertion brought home to you, try writing a composition on this topic: "Discuss the ways in which you adjust your language usage to fit different circumstances." If you do enough thinking to write a good theme on this topic, you will see that you do manipulate levels of diction to suit circumstances.

But level of diction determines only the social respectability of language, not its **precision** and **vigor.** Some words on all levels are vague and limp and some on all levels are precise and vigorous. *Regardless of level, you should choose the most precise and vigorous words you have at your command.* Precise and vigorous slang is to be preferred over limp and vague diction of a higher level.

Now it is one thing to learn this italicized precept and to repeat it knowingly and to say on proper occasions that the right word in the right place is the key to good writing style. It is entirely another matter to think about your own individual word choice. Few of us have the habit of focusing on an individual word in our own writing and asking ourselves whether that is the best word we can select for that spot. We think the above precept applies only to other people's writing. You should come to realize that it also applies to your writing and that you can form the habit of thinking about your individual word choice. Such a habit can bring a noticeable improvement in the quality of your writing. Of course many or most of the words in any one sentence are hardly subject to choice. But some are, and you should think about those. Any time you have even the vaguest feeling of uneasiness about a word, ask yourself if you have a different and better word choice for that spot.

A precise word is one that says **exactly** what you mean. A vigorous word is one that has **strength of meaning** and **strength of sound.** Vigor and precision in diction are desirable for they both contribute to clear meaning and to the esthetic pleasure that writing can give. Following are some principles of word choice that will help you learn to choose more precise and vigorous diction.

Specific and general words

The more specific a word is, the more precise it is; the more general, the less precise. A general word covers many different varieties of whatever the word applies to; a specific word covers only one or a few varieties—there are degrees of specificity. For example, here are three sentences in descending order from the general to the specific:

> An animal hurt a person.
> A dog bit a boy.
> A boxer nipped Freddie Spivak.

Even this simple paradigm illustrates the value of specific diction. It shows that the more clearly you specify the particular variety of whatever you are mentioning, the more exact your meaning becomes. Note that there are degrees of specificity in verbs as well as in nouns.

You can improve your word choice, then, by replacing general words that occur to you first with more specific words that occur to you after you start thinking about the words you have chosen. Here are some illustrative pairs:

> another thing
> another idea, accident, proposal, habit, gambit
>
> another factor
> another cause, detail, point of view, aspect, character trait
>
> a book
> a novel, biography, anthology, textbook of chemistry
>
> bad weather
> a tornado, cyclone, a windstorm, a bitter or foggy day
>
> a game
> bridge, poker, tiddly winks, post office, soccer
>
> illness
> mumps, cancer, respiratory ills, undiagnosed aches and pains

good looks
trim figure, flawless complexion, regular features, even teeth

a professional man
doctor, lawyer, dentist, professor, confidence man

made a noise
rattled, boomed, scratched, thundered, whistled

talked
jabbered, rambled, gossiped, preached, inquired, lectured

misbehaved
stole cookies, broke a chair, teased a cat, refused to wash

If you will develop the habit of actively inspecting your own writing to see whether you can make substitutions like those in the above examples, you will noticeably improve the precision of your diction. And you will also find that such substitutions often increase the vigor of your diction. Remember, you cannot make the improvement by just learning a list of words. You must also learn to focus on and think about your own individual word choice.

Among the most common offenders in nonspecific diction are the adjectives that we use for general approval or disapproval without specifying a particularity that causes our attitude. Here are the most common ones:

General Approval	General Disapproval
swell	lousy
terrific	terrible
nice	awful
fine	wretched
splendid	horrid
grand	foul
marvelous	abysmal
wonderful	horrible

Most of these words once had specific meanings. For example, *wonderful* originally was applied to an event or object that struck wonder or amazement in the viewer, and *terrific* once meant causing great fear. Now these are just generalized terms of approval that do not specify just what characteristic the writer or speaker is praising. So with all the words in both columns. They are of little value when used for their generalized meanings. As an exercise, compare the original meanings of these words with their present generalized meanings.

You should avoid the nonspecific words because they are not accurate. You should, instead, choose words like the following, making a choice according to the precise meaning you want:

Specific Approval	Specific Disapproval
reliable	irritable
valid	false
skillful	untrustworthy
adept	boring
stimulating	awkward
agreeable	repulsive
cheerful	headachy
vivacious	distressing
sympathetic	insipid
helpful	dull
moving	stereotyped
touching	childish
sweet	malodorous
kind	monotonous
effective	sentimental

Specific words like these are much to be preferred over the indiscriminate terms of blanket approval or disapproval. Remember, increasing the precision of your diction will not be just a matter of learning new words but of learning to reject your first word choice in favor of a more specific term. Also remember that you should be more concerned with the precision of your diction than with its level.

EXERCISE 39. Improving Sentence Precision and Vigor

DIRECTIONS: *Improve the precision and vigor of the following sentences by replacing general diction with specific.*

1. An animal injured my property.
2. A book led to my taking the job.
3. The reading material affected my attitude.
4. The injury was caused by a blunt instrument.
5. The accident resulted in part of his clothes being damaged.
6. The man treated his wife badly.

7. The tree was diseased.
8. The men talked about the issues.
9. A workman damaged a piece of art.
10. Just one thing about the affair bothered me.

Concrete and abstract words

As we have seen, specific words are more precise and vigorous than general words. Similarly, concrete words tend to be more precise and vigorous than abstract words. A concrete word is one that names an object that really exists and can be perceived by the human senses. An abstract word names a quality that an object can have, but that cannot be detached from that object so that it has a separate existence of its own. For example, the word *girl* names something you can see or touch. Therefore it is a concrete word. But the word *beauty* does not name a thing that you can see or touch by itself. It does not have an independent existence; something or someone must be beautiful if beauty is to exist. So *beauty* is an abstract word.

The word *abstract* comes from the Latin *abstrahere,* meaning to draw from or separate. Thus abstract words are those that express qualities apart from the things that have the qualities. Perhaps this concept can be made clearer to you with an illustration from *Alice in Wonderland.* Do you remember that Alice saw a Chesire cat that had the ability gradually to fade away? As Alice looked at the cat, it gradually faded until nothing but its grin was left. The grin was just there without the cat. That grin was abstract—literally separated from the object that owned it. Thus a grinning cat is concrete, but a grin by itself is abstract.

We use abstract words in almost all of our utterances. Here are a few of the common ones we depend upon: *courage, glory, fame, goodness, patriotism, devotion, love, honor, pride, humility, cunning, piety, generosity, pain, sweetness, kindness, joy, contentment, greed, hate, sympathy, jealousy, cowardice, fear, despair, hope, foolishness, wisdom, ignorance, faith, anger, remorse, pity, cruelty, snobbishness,* and *treachery.* The list could be almost endless.

Words like these are indispensable in our language. They are good words and should not necessarily be avoided. However, an overuse of abstractions weakens the precision and vigor of writing because abstractions cannot create mental images for the reader nearly as successfully as concrete words can. As we read, our minds try to picture (to form images of) what we read. Thus if we read that General Trotter is patriotic, we try to visualize what he is, and we have a hard time. The image will at best be vague in our minds. But if we read that he pledges allegiance to the flag each morning and spends one-third of his salary on savings bonds, we have actions we can picture in our minds. Thus writing that names objects and actions is usually more precise and vigorous than writing that names abstractions. The difference lies in the varying capacity of words to form images in our minds.

It is true that we do form images in our minds when we read abstract words. We do so by relating the abstraction to some concrete object or action that we associate with it. For example, when we read that someone has acted *foolishly* (an abstraction), we tend to think of foolish actions that we have committed, such as buying lavish gifts for an insincere girl friend. But the user of the word may have been referring to an entirely different kind of foolish action. As you can see, the more you use abstractions, the more you allow your reader to place his own interpretation on your meaning, for he will form his own rather than your images in interpreting your abstractions.

The general term *abstract writing* is applied to writing that is hard to comprehend because it has so few image-forming words in it. *Concrete writing,* on the other hand, is easier to comprehend and, other things being equal, more interesting because it gives the reader something to visualize. Philosophic writing is usually quite abstract, for it deals with concepts (abstractions) rather than with things. Narrative writing is usually concrete, for the author tells a story about things and actions. Philosophic and expository writing need not be highly abstract, however, for writers can always relate concepts to specific things and actions by using examples to illustrate terms like *patriotism, morality, piety, modesty, idealism, virtue, democracy, communism, justice, liberty, reality,* and *statesmanship.* Expository writing can and should make some use of the narrative technique of naming things and actions so that the reader's mind can form images.

To illustrate to you the value of concrete words in expository writing, a speech by Chief Seattle, one of the great American Indian chiefs, is reproduced below. This speech has considerable literary merit, much of which is due to the use of concrete language. Since the Indians lived close to the earth, it was, perhaps, natural for them to avoid abstractions and to rely on concrete terms to deliver their meaning. As an exercise for this section, point out concrete words in Chief Seattle's speech.

MESSAGE TO THE WHITE CHIEF

Yonder sky that has wept tears of compassion upon my people for centuries untold, and which to us appears changeless and eternal, may change. Today is fair. Tomorrow may be overcast with clouds. My words are like the stars which never change. Whatever Seattle says the great chief at Washington can rely upon with as much certainty as he can upon the return of the sun or the seasons. The White Chief says that Big Chief at Washington sends us greetings of friendship and goodwill. That is kind of him for we know he has little need of our friendship in return. His people are many. They are like the grass that covers vast prairies. My people are few. They resemble the scattering trees of a storm-swept plain. The great, and I presume—good, White Chief sends us word that he wishes to buy our lands but is willing to allow us enough to live comfortably. This indeed appears just, even generous, for the Red Man no longer has rights that he need respect, and the offer may be wise also, as we are no longer in need of an extensive country. . . . I will not dwell on, nor mourn over, our untimely decay, nor reproach our paleface brothers with hastening it, as we too may have been somewhat to blame.

Youth is impulsive. When our young men grow angry at some real or imaginary wrong, and disfigure their faces with black paint, it denotes that their hearts are black, and then they are often cruel and relentless, and our old men and old women are unable to restrain them. Thus it has ever been. Thus it was when the white men first began to push our forefathers further westward. But let us hope that the hostilities between us may never return. We would have everything to lose and nothing to gain. Revenge by young men is considered gain, even at the cost of their own lives, but old men who stay at home in times of war, and mothers who have sons to lose, know better.

Our good father at Washington—for I presume he is now our father as well as yours, since King George has moved his boundaries further north—our great good father, I say, sends us word that if we do as he desires he will protect us. His brave warriors will be to us a bristling wall of strength, and his wonderful ships of war will fill our harbors so that our ancient enemies far to the northward—the Hydas and Tsimpsians—will cease to frighten our women, children and old men. Then in reality will he be our father and we his children. But can that ever be? Your God is not our God! Your God loves your people and hates mine. He folds His strong and protecting arms lovingly about the pale-face and leads him by the hand as a father leads his infant son— but He has forsaken His red children—if they really are His. Our God, the Great Spirit, seems also to have forsaken us. Your God makes your people wax strong every day. Soon they will fill the land. Our people are ebbing away like a rapidly receding tide that will never return. The white man's God cannot love our people or He would protect them. They seem to be orphans who can look nowhere for help. How then can we be brothers? How can your God become our God and renew our prosperity and awaken in us dreams of returning greatness? If we have a common heavenly father He must be partial—for He came to his paleface children. We never saw Him. He gave you laws but He had no word for His red children whose teeming multitudes once filled this vast continent as stars fill the firmament. No; we are two distinct races with separate origins and separate destinies. There is little in common between us.

To us the ashes of our ancestors are sacred and their resting place is hallowed ground. You wander far from the graves of your ancestors and seemingly without regret. Your religion was written upon tables of stone by the iron finger of your God so that you could not forget. The Red man could never comprehend nor remember it. Our religion is the traditions of our ancestors—the dreams of our old men, given them in solemn hours of night by the Great Spirit; and the visions of our sachems; and it is written in the hearts of our people.

Your dead cease to love you and the land of their nativity as soon as they pass the portals of the tomb and wander way beyond the stars. They are soon forgotten and never return. Our dead never forget the beautiful world that gave them being.

Day and night cannot dwell together. The Red Man has ever fled the approach of the White Man, as the morning mist flees before the morning sun. However, your proposition seems fair and I think that my people will accept it and will retire to the reservation you offer them. Then we will dwell apart in peace, for the words of the Great White Chief seem to be the words of nature speaking to my people out of dense darkness.

It matters little where we pass the remnant of our days. They will not be many. A few more moons; a few more winters— and not one of the descendants of the mighty hosts that once moved over this broad land or lived in happy homes, protected by the Great Spirit, will remain to mourn over the graves of a people once more powerful and hopeful than yours. But why should I mourn at the untimely fate of my people? Tribe follows tribe, and nation follows nation, like the waves of the sea. It is the order of nature, and regret is useless. Your time of decay may be distant, but it will surely come, for even the White Man, whose God walked and talked with him as friend with friend, cannot be exempt from the common destiny. We may be brothers after all. We will see.

We will ponder your proposition, and when we decide we will let you know. But should we accept it, I here and now make this condition that we will not be denied the privilege without molestation of visiting at any time the tombs of our ancestors, friends and children. Every part of this soil is sacred in the estimation of my people. Every hillside, every valley, every plain and grove, has been hallowed by some sad or happy event in days long vanished. . . . The very dust upon which you now stand responds more lovingly to their footsteps than to yours, because it is rich with the blood of our ancestors and our bare feet are conscious of the sympathetic touch. . . . Even the little children who lived here and rejoiced here for a brief season will love these somber solitudes and at eventide they greet shadowy returning spirits. And when the last Red Man shall have perished, and the memory of my tribe shall have become a myth among the White Men, these shores will swarm with the invisible dead of my tribe, and when your children's children think themselves alone in the field, the store, the shop, upon the highway, or in the silence of the pathless woods, they will not be alone. . . . At night when the streets of your cities and villages are silent and you think them deserted, they will throng with the returning hosts that once filled and still love this beautiful land. The White Man will never be alone.

Let him be just and deal kindly with my people, for the dead are not powerless. Dead, did I say? There is no death, only a change of worlds.

Colloquial phrases and single-word equivalents

More vigor, and sometimes more precision, can be achieved in a sentence through the use of a single word to replace a weak colloquial phrase of two or more words. English is full of multiple-word colloquial phrases that have single-word equivalents. In our conversation we tend to use the phrases, but in writing the single-word equivalents are usually superior. Here are some examples:

play a big part in	dominate
do away with	abolish
get a hold of	control
cut down on	decrease
on account of the fact that	because
get a kick out of	enjoy
run into	meet
put up a fuss	quarrel
get down off of	dismount
run rings around	outperform
come up with	suggest
talk a lot about	discuss
make a hit with	impress
come in contact with	encounter
find out	discover
take a lot away from	diminish
leave out	omit
catch up with	overtake

In sentences you can feel the greater power of the single-word equivalents in this list. For example, "He dominated the meeting" has more strength and precision than "He played a big part in the meeting."

EXERCISE 40.   Improving Sentence Precision and Vigor

DIRECTIONS: *Improve the precision and vigor of the following sentences by substituting single-word equivalents for colloquial phrases.*

1. His attitude took a lot away from our enjoyment of the play.
2. We went down into the canyon and looked closely at its rock walls.
3. We got off of the ship just after it pulled in to the pier.
4. He let go of the rope in order to keep a disaster from happening.
5. I can't put up with Tom's attempts to buy off the policeman.
6. The speaker made fun of pacifist proposals to do away with nuclear weapons.
7. Manski took the place of the first-string quarterback, who did not have the academic right to play.

8. While looking into the treasurer's report, the committee found several discrepancies that needed to be straightened out.
9. The workmen bound themselves into one group to make their cause have more strength.
10. I got a great deal of pleasure out of that novel.

Idiomatic diction

If writing is to be precise and vigorous, it must be idiomatic. This means that the phrases used must be native to the language and must sound natural to the ear of the reader. For example, if you were to write "Tom can't put up with Jane's antics," you would have used a natural, native, idiomatic expression (though one more suitable for conversation than for exposition). If, however, you were to write "Tom can't put up against Jane's antics," you would have used an unidiomatic expression—unidiomatic because it is un-English. There is no logical reason why *with* should be used instead of *against* in the above phrase (think of *slow up* and *slow down*).

Most phrases in English that are thought of as idioms involve prepositions or words that look like prepositions.[2] The following list of idiomatic expressions will give you an understanding of the variety of English idioms:

get out of a car
get away from the scene of a crime
get down from a horse
get up into the attic
get up out of a chair
come up against a problem
come around to a point of view
come across with a blackmail payment
be in the movies
be on television
be in on a good thing

---

[2] In a phrase such as "put up with," neither *up* nor *with* is a preposition, nor is *up* an adverb. That is, Tom did not "put" with Jane's antics in an "up" fashion. (Compare, for example, "Tom walked rapidly with Jane." *Antics* is the object of the whole phrase, not just the word *with*. *Up* and *with* may be called particles and the whole phrase a merged-verb or a verb-adverbial composite. Note that the single verb *tolerate* (a better word choice for exposition) can be substituted for the whole phrase.

contrary to one's code of morals
in conflict with one's code of morals
a stand on a question
an opinion of a question
advantages of a separate peace treaty
reasons for a separate peace treaty
ways by which a problem can be solved
ways in which a problem can be stated
angry with one's teacher
angry at a delay
happy for one's uncle
pleased with one's wife
opposed to the legislation
in favor of the legislation
grateful for one's advice
appreciative of one's service
an opinion of a book
an attitude toward a book
reach an agreement on a proposal
reach an agreement with one's neighbor
ashamed of one's behavior
sorry for one's behavior

Idiomatic expressions like these follow no clear linguistic principles. They just are what they are, and we learn them naturally as we learn our native language. But since there is such a variety of idioms in English and since they do not obey simple rules of grammar, writers occasionally get their phrases confused and write unidiomatic—or un-English—sentences. For example, in haste or panic one might write "sorry of my behavior." Such a faulty idiom weakens sentence precision and vigor because it distracts the reader.

English has a number of widely used colloquial idioms that some people think are improper for semiformal usage. Here are a few of the most common ones:

Pleased with is standard.
    STANDARD: I was pleased with his reply.
    COLLOQUIAL: I was pleased at his reply.

Listen to is standard.
    STANDARD: I listened intently to his story.
    COLLOQUIAL: I listened intently at his story.

Because of is best used as an adverb.
    STANDARD: Because of the accident, I was late.
    COLLOQUIAL: My tardiness was because of the accident.

Due to is best used as an adjective.
    STANDARD: My tardiness was due to an accident.
    COLLOQUIAL: Due to an accident, I was tardy.

Different from is considered the proper idiom.
    STANDARD: My answer is different from yours.
    COLLOQUIAL: My answer is different than yours.
    COLLOQUIAL (*chiefly British*): My answer is different to yours.

Try to do is preferable to *try and do*.
    STANDARD: I will try to do my best.
    COLLOQUIAL: I will try and do my best.

Within is preferable to *inside of*.
    STANDARD: I will call within a week.
    COLLOQUIAL: I will call inside of a week.

In regards to is considered nonstandard.
    STANDARD: I have nothing to say in regard to his proposal.

Like as a conjunction is colloquial.
    STANDARD: It looks as though it may rain.
    COLLOQUIAL: It looks like it may rain.

Reason is because is colloquial.
    STANDARD: The reason he laughed was that he misunderstood the joke.
    COLLOQUIAL: The reason he laughed was because he misunderstood the joke.

Plan to is considered preferable to *plan on*.
    STANDARD: We plan to cooperate.
    COLLOQUIAL: We plan on cooperating.

Sure and is colloquial.
    STANDARD: Be sure to inspect the motor.
    COLLOQUIAL: Be sure and inspect the motor.

Had is preferable to *would have* in an *if* clause.
    STANDARD: If I had gone, I would have seen him.
    COLLOQUIAL: If I would have gone, I would have seen him.

You can learn to avoid colloquial idioms if you want your usage to be acceptable on all levels. But if you use a colloquial idiom, you can be sure you haven't made a serious error.

The use of two idioms together with the careless omission of one of the particles or prepositions is a source of faulty idiom. For example:

> OMITTED PREPOSITION: When a person has a goal to hope and work toward, he will be happy.
> RIGHT: When a person has a goal to hope for and work toward, he will be happy.

Note that the first sentence has either the faulty idiom "hope a goal" or the equally faulty "hope toward a goal." Here is another example:

> OMITTED PREPOSITION: Neither his interest nor concern for his employees' welfare brought him respect.
> RIGHT: Neither his interest in nor his concern for his employees' welfare brought him respect.

Note that "interest for" is not the correct idiom. Errors of this sort are due mostly to carelessness.

The use of a colloquial idiom does not constitute a serious error. The omission of one preposition in using a double idiom is not excusable but is, after all, a minor error of carelessness. Some errors in idiom, however, are truly serious. They are also hard to deal with, for they may be made only one time by one writer on one paper. That is, a frequently used faulty idiom is almost always a colloquial one and therefore informally acceptable. The true error in idiom is generally not a commonly recurring one. For example, the following sentences, taken from student papers, contain errors in idioms that may never have been made before or since:

> This contradicts with my own opinion.
> Our government should keep things at an equal basis.
> Our economy should grow at the rate for which it has in the past.
> There are several advantages toward federal aid being given to church schools.
> There are different ways into which the problem might be interpreted.
> Poe was a completely different person to which you pictured him.
> My grandfather had many books toward which I was interested.

I do not know upon what he used as a basis for his statement.

No rules can be given to help writers avoid such errors in idiom. Each error is a separate case with no general grammatical principle applying to it. The best advice that can be given you is for you not to write in haste or panic but to examine each of your sentences to be sure that each is naturally phrased.

EXERCISE 41. Improving Sentence Precision and Vigor

DIRECTIONS: *Improve the precision and vigor of the following sentences by eliminating faulty idioms.*

1. People are deceived in many ways of advertising.
2. Delinquents never really look into the situation in which they are faced with.
3. The whole problem must be given time to work out.
4. One important factor to the success of doctors is tactfulness.
5. The student will value from what the film has to offer.
6. They are in their own little shell of living of which a Peace Corps worker must try to bring them out.
7. I have proof to the fact that he took bribes.
8. The American newspaper reader is more intelligent than to read the sports page first.
9. When so much is stressed on education, students get nervous.
10. Since we are rated upon nothing but grades, we try to get high grades.
11. When one reaches the legal age of voting, he should become interested about politics.
12. He found himself in an entirely different situation from that of which he was formerly accustomed.
13. The only reason of any value in dividing classes into different levels is to benefit the brightest students.
14. I believe strongly against birth control.
15. What I do has little or no bearing to others.
16. He wanted to follow the late President's footsteps.
17. All students should keep up on current events.
18. For those who prefer relaxing a bit on edge, there are situation comedies.
19. If he continues his good work, he will accomplish helping the students.
20. Americans take great pride and respect for sports.

Overuse of modifiers

The overuse of modifiers can reduce the vigor, and often the precision, of writing. Some writers seem to think that the more adjectives they can attach to a noun, the more precise their sentence will be. Often the reverse is true. Cluttered writing is weak writing, and nothing clutters up a sentence more than useless modifiers. You should follow this precept: *when a noun or verb by itself says all you want to say, do not add adjectives or adverbs.* The following examples illustrate the improved vigor and precision of sentences stripped of excess modifiers:

> The worthy minister of the First Methodist Church magnanimously assisted the hard-working lay committee.
> The minister of the First Methodist Church assisted the lay committee.
>
> Our duly elected new Speaker opened the legislative session with a fine prayer.
> Our new Speaker opened the legislative session with a prayer.
>
> The wonderful example set by our grand scoutmaster taught the boys valuable self-reliance.
> The examples set by our scoutmaster taught the boys self-reliance.

The first sentence in each example illustrates a gratuitous use of modifiers—that is, the inclusion of modifiers just for the sake of having them, not because they are needed. The modifiers sound as though they were added by force. Such excessive use of adjectives and adverbs weakens vigor and precision. You should make it a habit to omit all modifiers not specifically needed.

You should be specially warned against the overuse of two particular modifiers: *very* and *definitely*. Though both of these words have legitimate uses, they are among the most overused and misused words in the language. They are intensifiers in that they are used to reinforce or intensify the meaning of other words. They have been so overused that they have lost their force and so no longer intensify to any noticeable extent. For example, to most people nowadays *very important* carries little more force than *important* and *I definitely believe* little more than *I believe*. These two intensifiers are somewhat like the little shepherd boy's cry of "wolf!" They have been used so much that no one any longer believes them. You will be well advised to be wary of the use of *very* and *definitely*. If you feel the need for an intensifier, try *especially, quite, considerably, truly,* or others of this type.

Euphemisms

Euphemisms can detract from sentence precision and vigor. The word comes from Greek roots meaning "to sound good." In English, a euphemism is a word or phrase that is less expressive or direct but also less offensive or distasteful than another. In short, we use euphemisms to avoid shocking the sensitive or to soften the blow for those who have suffered a loss. Here are some euphemistic statements, with more direct and expressive counterparts:

> I just learned that you lost your son in the war.
> I just learned that your son has been killed in the war.

> His remains will be shiped to Arlington.
> His corpse will be shipped to Arlington.

> A portly matron bought a foundation garment.
> A fat woman bought a corset.

> Paying guests are welcome.
> Boarders are welcome

> Fudd's Department Store experienced a considerable inventory shrinkage.
> A large amount of goods was stolen from Fudd's Department Store.

> My seatmate had an unpleasant odor.
> My seatmate stank.

> The play offers mature entertainment.
> The play is full of illicit sex.

> Alvin had a social disease.
> Alvin had syphilis.

As you can see, euphemisms run to mild vagueness, as opposed to the blunt precision of their counterparts. Often the blunt precision is preferable. Incidentally, it might amuse you to know that your Victorian great-grandparents felt the use of the words *legs* and *arms* to be indelicate; they spoke of *limbs*. In satirizing this absurd delicacy of language, Ambrose Bierce called toes *twigs*.

Disturbing sound patterns

A careless handling of sentence sounds can weaken the vigor of your diction. Rhyming words can be especially distracting in exposition. For example: "When you have a choice, always choose the active voice." Similarly, the close repetition of words or syllables can create distracting sound patterns in prose and thus reduce vigor. Examples:

> The players played their parts well in the play.
> A sentence should make sense, since it is a complete unit.
> It's cheaper to ship freight by ship than to ship it by train.
> We had a restful rest while the rest of the group worked without rest.

You can avoid such annoying repetition either by recasting your sentence or by substituting synonyms. For example:

> The actors played their parts well in the drama.
> While we rested comfortably, the remainder of the group continued to work.

You should not feel, however, that you must avoid all word repetition, for it is often necessary for coherence and clarity. But you should avoid jarring repetition.

Excessive alliteration (the close repetition of consonant sounds) is thought by most stylists to be out of place in prose. Examples:

> Avoid writing a sequence of similar sentences.
> The playful pups pranced proudly in their pen.

In poetry, alliteration can have a pleasing effect; in prose, it usually distracts the reader's attention from the meaning.

The sound of too many *tion* words in a sequence also is annoying. Examples:

> The celebration of the birth of the nation was an occasion for wild jubilation.
> The approbation of the delegation insured the adoption of the proposition.

You can achieve more vigor in your writing by being alert to the various annoying sound patterns that can accidentally slip into prose. When you encounter sing-song or jarring sounds, recast your sentence to eliminate them.

EXERCISE 42. Improving Sentence Precision and Vigor

DIRECTIONS: *Improve the precision and vigor of the following sentences by eliminating excessive modification in the first five, substituting direct expressions for euphemisms in the second five, and recasting the third five to eliminate distracting sound patterns.*

1. Our great and glorious leader gave a splendid speech on the absolute necessity of preparedness.
2. This grand occasion is definitely reminiscent of our first great demonstration.
3. This modest and demure young lady has gallant and admiring beaux by the plentiful dozens.
4. Our devoted and well-trained medical doctors most certainly believe that most highly touted patent medicines are absolutely worthless.
5. Our able and hardworking Governor made a very important announcement about our noble youths' elegibility to serve patriotically in the splendidly altruistic Peace Corps.
6. The battle injury left his intestines hanging from his abdomen.
7. Educational programs for exceptional children need to be adjusted to accommodate modern educational theory.
8. The liberating army undertook the task of pacifying the population.
9. The sanitation engineer complained that the extermination engineer left dead bodies for him to collect.
10. Mr. Jones's neighbor made some uncomplimentary remarks about his use of natural fertilizer on his lawns.
11. The students thought the teacher ought to have taught his class from the books they bought.
12. The opposition opposed the contribution of the delegation.
13. The athlete felt that he could not face the race against such a strong pace setter.
14. Television teaches teen-agers to tackle tasks with togetherness.
15. The devotion of the congregation was an inspiration to the visiting Committee for Integration.

Trite diction

One of the most common enemies of vigor, and consequently of precision, in diction is the cliché. This is the trite or hackneyed or overused phrase that the unthinking or unimaginative writer habitually depends upon. Much writing and many speeches consist of little more than strings of phrases that have been used over and over in other such writing or speeches. As we read or listen we pick up the pattern of clichés, and then, unfortunately, tend to use them ourselves when we are faced with thinking of something to say. The less willing we are to phrase our sentences with care, the more likely we are to use clichés. And the more we use them, the more dull, imprecise, and empty our writing is.

Probably no single occasion produces more cliché-ridden language than Fourth of July oratory. The following, for example, is hardly more outrageously trite than actual speeches produced by hundreds of orators on our chief national holiday.

> Fellow Americans,
>
> It gives me great pleasure to stand before you today to remind you of the glorious heritage that is ours. My poor words will not be able to do justice to this occasion. But there above you, in all its glory, hangs the symbol of our freedom, our unsullied flag. There may be some in our midst who do not feel patriotic fervor each time they see it waving in freedom. If so, I address them more in sorrow than in anger, for I would like to think that every heart that beats here belongs to a true American who will be vigilant so that our great flag will ever reign supreme.

The nauseating quality of clichés becomes quite apparent when many are strung together.

Not only Fourth of July oratory but almost every area of human activity has its quota of clichés. This has been wittily demonstrated by Frank Sullivan, one of America's best humorists, who created Dr. Arbuthnot, the cliché expert. In many articles in *The New Yorker*, Sullivan's Dr. Arbuthnot has gathered clichés from fields as diverse as baseball, atomic energy, dramatic criticism, political oratory, and tabloid journalism. Here are a few from baseball journalism; they will certainly ring familiarly in your ears (!):

> towering first baseman
> fleet baserunner
> scrappy little shortstop
> veteran spark plug
> sensational newcomer
> mound adversary
> rival hurler
> aging twirler
> mound duel

driven off the mound
erratic southpaw
heated argument
relegated to the showers
keystone sack
hot corner
connect with the old apple

Here are a few clichés Dr. Arbuthnot garnered from writings about atomic energy:

usher in the atomic age
tremendous scientific discovery
never be the same world again
prove a boon to mankind
pave the way to a bright new world
spell the doom of civilization as we know it
vast possibilities for good or evil
boggles the imagination
threshold of a new era
world at the crossroads
dire need of control by international authority
terms so simple a layman can understand
spells the doom of large armies

Dr. Arbuthnot also reads the drama critics:

battle-scarred veterans of not a few first nights
powerfully wrought
richly rewarding
wholly convincing
admirably played
poorly contrived
masterly performance
stole the show
brought the house down
captivate the audience
radiated charm
skyrocketed to fame
rare and refreshing talent
elevated to stardom
stellar role
immortal heroine
eternal verities

He listens to political oratory:

Fellow Americans
say with all due modesty
point with pride
view with alarm
four-square
worthy of trust
carry the banner
prophetic view
sterling character
burning questions
forces of reaction
enemies of America
troubled times
eternal vigilance
dedicate ourselves anew
generations yet unborn

And he reads the stories of love and murder in the tabloid newspapers:

bared in court
morals being impaired
striking blonde
stunning brunette
erring mates
pretty ex-model
much-married film star
swank penthouse apartment
love nest
sizzling love missives
cold-blooded slaying
gangland killings
love-crazed suitor
stumbled on the corpse
met with foul play
nabbed the suspect
held incommunicado
wring a confession out of
scene of the crime
morbid curiosity seekers
rain of bullets
refused to name his assailants

Such lists of clichés could be extended to hundreds of phrases and dozens of categories. Indeed, such a list could be prepared about English composition texts themselves. Clichés are so common, in fact, that no writer can avoid them altogether. But excessive use of them means dull, limp, near-meaningless writing. Therefore you should learn the nature of this sort of trite language and should guard against its use in your own writing.

EXERCISE 43. Improving Sentence Precision and Vigor

DIRECTIONS: *Recast the following sentences to eliminate clichés.*

1. After an uphill climb I realized my dearest ambition.
2. If you will take off your rose-colored glasses, you will see that life is a snare and a delusion.
3. By and large, I have a sneaking suspicion that all is not right with the world.
4. The measure of one's success is how he played the game.
5. At the crack of dawn I beat a hasty retreat to the arms of Morpheus.
6. Tired but happy, we arrived home in the wee small hours and slept the sleep of the just.
7. Poor but honest and pretty as a picture, she seemed none the worse for wear.
8. The fate of the world hung in the balance.
9. Earlier she had been the picture of health but now she was pale as death.
10. We must strike while the iron is hot, for in this broad land of ours time and tide wait for no man.

CORRECT DICTION

There is a difference between vague, imprecise diction and incorrect diction. In using an imprecise word, you say approximately, but not exactly, what you mean. In using incorrect diction you choose the wrong word. Imprecise diction reflects fuzzy thinking; incorrect diction indicates ignorance. For example, if you say that it takes a good many nickels to make a dollar, you are imprecise.

But if you say that it takes nineteen nickels to make a dollar, you are simply wrong.

There are two broad kinds of incorrect diction. One is the infrequent or even nonrecurring use of a wrong word. For example, if you were to write "I am solicitous for spring" or "He behaved redundantly," you would be guilty of using a wrong word in an attempt to choose impressive diction. Such misused words are called *malapropisms*. No rules can be given to help you avoid such mistakes, for they are generally nonrecurring. Examples of such mistakes from other people's writing would not help you, since you are not likely to make the same mistakes. The best suggestion to give you is for you to use your dictionary when in doubt.

The other kind of incorrect diction involves a few dozen frequently confused pairs of words, such as "affect" and "effect." The confusion of some of these pairs represents a real error due to ignorance; the confusion of others involves only a failure to distinguish between colloquial and more formal usage.

Following is an exercise in using correct diction based on words from the **Glossary of Usage,** which appears on pages 425–433. Look over the glossary in preparation for this exercise, and then use the glossary whenever you are in doubt about a particular word.

EXERCISE 44. Revising Incorrect Diction

DIRECTIONS: *In the following sentences identify and correct any instances of incorrect diction.*

1. John inferred that he would vote Republican.
2. Henry is a contemptuous person of low morales.
3. I was all ready on my way when I met my high school principle.
4. I am anxious to date Joan, for I am much effected by her beauty.
5. The members of the city counsel seem disinterested in reform.
6. In fact, I expect the councilmen will except bribes.
7. John wasn't suppose to loose his temper.
8. Therefore he laid down for a while to quite his nerves.
9. It seems incredulous that such a rascal as the Governor would feel a twinge of conscious.
10. A large amount of people wanted less changes than the council seemed prepared to make.

FIGURES OF SPEECH

The nature of figurative language

Language may be used for communication on a **literal** or on a **figurative** level. Literal language uses words only for their actual, basic meanings. It may be taken at face value; it means just what it says on the surface. Thus in literal use *fire* means a flame-producing oxidation of combustible material; *naked* means unclothed or without artificial covering; a *cloud* is a visible mass of vapor suspended in the atmosphere; *gold* is a metal of high value; *to throw* means to cause an object to fly through the air; *ears* are anatomical organs for registering sound. What do we mean then when we say

> My heart is on fire with love for you.
> I was determined to tell the naked truth.
> He left town under a cloud of suspicion.
> She had a heart of gold.
> He threw himself on the mercy of the court.
> When her friends gossiped, she was all ears.

Obviously, we do not mean the underscored words to be taken literally. To see why, try to visualize the concrete, literal meanings of these sentences.

The underscored words above are used figuratively. Figurative language, then, is language wrenched from its literal meaning—that is, it cannot be true literally. It in effect tells a lie on the surface in order to express a truth beneath the surface. For example, since one's heart cannot literally be on fire (at least while he is alive), such a use of the word *fire* is nonliteral or figurative.

In interpreting figurative language, the mind makes a transfer of meaning based on a comparison: for example, between the feeling of love and the heat of a fire; between the startling quality of a surprising truth and the shocking quality of a naked body; between the dimly understood nature of a suspected wrongdoing and the mistiness of a cloud; between the desirable qualities of a good and kind person and the value of gold; between a body tossed into a position of subjection and one's giving himself up to a court's decision; between one's being composed of nothing but ears and his eager interest in hearing all that is being said. Such comparisons in figurative language are literally false but they nevertheless deliver understandable and expressive meaning.

Much of our language usage is basically figurative without our realizing it. In fact, so many originally concrete words have been given expanded meanings that we can hardly utter two or three sentences together without using figurative language. For illustration, pick out the figuratively used words in the following sentences.

> She is a sweet-tempered girl.
> He is a blackhearted rogue.
> His high position gave weight to his proposal.
> We have only scratched the surface of that market.
> He played a devilish trick on me.
> She maintained a stony silence.
> He's just a green youth with no experience.
> With heavy hearts, we paid for our crimes.

The original, basic, core meanings of the words you picked out have been extended so that, for example, we accept *sweet* as a word to be applied to temperament. But actually such usage must be figurative, for *sweet* literally means having the taste of sugar.

Most figurative language is used by custom. But much is used by choice—that is, is consciously created—and that is the kind you want to learn about so that you can improve your own writing. But before you are given suggestions for using figures of speech, you should learn the names of the major ones.

The chief figures of speech

Many different kinds of figures of speech have been identified by students of rhetoric. One of them is of especial value in the study of expository writing, but an explanation of the chief figures of speech may be of interest to you and may increase your general knowledge of how language delivers meaning.

Personification attributes human qualities to nonhuman objects or entities. For example:

> All nature mourned the death of the King.
> The surf flung its arm around the swimmers and enveloped them with love.
> God frowned with displeasure.

Metonymy is the use of the name of one thing for that of another suggested by it or associated with it. For example:

The White House (meaning the President) issued a denial of Mr. Appleson's accusation.

Reading Mark Twain (meaning his works) is always fun.

The table (meaning the food on the table) looked delicious.

My transportation (meaning car) broke down.

Synecdoche is a type of metonymy in which a part is used for a whole, or vice versa. For example:

I'll go with you if you have wheels (meaning a car).

We hired two extra trombones (meaning trombone players).

The law (meaning a policeman) arrived.

Here comes the Navy (meaning one sailor).

Hyperbole is a figure of exaggeration. It tells more than the truth about the size, number, or degree of something without intending to deceive. For example:

The comedy team had them rolling in the aisles.

My sweetheart is perfection itself, flawless and divine.

His dormitory room was filled with books.

Rivers of tears were flowing as the heroine died.

Litotes is a figure of understatement. It uses terms less strong than is to be expected. For example:

The Prime Minister explained that war would mean some inconveniences for the home front.

I have a line or two of Cicero to translate for tomorrow's Latin class.

Rockefeller was content to make a dollar here and there.

Haven't you lost a little weight (meaning fifty or more pounds)?

Some other nonliteral uses of language are *analogy, allegory, irony,* and *symbolism.* These represent figurative uses of language, for in grappling with them the reader's mind must make a transfer of meaning in order to undersand the author's true intent. An analogy is an extended comparison of two essentially unlike ideas or processes, the intent of which is to make one clear in terms of the other. For example, a writer might try to explain the arcane features of high finance in terms of a child's game. An allegory is a story in which the characters and actions really represent people and events not literally expressed in the story. For example, the conflict between communism and the free world could be told allegorically in a story about rival neighborhood clubs. Verbal irony is language in which the author's intent is in contrast to what his words seem to say on the surface. For example, when you praise someone sarcastically with the true intent of disparaging him you are using irony. Symbolism is a complex term, but basically a symbol in writing is the use of the name of an object to represent a complex and abstract idea. For example, a story writer might use the recurring symbol of a liquor bottle to represent the degradation of one of his characters. Analogies and irony can be highly useful in expository writing, but allegory and symbolism are chiefly used in imaginative writing.

The above figures of speech are interesting to know about but do not contribute much to expository writing. The kind of figurative language which is most commonly used in exposition is called *metaphorical*. Two figures of speech are included in this term: *metaphor* and *simile*. A simile is a comparison of two essentially unlike things with the use of *like* or *as*. For example:

> His face was like a piece of stone sculpture.
> Learning a new language is like building a new window in the mind.

A metaphor is a direct identification of two essentially unlike things. For example:

> His face was made of stone.
> To learn a new language is to build a new window in the mind.

The technical distinction between metaphors and similes is unimportant. They represent the same kind of figurative use of language: a comparison of two objects, ideas, or situations essentially dissimilar but having points of resemblance that make one clear in terms of the other. Most figurative language is metaphorical.

The use of figures of speech in exposition

It is true that metaphors and similes are more common and important in imaginative writing, but, unless overused, they may be quite useful in exposition. They can add both color and clarity to factual writing. They add color because, when successfully created, they form interesting, vivid images and impart the flavor of concreteness. They add clarity by making abstract ideas and concepts more readily accessible to the reader's mind through relating them to concrete objects or actions that he is already familiar with.

Successful metaphors are created for specific purposes. When a writer of exposition has a particular idea or concept that he would like to make clearer or more engaging, he will often create a figure of speech to explain it. If he creates a fresh, original, and appropriate one, his writing will be improved. If he relies on an established, trite figure, his writing is likely to be limp and dull. Most clichés are overused figures of speech. For example, you will not add much color or clarity to your writing by using such hackneyed figures as these:

> pretty as a picture
> tired as a dog
> dead as a doornail
> sharp as a razor
> ugly as sin
> brown as a berry
> the lap of luxury
> fly off the handle
> a face that would stop a clock
> hitch your wagon to a star
> a bonehead
> a wet blanket
> an ace in the hole

Of course you can't avoid occasional use of an established figure, and such occasional use will not weaken your writing. But you cannot depend on established figures to add much color or extra clarity to your exposition.

You should avoid not only trite but also mixed or inconsistent figures. When a metaphor is continued through two or more phases, all the phases should be based on the same kind of comparison, or at least not on clashing comparisons. For example, the following metaphors are mixed:

> Mr. Beane headed into the wild blue yonder of stock speculation, confident that he could keep his feet on the ground and make money as easily as falling off a log.
> As his temper was about to boil over, Mr. Bang caught hold of the reins of his passion and locked his anger inside his stormy breast.

In the first example, Mr. Beane is, figuratively, in the air, standing on the ground, and falling off a log at the same time. In the second there is a figure of cooking, one of driving a horse, and one of locking a door, all mixed up together. Such inconsistency in metaphors is distracting; the reader does not know where to focus his attention. In exposition, the single-phase metaphor is the most useful; piled-up metaphors are not often effective.

Successfully used metaphors, then, should be fresh, consistent, and appropriate. In exposition especially, they should contribute to meaning as well as style. Their function is dual: to clarify ideas by establishing meaningful comparisons and to enliven style by adding color, flavor, and vividness. Here are a few original and colorful figures:

as disappointed as a worm on a wax apple
yielded as graciously as a wild horse to bit and reins
as stuffed with knowledge as the New York Public Library
muscle reflexes like a stretched rubber band
as selfless as a ten-year colonel bucking for general
like pouring water into a bucket seat
as pious as the spirit of Christmas at Gimbel's
groomed like an untrimmed poodle
as free of prejudice as a fox in a henhouse
an idea as weightless as a man in orbit
an idea as dangerous as a drunken navigator on a spaceship
an idea as deceptive as a black widow spider at mating time
as carefully planned as a spontaneous Communist demonstration
an idea as sound as the axioms of Euclid

Some of the above figures are ironical; point them out.

EXERCISE 45. Creating Figures of Speech

DIRECTIONS: *Think of a figurative way to express each of the following ideas or situations.*

1. A student sleeping in class
2. A salesman stretching the truth
3. A bashful man proposing
4. Reading a boring book
5. A person being obnoxious at a party
6. A teacher wandering from the subject matter

7. Arguing with an adamant traffic cop
8. Studying while friends talk or listen to TV
9. A poor product highly advertised
10. A politician speaking in meaningless generalities

CONNOTATION AND SLANTED DICTION

So far in this chapter we have discussed the principles of word choice you should apply in expository writing. Since the purpose of this kind of writing is to explain or make clear or analyze, you should choose precise words that will deliver honest, full, and comprehensible meaning. But much writing is designed not just to make facts and ideas clear but to sway or hoodwink the reader. Much political, economic, social, and religious writing, and almost all advertising copy, is of this sort. Writers of material intended to sway rather than inform often use some principles of word choice different from those proper for pure exposition. They use words for their connotative value, and in more rapscalion cases they use slanted diction or loaded words.

Words are said to have **denotative** and **connotative** meanings. The denotative meaning of a word is its basic dictionary definition—what the word means to all who know it. For example, the denotative meaning of *orchid* is "any of a number of related plants having flowers with three petals, two regularly shaped and the third enlarged and irregular in form." This, the denotative meaning, is just a bare, factual definition without emotional suggestions. All nouns, verbs, adjectives, and adverbs have denotative meanings that form the basis of their use for language communication.

Many content words also have connotative meanings. These are the suggested or associated meanings of words beyond their core denotative definitions. These meanings often differ with individuals or groups and so cannot be put into dictionaries. Connotative meanings have emotional overtones because they reflect the attitude of an individual or a group toward a word. Thus if you respond emotionally to a word, it has a connotative meaning for you. The term *associated meaning* is also applied to this language phenomenon because our reason for having an emotional attitude toward a word is that we associate it with some public event or situation or with some private event in our lives. For example, to a young girl the word *orchid* may have an unspoken and favorable connotation if she has just received one to wear to her first formal dance. To her it is not just a three-petaled flower, but a symbol of expected romance and youthful pleasure. If her expectations should be met, the word *orchid* will continue to have strong connotative meaning for her for at least several days.

Consider the different emotional impact that the following words will have on the two different persons mentioned:

> The word *funeral* to an undertaker and to a man who has just buried his young son.
> The word *teacher* to a disturbed problem child and to a responsive youngster who makes good grades and likes school.
> The word *politician* to a dedicated elected public official and to a chronic failure who blames the government for all ills.
> The word *poetry* to a badly taught, tough young hoodlum and to a sensitive, well-educated youth.
> The word *husband* to a deserted wife with six children and to a young and happy bride.
> The word *revolution* to a radical with a cause and to a wealthy, privileged aristocrat.

From these examples you can readily see that words can vary widely in their connotative value. What a word really means to an individual may depend partly on his point of view and not just on its core definition.

Much connotation is of course public rather than private— that is, the suggested meaning is about the same for all persons who hear or read the word. Therefore writers with prejudices and biases or with commercial aims will often choose a word for its calculated emotional influence rather than for its precision and honesty. Such word choice is notoriously common among advertising copywriters. Why, for example, has the phrase "the seventy-cent spread" been used? Obviously because the word *butter* has a connotation of richness and luxury that the word *oleomargarine* will probably never have. A copywriter for a wine company has an easier task than one for a beer company because the word *wine* has, for many, a permanent connotation of gracious living and refined taste, whereas the word *beer* has a lowbrow connotation in spite of the fact that many highly cultivated people relish it. The word *country* has for many a connotation of crudeness or lack of sophistication; but add the word *club* to it and you have a compound word with a connotation that helps sell everything from high-priced beauty creams to expensive automobiles. A few truly cultured people may laugh at the phrase "the country-club set" but most Americans will associate it with elegance and wished-for luxury. Like advertising copywriters, the creators of movie titles also work on connotative meanings. Can you, for example, imagine the title "Days of Wine and Roses" being changed to "Days of Beer and Petunias"?

The copywriter's addiction to words with strong connotative values is perhaps annoying, but it is probably not especially harmful or wicked. The same manipulation of language by political, religious, social, and economic propagandists, however, is the cause of much ignorance, misunderstanding, hatred, and bigotry. For example, one United States Senator always used to refer to another as "the Jewish Senator from New York." He intended the word *Jewish* to carry an unfavorable connotation. But writers and speakers with strong biases usually do not stop with connotative manipulations. They pervert language communication even further by using slanted diction or loaded words.

The use of slanted diction involves more than the choice of a word for its connotative value. Since connotation may vary with individuals or groups, a biased writer must know his audience if he is to produce successful connotative effects. For example, a highly conservative politician speaking to a like-minded group might use the word *liberal* for its suggestive meaning to that group. But he could not depend on a common reaction from everyone, for many think of *liberal* as a "good" word.

When a writer uses slanted diction, he expects everybody to react in about the same way. He tries to present an event, situation, or idea from his biased point of view by choosing words that give his own "slant." Thus a situation can be made to appear desirable or undesirable, according to the words used to describe it. For example, both of the sentences in each of the following pairs could easily be written about the same situation.

The good-natured Governor tried to please everyone.
The easily influenced Governor bumbled along.

Coach Fox is a notable competitor.
Coach Fox will use any tactics to win.

The General controlled his troops with firm discipline.
The General behaved like a martinet.

> The sweet-tempered teacher let the children have fun.
> The lax teacher permitted the children to misbehave.

In its extreme form slanted diction is called *loaded words*. These are highly charged words that are always at the disposal of propagandists or prejudiced writers. Consider such sentences as these:

> Left-wing pressure groups threatened the stability of the loyal union members.
> The reactionary National Association of Manufacturers is trying to keep workers in sweat-shop conditions.
> One-hundred-percent Americans will resist this foreign attempt to pervert our principles.
> The Communist-dominated Senator from New York ranted and raved as he propagandized for federal aid to education.

The very tone of such slanted diction will, to perceptive readers, reveal the writer's intent to sway rather than to inform.

The more factual and honest writing is, the more it depends on denotative meanings or widely accepted and unprejudiced connotations. The more argumentative, persuasive, or propagandistic, the more it uses calculated connotations and slanted diction. In college, then, the study of connotation and slanted diction is more a part of training in reading than in writing. You need to be taught to protect yourself against editorially slanted writing and other propaganda (including advertising), but, at this point at any rate, you do not need to be taught to manipulate language for the purpose of spreading prejudice. In your college exposition you should try to be honest, open-minded, fair, and factual. If you become a gossip columnist, a hack political journalist, or an advertising copywriter, you will quickly enough learn your lessons about connotative meanings and slanted diction. In your college writing, choose words for their honesty and precision.

CHAPTER 6

Conventions
of Usage

THE CONVENTIONAL ASPECTS
OF WRITING

Chapters 4 and 5 of this book have identified various kinds of errors and weaknesses which affect the logic, clarity, or precision of writing: confused sentence structure; faulty pronoun reference; improper shifts in number, person, voice, tense or mood; faulty parallelism; misplaced modifiers; vague and incorrect word choice; and so forth. These errors and weaknesses range from the very serious, which can obscure meaning altogether, to the minor, which are only mildly confusing. But all have to do with the way sentences deliver **meaning.**

Other errors—such as those in spelling, capitalization, and the use of the apostrophe—have to do with the **social acceptability** rather than with the meaning of writing. When such errors are committed, meaning is really not affected, for the conventional rather than the logical aspects of writing are violated.

The word *convention* comes from the Latin *venire,* meaning to come, and *con,* meaning together. So, literally, a convention is a coming together. Figuratively, it is a custom that the members of a particular society have come to accept as proper and right for them. Thus in writing, conventions are just standard forms that a particular group of writers (for us, educated writers of English) accept as proper and correct for them. For example, signaling a new paragraph by indenting its first line five spaces is just a convention. In business writing nowadays, it is also a common practice not to indent a paragraph at all but to double space between paragraphs. Either convention for signaling a new paragraph is perfectly satisfactory provided those concerned agree on it. Or, for another example, it has been conventional in the past to form the plural of a letter or a numeral with an *'s*: E's, T's, 3's, 7's. But nowadays many professional writers and book publishers form such plurals with an *s* only: Es, Ts, 3s, 7s. Either convention is quite satisfactory for those who accept it. A liberal-minded person will accept both conventions, since both are practiced by educated writers.

All spelling is, of course, conventional. Any method of spelling a word is satisfactory provided those who use the word agree on that spelling. For example, convention dictates that we use such spellings as *cough, bough, rough, though,* and *through,* and so for centuries these odd spellings have been satisfactory for hundreds of millions of writers.

The use of capital letters, apostrophes, and hyphens is also conventional. For example, in German all nouns are capitalized and apostrophes are not used to show possession; but in English most nouns are not capitalized and apostrophes are used to show possession. Such differences are purely conventional and really do not affect meaning.

Punctuation is, of course, a great aid to clarity in writing, and in a few cases it can determine the meaning of a sentence. But for the most part, punctuation is conventional, and fashions in it have changed in English over the centuries. Consider, for example, the following passage:

> I had rather beleeve all the fables in the Legend, and the

Talmud, and the Alcoran, then that this universall frame is without a minde. It is true, that a little philosophy inclineth man's minde to Atheisme; but depth in philosophy bringeth men's mindes about to religion.

Will educated people say this passage is unclear, imprecise, or illogical? No, they will understand it perfectly. But some might point out that it has "errors" in spelling, capitalization, and punctuation. The fact is, however, that it was written by Sir Francis Bacon, one of the greatest of all English writers and thinkers. Certain conventions acceptable in his day are not now standard; the change in conventions, however, has not affected the logic, clarity, or precision—in short, the meaning—of the passage. As a brief exercise, rewrite the passage using modern spelling, capitalization, and punctuation.

The word *usage* is applied to our handling of the above-mentioned conventions of writing, and it is also applied to certain aspects of grammar. But *grammar* and *usage* are not synonymous terms. Grammar involves a study of the whole structure of a language. You could not learn everything about English grammar even in an advanced college course. But that is not of especial importance, for every native speaker of English—even an illiterate—has an unconscious knowledge of all the indispensable aspects of English grammar. The "mistakes" made by the uneducated involve only the tiniest fraction of the whole of grammar.

Usage is a term applied not only to spelling and capitalization, but also to certain aspects of grammar in which variations do appear among native users of the language. These variations are largely limited to the different forms or endings that are given verbs, pronouns, and certain modifiers. For example all users of English know how to distinguish between the various tenses, but not all use the same form of a verb for a particular tense. One person may say, "I took the money, but I don't have it now." And another may say, "I taken the money, but I ain't got it now." These sentences are identical in most aspects of their grammar, but vary in the verb forms used for tenses. Both sentences are clear, however, and no one could misunderstand which tenses are meant. But the sentences are not equal in their social acceptability.

The aspects of grammar that have to do with usage may be called conventional, for they do not affect the meaning of a sentence but only its social acceptability. Observing the various conventions of educated usage is analogous to observing social conventions of proper dress, neat grooming, and polite manners. You should observe those conventions suitable for the society you are active in.

The following illustration can help you understand better the distinction between convention and logic in language. It is easily possible that a century or less from now the most highly educated speakers of English may naturally use such expressions as, "I ain't interested in stock speculation." Or, "I don't have no money for real estate investment." Such a shift in conventional usage would not at all affect clarity or meaning. But it is highly unlikely that sentences like the following can ever become standard:

> We found a picture of her swimming with him after he died.
> He described the faults that his wife has clearly.

In these sentences the misplacement of the modifiers *after he died* and *clearly* makes for awkward or humorous ambiguity. The difference between the two sets of sentences is that the first two have only nonstandard grammatical forms which do not interfere with clarity, while the second two have faults of word order which make them difficult to understand.

The difference between matters of sentence structure that affect clarity, precision, and logic and the conventions of grammar that affect only social acceptability can also be illustrated by a close look at the so-called bad grammar of uneducated people:

> ain't
> he don't have none
> had took
> him and me have went
> them books

Do educated people object to this language because they don't readily understand it? Of course not. They object to it because it is, to them, socially unacceptable, like dirty or rumpled clothing worn to fashionable banquet. It is clear then that word forms in grammar are conventional. For many people with little or no formal education, certain forms are conventional, while other forms are conventional for those with more formal education.

There is, however, no immutable, fixed system of educated usage, for language is in constant change. Most well-schooled Americans agree on most points of usage, but there are areas of variant practices (for example, capitalization), and therefore you will not be able to please all educated people in all aspects of your usage. You can only hope to be "right" most of the time and to hold criticisms of your usage to a minimum. In fact, a few deviations from so-called standard usage are likely to appear in anybody's writing. It is a mistake to think that observance of a few rules of grammar will make a person's writing good, or that violation of a few will make it bad. Much English teaching in the past has overemphasized a few minor matters of usage that play only the tiniest part in the whole process of writing, such as the distinctions between *shall* and *will, good* and *well, who* and *whom, sure* and *surely, it's me* and *it's I, none is* and *none are,* and *everyone . . . his* and *everyone . . . their.* Such matters are minor; you should not think that points of usage such as these are as important as clarity, precision, and logic in writing. And as for split infinitives, sentences beginning with *and,* and sentences ending with prepositions, no informed person today can reasonably object to such usage.

A nineteenth-century writer, later identified as Mark Twain, once received the following letter:

> Dear Mr——:
>
> Your writings interest me very much; but I cannot help wishing you would not place adverbs between the particle and verb in the Infinitive. For example: "to *even* realize," "to *mysteriously* disappear" "to *wholly* do away." You should say, *even* to realize; to disappear mysteriously etc. "rose up" is another mistake—tautology, you know. Yours truly
>
> A Boston Girl.

Part of Mark Twain's anonymous comment on this letter was as follows:

> . . . . Now I have certain instincts, and I wholly lack certain others. (Is that "wholly" in the right place?) For instance, I am dead to adverbs; they cannot excite me. To misplace an adverb is a thing which I am able to do with frozen indifference; it can never give me a pang. But when my young lady puts no point [period] after "Mr.;" when she begins "adverb," "verb," and "particle" with the small letter, and aggrandizes "Infinitive" with a capital; and when she puts no comma after "to mysteriously disappear," etc., I am troubled; and when she begins a sentence with a small letter I even *suffer.* Or I suffer, *even,*—I do not know which it is; but she will, because the adverb is in her line, whereas

only those minor matters are in mine. Mark these prophetic words: though this young lady's grammar be as the drifted snow for purity, she will never, never, never learn to punctuate while she lives; this is her demon, the adverb is mine. I thank her, honestly and kindly, for her lesson, but I know thoroughly well that I shall never be able to get it into my head. Mind, I do not say I shall not be able to make it *stay* there; I say and mean that I am not capable of *getting it into* my head. There are subtleties which I cannot master at all,—they confuse me, they mean absolutely nothing to me,—and this adverb plague is one of them.

We all have our limitations in the matter of grammar, I suppose. I have never seen a book which had no grammatical defects in it. This leads me to believe that all people have my infirmity, and are afflicted with an inborn inability to feel or mind certain sorts of grammatical particularities. There are people who were not born to spell; these can never be taught to spell correctly. The enviable ones among them are those who do not take the trouble to care whether they spell well or not,—though in truth these latter are absurdly scarce. I have been a correct speller, always; but it is a low accomplishment, and not a thing to be vain of. Why should one take pride in spelling a word rightly when he knows he is spelling it wrongly? *Though* is the right way to spell "though," but it is not *the* right way to spell it. Do I make myself understood?

Some people were not born to punctuate; these cannot learn the art. They can learn only a rude fashion of it; they cannot attain to its niceties, for these must be *felt;* they cannot be reasoned out. Cast-iron rules will not answer, here, any way; what is one man's comma is another man's colon. One man can't punctuate another man's manuscript any more than one person can make the gestures for another person's speech.[1]

These sensible and refreshing statements have a sound lesson for students of language.

SPELLING

Spelling is a convention of writing and therefore does not affect meaning (except in those rare cases in which a word is so badly misspelled that its identity is obscured). It is a mistake to assume

---

[1] The Boston girl's letter and Twain's reply were published anonymously in "The Contributors' Club" of *The Atlantic Monthly*, XLV (June 1880), pp. 849–860.

that one cannot write with clarity and precision unless he spells properly. One pamphlet of dictionary study, for example, says, "To achieve precision in writing, it is necessary to spell correctly." But this very sentence loses none of its precision when written in this fashion: "To acheeve precision in riting, it is necessary to spel corectly." The two versions are identical in meaning. The second, however, lacks social respectability because of its misspellings. But social respectability and precision are entirely different matters.

Further proof that "correct" spelling is not necessary for precision lies in the history of our language. It was not until the eighteenth century that the movement for standardized English spelling became strong. Prior to that time many variations in spelling occurred in the writings of the most learned men. In fact, the greatest writers—Shakespeare, Bacon, Milton, Dryden, for example—often spelled a word in two or three different ways, sometimes on the same page. Their writings, needless to say, are the essence of precision.

But later generations have come to be very spelling-conscious, mostly because of the establishment of "the dictionary" as an authority. Since 1755 a series of excellent English dictionaries have standardized spelling, and our public schools have fostered the notion that failure to follow dictionary spellings is a positive sign of ignorance. Hence there currently exists a colossal public prejudice against misspellings. (Strangely, this prejudice seems to be strongest among poor spellers.) One result is that students with a natural facility for learning to spell English are thought to be especially bright and those without such a facility are often thought to be dull. Actually, many very bright people just don't have the knack of spelling. (Rumor has it that one of the most intelligent United States presidents of this century was quite a poor speller, though an excellent writer.) In school, poor spellers are often punished for what may well be just a minor oversight on the part of the Giver of natural abilities.

But whatever one's theory of spelling may be, it is a social fact in present-day America that misspellings reduce the social acceptability of writing. Hence college writers must hold their spelling mistakes to a reasonable minimum. You should cultivate an attitude toward spelling somewhat like your attitude toward dress or other customs. You may often think it unreasonable and onerous to be required to dress in a certain fashion for certain occasions, but though you may complain you are likely to go along with the conventions. You may even study to follow them accurately if you want to be an acceptable member of a group. You simply have to cultivate a similar attitude toward spelling conventions. But it is well to remember that no one is always perfect in his spelling. The following sections will give you practical advice on how to improve your spelling.

Spelling by phonemics

The "Mark Twain" article on page 243 says "*Though* is the right way to spell 'though,' but it is not *the* right way to spell it." He meant, of course, that we would spell it *tho* if we spelled it as we pronounce it. In his view, *the* right way to spell is the phonemic way, that is, according to pronunciation.

Human vocal cords produce discrete sounds that are merged together to form speech. Linguists call these separate sounds *phonemes,* and one or more phonemes used as a meaningful unit they call a *morpheme.* In spelling, we speak of letters and syllables. When one letter represents one—and only one—phoneme, spelling is phonemic. For example, *put* is composed of three letters representing three phonemes (one morpheme) and is spelled phonemically provided we think of *p, u,* and *t* as always representing only the three sounds in the word. Thus if we had one letter in our alphabet for each phoneme, our spelling could be phonemic.

But as every student knows, much English spelling is not phonemic. And with our present alphabet English spelling could not be wholly phonemic, for we use at least thirty-three phonemes but have only twenty-six letters in our alphabet, three of which (*c, q,* and *x*) are useless. Obviously, some letters, chiefly the vowels, must do double (or even triple or quadruple) duty. And not only that, sometimes one phoneme is represented by one letter in one spelling and then by another letter in another spelling. For example, the sound *z* is sometimes represented by the letter *z (lizard)* and sometimes by the letter *s (is, was).* Or, for another example, the sound *k* is sometimes represented by *k,* sometimes by *ck (kick),* sometimes by *c (car),* sometimes by *ch (Christmas),* and sometimes by *que (clique).* Many more such examples could be given.

But even though, with our present alphabet, English spelling can never be absolutely phonemic and though it is often quite unphomenic, it is more phonemic than is generally believed. Many of our words are spelled approximately as they are pronounced. And in addition, many phonemic principles operate in words that appear to be senselessly unphonemic. Some of these principles (most are too minor and obscure or too riddled with exceptions to be mentioned here) are explained below.[2] Students unconsciously absorb some of these principles, but a conscious knowledge of the most important ones will give you greater confidence in spelling. The common spelling rules are also based on phomenic principles, but, since they form a traditional body of spelling lore, they will be explained separately in the following section on spelling by rules.

The *tion* and *sion* syllables are often confused in spelling. They are sometimes pronounced *shun* (*nation*) and sometimes *zyun* (*vision*). When the pronunciation is *zyun,* the spelling is always *sion:*

aversion	incision
confusion	invasion
decision	occasion
diversion	persuasion
division	revision
evasion	submersion
explosion	suffusion

When the syllable is pronounced *shun,* the spelling is usually *sion* after *l* and *s:*

commission	expulsion
convulsion	passion
discussion	permission
digression	propulsion
dismission	remission
emulsion	revulsion
expression	submission

There are of course exceptions, but in most other cases the syllable is spelled *tion.*

The *ance* (*ant*) and *ence* (*ent*) endings give a great deal of trouble in spelling. The spelling is *ance* when the syllable is preceded by *nd:*

---

[2] In linguistic texts, phonemic symbols rather than letters are used to identify phonemes. Here we will just use the letters that you are familiar with.

abundance
ascendance
attendance
dependant
pendant
redundance

Exceptions:
independence
tendency

The spelling is *ence* after a *d* preceded by a vowel:

accident
coincidence
confidence

evidence
impudence
residence

The spelling is *ance* after a hard *g* (pronounced *guh*) or a hard *c* (pronounced as a *k*):

applicant
elegance

extravagance
significance

The spelling is *ence* after a soft *g* (pronounced as a *j*) or a soft *c* (pronounced as an *s*):

adolescence
diligence
indigence

innocence
intelligence
munificence

The spelling is *ence* when the syllable is preceded by an *r* in an accented syllable:

abhorrence
coherence
concurrence
deterrence

interference
occurrence
recurrence
transference

The spelling is *ence* when preceded by *i* or *l*:

benevolence
convenience
conscience
efficient
excellent
omniscience
prevalent
resilience
sufficient

expedience
experience
insolence
lenient
obedience
Exceptions:
alliance
petulant
vigilant

When a long *a* sound occurs before *ght, gh, ge, gn,* and *n,* it is often spelled *ei* but never *ie:*

beige	neighbor
deign	reign
feign	rein
freight	skein
inveigle	vein
neigh	weight

The *c* in the syllable *ice* is sounded as an *s;* the *s* in the syllable *ise* is sounded as a *z:*

advice	device
advise	devise

Words ending in the *f* sound are sometimes spelled with one *f*, sometimes with *ff*, and sometimes with *gh*. If the sound before the *f* is a short vowel (except short *e*), the *f* is usually doubled:

buff	staff
chaff	tariff
doff	whiff
plaintiff	*Exception:*
sheriff	graph

If the sound before the *f* is a consonant or a long vowel, the *f* is not doubled:

brief	half
belief	leaf
dwarf	proof
golf	surf
grief	waif

When the letters before the final *f* sound are *au* or *ou,* the *f* sound is usually spelled *gh:*

cough	rough
enough	tough
laugh	trough

When a *g* is given a hard (*guh*) sound, it usually ends a word or is followed by a consonant or by *a, o,* or *u:*

analogous	rang
angle	sing
bungle	spangle
haggle	tangle
hung	tingle
lung	wrangle

When a *g* is given a soft (*j*) sound, it usually is followed by *e, i,* or *y:*

advantageous	mangy
angel	pungent
change	range
courageous	rangy
lunge	singe

Note particularly the *angle-angel, lung-lunge, rang-range,* and *sing-singe* pairs.

Sometimes the *ch* sound is spelled *ch* and sometimes *tch*. It is spelled *tch* in most monosyllabic words with a short vowel before the *tch:*

catch	fetch
crutch	notch
ditch	pitch

Sometimes prefixes or suffixes are added to such words:

bewitch	catching
rehitch	clutched

In polysyllabic words and in words with a long vowel or a consonant before the *ch* sound, the spelling is *ch:*

attach	reach
beach	sandwich
branch	squelch
coach	*Exceptions:*
couch	dispatch
detach	hatchet
ostrich	kitchen

Words ending in *ge* and *dge* cause spelling confusion. Those ending in *dge* are mostly monosyllabic words with a short vowel preceding the *dge:*

badge	judge
bridge	ledge
budge	lodge
dodge	pledge
hedge	trudge

Sometimes prefixes are added to such words:

adjudge	dislodge
begrudge	prejudge

In polysyllabic words and in words with a long vowel sound or a consonant before the *ge* sound, the spelling is *ge:*

allege	privilege
college	sacrilege
decoltage	siege
forage	stooge
huge	*Exception:*
marriage	knowledge

Though they are not phonemic principles, certain facts about prefixes and suffixes will be mentioned here because they pertain to phonemic spelling. The following examples are hyphenated to show phonemic spelling. *None of the words is hyphenated in ordinary writing.*

There is no such prefix as *diss* (though *dis* is often added to words beginning with *s*):

dis-appear	dis-appoint
dis-agree	dis-approve

When the prefix *dis* or *mis* is added to a root beginning with *s,* both *s*'s are retained:

dis-similar	dis-solve
dis-sect	dis-suade
dis-satisfaction	mis-sent
dis-service	mis-spell
dis-social	mis-statement

The prefixes *de, pro,* and *re* are never followed by a double consonant:

de-duction	pro-fessor
de-ficient	pro-gress
de-finite	re-collect
de-legate	re-ference
de-pression	re-frain
pro-gram	re-solution

The prefix *e* is attached to many roots beginning with *l,* and the prefix *el* is added to many roots not beginning with *l*. But only one root beginning with *l* has *el* as a prefix: *ellipse* (several words are formed from it). Therefore extra *l*'s should not be put in words like the following:

e-lastic	e-lucidate
e-late	e-lude
e-lection	e-lusive
e-lectric	el-egant
e-licit	el-egy
e-lide	el-ement
e-liminate	el-ephant
e-lision	el-evate
e-longate	el-igible
e-lope	el-oquent

When *ly* is added to a word ending in *l*, both *l*'s are retained:

accidental-ly	natural-ly
fatal-ly	real-ly
final-ly	total-ly

When the suffix *ly* is added to a word ending in a silent *e*, the *e* should not be dropped:

approximate-ly	like-ly
immediate-ly	rude-ly
lame-ly	*Exception:*
late-ly	truly

Words ending in *able* or *ible* do not follow the above principle:

ably	incredibly
dependably	notably

Though minor, the above phonemic principles will help you spell many difficult words. There is also another principle—a major one—that you must understand if you want to spell English with reasonable accuracy. Most students just absorb an understanding of this principle and apply it subconsciously, but illustration of it here may help you avoid pitfalls in spelling. Though there are exceptions to it, this principle in general holds true: In a vowel-consonant-vowel sequence the first vowel, *if accented,* is long; in a vowel-consonant-consonant sequence or a vowel-consonant-end-of-word sequence, the first vowel is short. Thus the first vowel in words like these is long:

bite	pate
cute	rate
dote	rote

But the first vowel in words like these is short:

bit	dotting
cut	pat
dot	patting

Quite clearly, the silent *e* in the first group is a device for spelling the long-vowel phonemes.[3]

The silent *e* is only a part of the principle. In words like these the first vowel is also long:

dating	roping
dative	total
duty	writing

The vowel-consonant-vowel principle is at work here. In words like these, however, the first vowel is short:

matting	stopping
smitten	toddler
smutty	written

Here the vowel-consonant-consonant principle is working.

There are—predictably in English—exceptions to the above principle. For example, *coming* is not pronounced with a long *o*. But in general the principle holds true and therefore a knowledge of it is essential for good spelling. Anyone who understands the principle will not confuse such pairs as these:

before-befor	quite-quit
campus-campuse	redder-reder
careful-carful	refer-refere
confuse-confus	safely-safly
forecast-forcast	scared-scarred
infer-infere	slur-slure
interfere-interfer	stopping-stoping
interpret-interprete	suppose-suppos
occasion-occassion	therefore-therefor
purely-purly	writing-writting

---

[3] Though *e*-consonant-silent *e* is sometimes used to spell the long *e* sound (discr*e*te, prec*e*de), the long *e* sound is most often spelled *ee, ea,* or *ie* rather than *e*-consonant-silent *e*.

By keeping in mind these phonemic principles and others that you absorb unconsciously (for example, the various sounds of *c, f, k,* and *s*), you can spell many, many English words phonemically, particularly long words. In so doing, you should sound out each syllable much more separately and emphatically than you normally would in using them in speech. For example, in spelling words like the following, sound each syllable separately and emphatically:

ab-bre-vi-ate	com-pe-ti-tion
ac-ci-den-tal-ly	e-rad-i-cate
ac-com-mo-date	pro-nun-ci-a-tion
ac-com-pa-ny-ing	tem-per-a-ture

If you will follow these suggestions, you will find English spelling much more phonemic than you thought.

Spelling by rules

The so-called rules of spelling are based on phonemic principles like those just explained and thus might have been included in that section. Five of these rules, however, are of such honorable and ancient standing in English textbooks that they are given separate entry here. These rules cover a large percentage of the most often misspelled English words. If you will **memorize** and **use** these rules, you can eliminate a great many of your spelling problems.

RULE 1:
Place i *before* e *when pronounced as* ee *except after* c; *place* e *before* i *when not pronounced as* ee.
This rule covers the troublesome *ie* and *ei* combinations. When the combination is pronounced as a long *e*, it is spelled *ei* after *c:*

ceiling	deceive
conceit	perceive
conceive	receive
deceit	receipt

When the combination is pronounced as a long *e* and follows a consonant other than *c,* it is spelled *ie:*

achieve	priest
believe	relief
brief	relieve
chief	shield
field	siege
grief	thief
niece	wield
piece	yield

Of course, there are a few exceptions. Here is a nonsense sentence that gives most of them: "Neither (either) species seized weird leisure." You should **memorize** this sentence and call it to mind whenever you want to spell one of the *ie* or *ei* words in it.

When the *e-i* combination is not pronounced as a long *e*, it is usually spelled *ei:*

foreign	neighbor
freight	reign
height	reins
inveigh	vein
inveigle	sleight
neigh	weight

An exception is *friend*.

The words of the *ie-ei* kind that give the most trouble are *receive, chief, niece,* and *seize*. You should never misspell these (or any of the others) if you will **memorize** the rule and the sentence of exceptions.

RULE 2:
Drop a final silent e *when adding a suffix beginning with a vowel:*

believe-believing	imagine-imaginative
condole-condolence	mange-mangy
create-creative	write-writing

In current practice this rule is sometimes ignored when *able* or *age* is added to a word ending in a silent *e:*

blame-blamable-blameable	make-makable-makeable
desire-desirable-desireable	mile-milage-mileage
like-likable-likeable	name-namable-nameable
live-livable-liveable	sale-salable-saleable
love-lovable-loveable	use-usable-useable

Probably there will be a general increase in the number of words that may retain the silent *e* when *able* or *age* is added.

Because of the vowel-consonant-consonant principle explained above, the silent *e* should not be dropped when a suffix beginning with a consonant is added. Note, for example, the different pronunciation (short *i* and *a*) that would be required with these spellings:

like-likness   safe-safty

In such spellings the silent *e* should be retained so that a vowel-consonant-vowel sequence will require a long vowel pronunciation:

fate-fateful   like-likeness
hate-hateful   safe-safety

Three common supposed exceptions to the above rule are these:

argue-argument   true-truly
awe-awful   whole-wholly

But the first three are not really exceptions, for the final *e* is not used in any of the three to produce a long vowel sound. (*Judgment* and *judgement* are both acceptable spellings.)

RULE 3:
When a word ends in a silent e *preceded by* c *or* g, *retain the* e *when adding a suffix beginning with* a, o, *or* u.

The reason for this rule is that normally *c* is pronounced as a *k* before *a, o, u,* or a consonant and as an *s* before *i, e,* or *y* and that *g* is normally pronounced *guh* before *a, o, u,* or a consonant and as a *j* before *e, i,* or *y*. The first mentioned pronunciations are called hard and the second soft. The silent *e* is retained to preserve the soft *c* and *g* pronunciations. For example, *noticable* would be pronounced *no-tik-able,* whereas *noticeable* is pronounced *note-is-able.* Here are examples of the rule in action:

advantage-advantageous   manage-manageable
arrange-arrangeable   peace-peaceable
change-changeable   replace-replaceable
courage-courageous   service-serviceable

When a suffix beginning with a vowel is added to a word ending in *c*, a *k* is added to retain the hard *c* sound. For example, *picnicing* would be pronounced *pick-nis-ing*. Examples of the rule:

picnic-picnicking   politic-politicking
panic-panicked   traffic-trafficking

RULE 4:
Change the y *to* i *when adding a suffix to a word ending in* y *preceded by a consonant:*

busy-business   heavy-heaviest
cry-crier   lonely-loneliness
dry-driest   necessary-necessarily
easy-easily   noisy-noisily
gloomy-gloomiest   ordinary-ordinarily
handy-handily   satisfactory-satisfactorily

This rule also applies in the spelling of the plural form of a word ending in *y* preceded by a consonant. The *y* is changed to *i* and *es* is added to make the plural:

baby-babies   harpy-harpies
copy-copies   lady-ladies
gravy-gravies   navy-navies

The rule also applies in spelling the third person singular of a verb ending in *y* preceded by a consonant. The *y* is changed to *i* and either *es* or *ed* is added:

deny-denies-denied   pry-pries-pried
envy-envies-envied   reply-replies-replied
fry-fries-fried   try-tries-tried

The rule does not apply when *ing* is added to a word:

deny-denying   reply-replying
envy-envying   study-studying
fry-frying   try-trying

When the final *y* of a word is preceded by a vowel, the *y* is not changed when a suffix is added:

annoy-annoys-annoyed   stay-stays-stayed
convey-conveys-conveyed   turkey-turkeys
employ-employs-employed   valley-valleys
play-plays-played   whey-wheys

There are three common exceptions to this rule:

lay-laid   say-said
pay-paid

Note: The *y*-to-*i* rule does not apply in the spelling of the plural proper names:

Brady-Bradys   Grady-Gradys
Crowly-Crowlys   Kennedy-Kennedys

RULE 5:

When adding a suffix beginning with a vowel to a word accented on the last syllable and ending in one consonant preceded by one vowel, double the final consonant.

This rule is due to the principle that in a vowel-consonant-vowel sequence the first vowel, if accented, is long and that in a vowel-consonant-consonant sequence the vowel is short. Thus *rate* has a long *a* sound and *rat* a short *a* sound. *Rating* also has a long *a* sound because of the vowel-consonant-vowel sequence. So if we want to spell *ratting* rather than *rating*, we must double the *t* in *rat* before adding *ing*. Then the vowel-consonant-consonant sequence will maintain the short *a* sound.

To understand the necessity of the rule, pronounce the misspelled words in the right-hand column following:

bid   biding
cut   cuting
pot   poted
tip   tiped

When the rule is applied, words will retain their proper pronunciation:

beg-begging   readmit-readmitted
compel-compelled   refer-referred
concur-concurred   rot-rotting
confer-conferred   scrub-scrubbed
debar-debarred   sip-sipping
occur-occurred   slap-slapped
pin-pinning   snub-snubbing
prefer-preferred   stab-stabbed

If the last syllable of a word is not accented, the consonant is not doubled when a prefix beginning with a vowel is added, nor is the final consonant doubled in any word if the added suffix begins with a consonant.

banter-bantering	honor-honorable
glad-gladness	leaven-leavening
happen-happened	prohibit-prohibited
hinder-hindered	sin-sinful

Spelling by mnemonic devices

Psychologists do not fully understand on a theoretical basis just how our memories work. But on a practical basis everyone knows that **association** is a great aid to memory. We can more easily remember something—a telephone number, a person's name, an address—if we associate it with something else which is easy for us to remember. For example, consider the telephone number 71165. A gambler might easily remember this number as a sequence of natural passes in a dice game: a seven, an eleven, and another eleven made up of six and five. Once the gambler made that association in his mind, he would never forget that particular telephone number. Clues of this sort that aid our memories are called **mnemonic devices,** from a Greek word meaning memory. Incidentally, you can remember that *mnemonic* begins with an *m* if you remember that its meaning is *memory;* or you can remember that it means *memory* if you remember that it begins with an *m*.

Mnemonic devices can be valuable aids in spelling troublesome words. Quite a number of these associational clues have been invented for particularly troublesome words. Some of these are listed below. Each individual can also invent private clues of his own for those words he finds difficult to spell.

all right—Pair it off with *all wrong*.

a lot—Think of buying a lot; so avoid *alot*.

amateur—The last syllable is *not* spelled as it sounds; so spell *teur*, not *ture* or *tuer*.

attendance—Think of *attend dance* and so use *ance*.

bargain—There is a *gain* in a bargain.

battalion—Think of a *batt*le against *a lion*.

breakfast—It is literally to break a fast.

bulletin—Who put a *bullet in* a bulletin?

calendar—Think of calend*ar art*.

courtesy—It is a habit with those who *court*.

definite—It comes from *finite*.
dessert—It has two *s*'s, like *s*trawberry *s*hortcake.
disease—The word literally means *dis ease*.
dissipation—It makes you dizzy, so use *dissi*, not *dissa*.
eighth—Remember the *h-t-h* sequence.
embarrass—Remember two *r*'s and two *s*'s.
familiar—Think of a *fami* (whatever that is) *liar*.
forty—It is not pronounced like *four*.
friend—Remember that he's a friend to the *end*.
grammar—The *rammar* part is spelled the same both ways.
handkerchief—You use your *hand* to pull out your kerchief.
holiday—It comes from *holy* and so has only one *l*.
occurrence—It has *rre* as in *current* event.
peculiar—Think of a *pecu* (whatever that is) *liar*.
principal—The principal of a school is a *pal* to you.
principle—The principle meaning a rule ends in *le* as rul*e* does.
rhythm—Remember the *rh-th* sequence.
separate—It's hard to spell; therefore there is *a rat* in it.
stationery—The word meaning pap*er* has an *er* in it; the other has an *ar*.
sugar—Both sug*a*r and s*a*lt have *a*'s.
together—Think of a date: *to get her*.
tragedy—There is a *rage* in tragedy.
until—The word with two syllables has one *l*; the word with one syllable (*till*) has two *l*'s.

Spelling by practice

Spelling problems can be overcome only through practice, and generally the practice available in college classes is not sufficient for poor spellers. If you need more practice than your instructor can allow time for, you should arrange practice sessions with a friend.

The kind of practice you undertake is important. Spelling individual words from lists will probably not help you much in your actual writing. Instead, you should practice from dictated sentences, for then you will be imitating a real writing situation and thus will be more likely to retain and be able to use what you learn.

A good plan to follow is to start with the twenty sentences below, which contain about 100 simple spelling problems. Have them dictated to you by a friend. Then have your friend compose another twenty sentences, using the words you missed from the first twenty sentences plus twenty-five or more words from the lists of words that also follow below. Your third practice session should be composed of dictated sentences that include the words you missed on the first and second tests plus another group from the lists. And so on. Before each practice session you should study the words you missed on the two previous tests and the next group from the study list. If you will get your roommate, sweetheart, or mother to help you with such a planned program of practice and if you yourself will work hard at it, you can soon cure most of your spelling ills. That's assuming, of course, that you have spelling problems.

SPELLING TEST FOR INDIVIDUAL PRACTICE

1. Always accept a friend's quiet advice.
2. It's all right to believe your principal's description.
3. Today's tragedy occurred as a necessary occasion.
4. The government's laboratory probably owns shining equipment.
5. Who's supposed to receive separate salaries?
6. I'm not coming until this peculiar weather truly changes.
7. James' (James's) puppies meant to disappear with the donkeys.
8. Whose library is therefore losing business?
9. Someone's neighbor is studying grammar.
10. Jane's babies are usually among ninety-eight enemies.
11. The forty priests are beginning their similar duties.
12. A woman is writing recipes for two hundred attorneys.
13. The professor is hoping his speech won't be omitted.
14. Mr. Jones' (Jones's) worries are too definite.
15. Everybody's courtesy doesn't need improving.
16. The bulletin described Betty's surprise marriage.
17. The dog injured itself while wagging its tail.
18. Sitting Bull's niece tries to be a beautiful amateur chief.
19. College is a bargain and a privilege.
20. A lot of desert sand is quite coarse.

COMMON WORDS QUITE FREQUENTLY MISSPELLED

accommodate
achieve
acquaint
acquire
affect
all right

altogether
among
analyze
analysis
answer
apparent

appear
appearance
argument
balance
before
beginning
believe
benefit
benefited
breathe
brilliant
buried
business
calendar
career
carrying
category
certain
changeable
choose
chose
clothes
coming
comparative
comparison
conscience
conscious
consistent
controlled
course
criticize
dealt
decided
definite
definitely
describe
description
despair
dining
disagree
disastrous
effect
eighth
embarrass

environment
equipped
especially
exaggerate
excellent
existence
experience
explanation
familiar
fascinate
foreign
forty
fourth
friend
government
grammar
height
imagination
immediately
incidentally
intelligence
interest
interpret
its
it's
itself
knowledge
led
literature
loneliness
lonely
lose
losing
marriage
meant
necessary
Negroes
noticcable
occasion
occurred
occurrence
original
paid
passed

past
perform
personnel
piece
pleasant
possess
possible
practical
precede
preferred
prejudice
prevalent
principal
principle
privilege
probably
proceed
procedure
professor
psychology
pursue
quiet
quite
really
realize
receive
recommend
referring
repetition
rhythm

sense
separate
shining
similar
studying
succeed
surprise
than
then
their
there
they're
thorough
tries
truly
two
to
too
until
usually
using
varies
various
weather
whether
woman
writing
yield
you're
yours

COMMON WORDS OFTEN MISSPELLED

accept
acceptable
accidentally
across
advice
advise
aggressive
article
athlete
attendant

attendance
authority
basically
Britain
careless
careful
challenge
character
characteristic
college

conceive
condemn
considerably
convenience
curious
dependent
difference
disappoint
discipline
dominant
efficient
extremely
finally
fulfil(l)
fundamental
further
guarantee
guidance
happiness
heroine
heroes
hindrance
hopeless
hoping
hopping
hospital
humor
humorous
hundred
hypocrisy
hypocrite
ideally
ignorance
immense
importance
increase
indefinite
independent
indispensable
individual
influential
inevitable
interfered
ingenious

intellect
involve
irrelevant
irreverent
jealousy
laboratory
laborer
later
latter
leisure
length
likely
livelihood
luxury
magnificent
maintenance
maneuver
mathematics
medieval
mere
miniature
ninety
ninth
omitted
operate
opinion
opportunity
opponent
optimism
parallel
particular
peculiar
permanent
permitted
philosophy
physically
planned
propaganda
quantity
relieve
religious
resources
response
ridicule

ridiculous	technique
satire	temperament
schedule	therefore
sergeant	tomorrow
significance	tragedy
speech	transferred
sponsor	undoubtedly
subtle	unusually
subtly	villain
summary	weird
supposed	who's
suppress	whose

CAPITALIZATION

Though capitalization is the most purely conventional of all aspects of writing, there is an elusiveness about its rules that constantly plagues all writers who want to be wholly "correct" in their usage. One of the questions most frequently asked of English teachers is, "Do you capitalize such-and-such a word in such-and-such a case?" There are two main sources of the uncertainty about capitalization. First, the rules often call for capital letters for specific reference and lower-case (small) letters for general reference, as in President-president, Mayor-mayor, and so forth. But frequently a writer is not sure whether he is making a specific or a general reference. For example, are the references in the following sentence specific or general? "One of the duties of the President (president?) is to appoint Supreme Court Justices (justices?)." Second, a capital letter is often used to give emphasis to an important word, as in this sentence: "A study of the Humanities is the only avenue to true education." But again, writers are often uncertain as to when a word warrants capitalization for emphasis. For example, is *Humanities* a more important word in the above sentence than *education?* Or consider this sentence from a business letter from a publishing company: "I am very happy to send you a Complimentary examination copy of this book." Is *Complimentary* important enough to warrant capitalization?

Because of these two sources of uncertainty, and perhaps also because of personal whim, practices in capitalization vary rather widely among professional writers. There is not, even, a discernible trend toward either more or less capitalization among professional writers. Some writers seem to be increasing and others decreasing the number of instances in which they use capital letters. For example, G. M. Trevelyan, one of the greatest English historians (and a great stylist) of this century, capitalized the following words (and many more like them) without specific reference:

Charity Schools	Librarian
Church	Mayor
Churchman	Nineteenth Century
Colonial	the Press
Deistic	Puritanism
Grammar School	Reform
Hell	State
History	Statute
Industrial Revolution	University

On the other hand, Alfred Kazin, a noted American critic, used lower-case letters in these words:

British army colonel	the Presbyterian church
fascism	socialism
hell	

But to complicate matters, in the same article he capitalized these:

Communism	Depression

Obviously, there can be considerable leeway in the practices of capitalization in English.

In spite of the wholly conventional nature of capitalization and in spite of the variant practices found among professional writers, the general public believes that "errors" in capitalization (like errors in spelling) indicate ignorance. For example, anyone who fails to capitalize the pronoun *I* is thought to be severely retarded educationally. Yet that pronoun is capitalized only because long ago someone thought the lower-case *i* was likely to be overlooked in a line of script or type. Or, for another example, the spelling of *English* with a lower-case *e* is particularly offensive to English teachers. Yet in German (a language rather closely related to English) such proper adjectives are conventionally spelled with lower-case letters. But logic aside, convention calls for adherence to the rules of capitalization, and so you should conform as best you can.

As a student, you should learn (if you have not already done so) the cut-and-dried rules adhered to by most writers, but you should be allowed to excercise your own judgement or preference in doubtful cases. Liberal-minded people do not, as a rule, force their preferences on other people because capitalization seldom affects clarity, logic, and precision. *The following words, for example, (and other comparable words or phrases) are now widely accepted with either capital or lower-case letters.* Often a writer will make his decision on the basis of context; that is, on one occasion he may want to capitalize one of these words, but not on another occasion.

> Army, Navy, Air Force
> Archbishop, Bishop, King, Pope
> Board of Directors
> Church
> Civil Service
> Communism, Democracy, Fascism, Socialism
> Congressman
> Deity
> Democrat, Republican
> Federal Court, Municipal Court
> Federal Government
> Fraternity Row
> Freshman Class
> Heaven, Hell
> Mayor, Principal, Professor
> Presidential Inauguration
> School Board
> Scripture
> Steering Committee
> State Government
> State Law
> Student Body, Student Government
> Sunday School

The following rules of capitalization include only those about which there is little or no disagreement among educated writers of English. You should follow these rules because most educated writers do. In doubtful cases, follow your own inclination.

RULE 1:
Capitalize the first word of each sentence, the pronoun I, *the interjection* O, *and the first word in each line of poetry unless the poet himself did not capitalize it:*

> Here lies my wife; here let her lie;
> Now she's at peace, and so am I.

RULE 2 :

Capitalize the first word and all other words except articles, pre-positions, and coordinating conjunctions in a title or chapter heading:

TITLE OF A BOOK: The Rise and Fall of the Third Reich
TITLE OF AN ESSAY: "Marriage Customs through the Ages"
CHAPTER HEADING: Symbolism in the American Short Story

RULE 3 :

Capitalize all proper names and adjectives formed from proper names:

African	French
Alabaman	Hollywoodish
Caucasian	Oriental
Chicagoan	Platonism
English	Swedish

Note: The word *Negro* is now often used with a lower-case *n*. The word *white* meaning race is capitalized by only a few writers. Either usage for these two words is acceptable.

RULE 4:

Capitalize references to the Deity, the names of divine books of all religions, and references to specific religions or religious sects:

Baptist	Koran
Bible	our Lord
Book of Mormon	Mormon
Catholic	New Testament
Christ	Pentateuch
God	Protestant
Holy Ghost	Seventh Day Adventist
Jehovah	the Trinity
Jewish	the Upanishads

Note: An increasing number of writers are using lower-case letters to spell Protestant, Catholic, Baptist, and so forth.

RULE 5:

Capitalize the titles of relatives when used with the person's name and when the person is addressed directly but not when used with the pronoun my:

Aunt Nellie   Grandfather Scarne
Uncle Josh   Cousin Margie
"Oh, Mother, can you come here?"
"My goodness, Grandfather, did you hurt yourself?"
"My mother is an excellent cellist."

RULE 6:
Capitalize the titles of officials when a specific individual is meant, whether or not the person's name is included:

Mayor Hartsfield   the Lieutenant
Vice-President Finlinson   the Senator
Colonel Wetzler   the Pastor
Dean Levinson   the Board Chairman
Principal Wallace   the Chairman

RULE 7:
Capitalize the days of the week and the months of the year but not the names of the seasons:

Monday   spring
January   winter

RULE 8:
Capitalize the names of streets, avenues, parks, rivers, mountains, cities, states, provinces, nations, continents, oceans, lakes, and specific geographical regions:

Tenth Street   the Strait of Magellan
Gayley Avenue   Africa
Central Park   the Midwest
the Red River   the Northeast
Ghana   the South
the Iberian Peninsula   Asia Minor
the North Pole   the Far East
the Allegheny Mountains   the Western Hemisphere
Bear Mountain   the Central Plains
Alaska   Lake Tahoe
Alberta   the Pacific Ocean
the West Coast   the Black Sea

Note: Do not capitalize the names of directions:

Go west, young man.
The farther south we drove, the hotter it got.

RULE 9:
Capitalize the names of buildings:

the Palace Theater	the Capitol
the First Methodist Church	the Sill Building
the Humanities Building	the Empire State Building

RULE 10:
Capitalize the names of private organizations:

Rotary	the Society of Individualists
the Elks Club	the American Legion

RULE 11:
Capitalize the names of governmental organizations:

the Veterans Administration	the U.S. Department of Agriculture
Congress	the Peace Corps
the House	
the United States Navy	

RULE 12:
Capitalize the names of historical documents, events, and periods or eras:

the Declaration of Independence	the Battle of Midway
the Bill of Rights	the Diet of Worms
the Atlantic Charter	the Middle Ages
the Missouri Compromise	the Renaissance
World War I	the Napoleonic Wars

Note: Some writers do not capitalize the names of periods such as the Romantic Age and the Baroque Era.

RULE 13:
Capitalize the names of specific school courses:

Senior Problems	Introduction to the Study of Poetry
Twentieth-Century Novels	American Literature
History 3A	Freshman Composition
Elementary Algebra	Advanced Organic Chemistry

RULE 14:
Capitalize brand names but not the name of the product:

a Ford car	Camay soap
Goodyear tires	Jerseymaid ice cream
Norwalk gasoline	Mum deodorant

Of course these rules about capitalization do not cover all the cases when you should not capitalize. A satisfactory rule to follow is not to capitalize a word unless you have a specific reason for doing so. However, many doubtful cases arise in the work of all writers. The best policy is to use your own judgment in doubtful cases and not to consider the problem important. For example, most writers do not capitalize the names of foods (rice, spaghetti), games (golf, bridge), diseases (cancer, mumps), occupations (engineer, doctor), animals (trout, robin, collie), plants (maple, rose), or musical instruments (piano, violoncello). But occasionally a specific context may call for the capitalization of words like these, and then you should not hesitate to capitalize them.

THE APOSTROPHE AND THE HYPHEN

Both the apostrophe and the hyphen look like marks of punctuation, and both have been defined as such, even in dictionaries. But actually neither is any more a mark of punctuation than is a letter of the alphabet. Marks of punctuation are used to clarify sentence structure in writing, just as pauses and intonation are used in oral language. Apostrophes and hyphens are used to clarify certain kinds of spelling situations; that is the whole extent of their use in English. They cannot be indicated by the voice as marks of punctuation can be.

Since the apostrophe and hyphen are used only in spelling, their use is conventional. We could actually do without them altogether or we could substitute other devices for them. But they are convenient marks and do help clarify English spelling. Therefore you should, if you have not already done so, learn the rules governing their use.

The use of the apostrophe in possessives

In oral English, the same pronunciation is used for the plural form, the singular possessive form, and the plural possessive form of most nouns. Listeners are seldom confused, however, as to which is meant, for context will almost always supply that information. In writing, not only context but also spelling tells the reader the meaning of a noun ending in an *s* sound. For example, the following triplets are pronounced alike, but have different meanings in sentences:

companies-company's-com-   peoples-people's-peoples'
   panies'   rats-rat's-rats'
days-day's-days'   waiters-waiter's-waiters'
ladies-lady's-ladies'

Even in writing, context will almost always tell a reader which of the three meanings is intended, but the apostrophe makes the distinctions crystal clear.

At one time the apostrophe was not used to spell possessives in English. Instead, an *es* was added to words ending in *x* and *s*, as in these phrases:

a foxes tail   a lionesses cubs
Jameses book   his mistresses eyes

And an *s* or an *es* was added to words not ending in *x* or *s*, as in these phrases:

a mans wife   a mannes wife
a dogs tail   a dogges tail
a birds wing   a birdes wing

In the sixteenth century writers began to use apostrophes in contractions, and, to make contractions, they often substituted an apostrophe for the *e* in the *es* possessive ending, in this way:

a fox's tail   a lioness's cubs
James's book   his mistress's eyes

Then gradually, through ignorance or carelessness, writers began using the apostrophe even when no *e* had necessarily been omitted, as in:

a bird's wing   a man's wife
two birds' wings   men's wives

The process of adopting the use of the apostrophe for all English possessives took about two centuries. As late as 1725 its use had not become wholly standardized.

Humorously enough, the use of the apostrophe in possessives led some scholars in the late sixteenth and early seventeenth centuries to believe that the possessive form was a contraction of the possessive pronoun *his*—that is, that the apostrophe marked the omission of the *hi*, in this way:

a man's wife = a man his wife
a dog's tail = a dog his tail

One notable writer even entitled a book *Purchas His Pilgrims*, meaning *Purchas's Pilgrims*.

The use of the apostrophe in spelling English possessives, then, is a historical mistake, growing out of the use of the mark to indicate contractions. Even the present pronunciation of the word occurred through ignorance. The four-syllable word *a-pós-tro-phe* means a certain figure of speech. The three-syllable French word *a-po-stróphe* is an entirely different word and is the one that came into English to designate the mark ('). So if early English writers had not made ignorant mistakes, writers nowadays would use a three-syllable apostrophe only to indicate contractions.

But the four-syllable apostrophe is with us now and is conventionally used in possessive spellings. And, as in all matters of spelling and capitalization, the public thinks that failure to use the apostrophe in possessives is a sure sign of ignorance. Even students who habitually fail to put apostrophes in possessives will, when questioned, assert that apostrophes are absolutely necessary. Since the public feels as it does, you must use apostrophes as conventionally dictated if you want your usage to be acceptable in educated circles.

Following are the conventional rules governing the use of the apostrophe in possessive spellings.

RULE 1:
The possessive form of a singular noun not ending in s *is spelled with the addition of an* 's:

John's coat   the teacher's temper
a sheep's fleece   the President's power

RULE 2:
The possessive form of a singular noun ending in s *is spelled with the addition of either an* 's *or just an* ':

a waitress' order *or* a waitress's order
a crocus' odor *or* a crocus's odor
James's book *or* James' book

RULE 3:

The possessive form of a plural noun ending in s *is spelled with the addition of an ' only:*

several boys' bicycles
the Supreme Court Justices' decision
the Board of Supervisors' tax cut

RULE 4:

The possessive form of a plural noun not ending in s *is spelled with the addition of an 's:*

the men's wives	six sheep's fleece
the women's husbands	the children's toys

Note: For those who have trouble with apostrophes, the previous four rules may be reduced to these two: (1) the possessive of a noun not ending in *s* is formed with an *'s*, (2) the possessive of a noun ending in *s* may be formed with just an '. (See note with Rule 6 following for determining placement of the apostrophe.)

RULE 5:

The possessive forms of the indefinite pronouns are spelled with the addition of an 's:

one's desire	nobody's business
someone's sweetheart	everybody's mistake
anybody's guess	everybody else's money

RULE 6:

Nouns expressing periods of time and amounts of money are given normal possessive spellings in possessive constructions.

one hour's time	the year's end
two hours' wait	a moment's delay
one month's salary	your money's worth
six years' delay	three dollars' worth
today's assignment	one nickel's difference

Note: The placement of an apostrophe can always be accurately determined by converting the possessive phrase into a "belonging to" phrase or an "of" phrase in order to get the base noun which will show possession. Examples:

1. James' book = a book belonging to *James*. The base noun is *James;* therefore the correct possessive form is *James'* or *James's*, not *Jame's* or *James'es*.
2. The men's wives = the wives belonging to the *men*. The base noun is *men;* therefore *men's* rather than *mens'* is the proper possessive form.
3. Three teachers' reports = the reports of three *teachers*. The base noun is *teachers;* therefore the proper possessive form is *teachers'* not *teacher's* or *teachers's*.
4. The Joneses' dog = the dog belonging to the *Joneses*. The base noun is *Joneses* (plural of Jones); therefore the correct possessive form is *Joneses'*, not *Jones'* or *Jones'es*.
5. Mr. Jones' dog = the dog belonging to Mr. *Jones*. The base noun is *Jones;* therefore the correct possessive form is *Jones's* or *Jones'*, not *Jone's* or *Joneses'*.
6. Nobody's business = the business belonging to *nobody*. The base word is *nobody;* therefore the proper possessive form is *nobody's*, not *nobodies'*.
7. Your money's worth = the worth of your *money*. The base noun is *money;* therefore the possessive form is *money's*.
8. Three months' vacation = the vacation of three *months*. The base noun is *months;* therefore the possessive form is *months'*.
9. An hour's delay = the delay of an *hour*. The base noun is *hour;* therefore the possessive form is *hour's*.

RULE 7:
The personal possessive pronouns are spelled without apostrophes.

Its paw is injured.	The profit is *ours*.
The book is *hers*.	The debt is *yours*.
The car is *theirs*.	*Whose* lunch is that?

General Note: Some stylists maintain that nouns which name inanimate objects should not have their possessive forms spelled with an *'s*. Instead, they recommend "of" phrases like these:

The entrance requirements of the school (*rather than* the school's entrance requirements)
The eraser of the pencil (*rather than* the pencil's eraser)

This precept, however, is not wholly valid. It is true that euphony will sometimes lead a writer to use an "of" phrase instead of a possessive form, as "the roof of the house" rather than "the house's roof." But such phrases as the following are common in the best writing:

the bank's cashier   the tree's roots
the book's frontispiece   the farm's value
the car's brakes   the light's gleam

The use of the apostrophe in contractions

The original use of the apostrophe in English was to show omission of one or more letters in a word. Such an omission is known as a contraction. The most widespread use of the apostrophe for this purpose was first made by poets to help the reader with his pronunciation. For example, in the original writings of Shakespeare the word *walk'd* is to be pronounced as one syllable and the word *walked* as two. Or, for another example, a poet in the earlier days of modern English might have used the phrase *th' apple* as two syllables instead of three. Even nowadays the spelling *o'er* is often used poetically to denote a one-syllable pronunciation.

The use of the apostrophe for poetic contractions has diminished, but we still use apostrophes for contractions in our ordinary writing. The rule is simple: *enter an apostrophe where one or more letters have been omitted.* Examples:

are not = aren't (*not* arn't *or* are'nt)
cannot = can't (*not* cant *or* ca'nt)
it is = it's (*not* its *or* its')
of the clock = o'clock

In speech, Americans often slur syllables. When reporting conversation, a writer may use apostrophes to indicate the intended pronunciation. Example: "Somethin' funny 'uz goin' on at fo' o'clock this mornin'." The apostrophe is also used in contractions of dates. Examples:

He owns a '68 Ford.
The '30's were a period of economic depression.
Some oldtimers still remember '88 as the year of the big blizzard.

Such contractions can be used only when the century involved is obvious. Unless another century has been clearly mentioned, such a contraction will always apply to the last ninety-nine years.

One of America's greatest contemporary authors, William Faulkner, who died in 1962, often spelled the common contractions without apostrophes, like this:

cant	oclock
dont	wont

He also used *ain't* and other vulgate expressions in his own speech. Mere college students, however, had best conform to convention.

The use of the apostrophe in plural spellings

Apostrophes should not be used in the spelling of ordinary plurals and verbs in the third person singular present tense. Almost every English teacher is far more tolerant of omitted apostrophes in possessive spellings than he is of their misuse in plurals and verbs. All of the apostrophes in the following examples are **misused:**

> My brother read's several book's each month.
> He tries' to read the monthly fare of all the book club's.
> He spend's about thirty dollar's a month just for books'.

When in doubt, always test with a "belonging to" phrase. Also remember that in general it is better to omit an apostrophe than to use one unnecessarily.

Apostrophes are frequently used in spelling the plurals of numerals, letters of the alphabet, and abbreviations consisting only of capital letters. Examples:

> There are four *s*'s and four *i*'s in Mississippi.
> I made five C's last semester.
> I own three old Colt .44's.
> His 9's look like 7's.
> The 1920's were an era of lawlessness.
> All the CPA's in town have gone to a convention.
> The FFA's are meeting tonight.

Though the use of apostrophes for these plural spellings has been standard, many professional writers and book publishers do not use them when clarity is not generally affected. Thus most writers and publishers would use apostrophes in spelling the plurals of lower-case letters (*a*'s, *i*'s, *t*'s, *p*'s) because of improved clarity but omit them in the spelling of the plurals of capital letters (Cs, Ps, PDQs) and numerals (3s, 9s, .44s, 1930s).

Sometimes words are used not for their meaning but as words, as in this sentence: "The word *so* is less often misspelled than the word *therefore*." The most commonly accepted practice is spelling the plural of a word used as a word is to *italicize* (underline in script or typewriting) the word and to add an *'s*. Examples:

> No proposal should be sprinkled with *if*'s.
> His sermon was full of *consequently*'s.

The use of the hyphen

Like the apostrophe, the hyphen is a mark used in spelling, not punctuation. Following are the rules governing its use.

RULE 1:
In dividing a word at the end of a line of script, typewriting, or print, divide between syllables and indicate division with a hyphen.

Careful pronunciation will usually disclose the syllabification of a word. When in doubt, consult a dictionary. Never divide a one-syllable word at the end of a line, such as *tw-elve, len-gth,* and *stop-ped.* Avoid dividing a word so that a one-letter syllable is left by itself, such as *a-void* or *mush-y.* Do not divide a word unless the maintenance of a margin demands it.

RULE 2:
Hyphenate compound numbers and fractions:

twenty-two	one-half
thirty-four	a half
one hundred and sixty-three	three-fourth
three thousand and forty-one	sixty-three and a third
fifty-fifth	sixty-three and one-third

RULE 3:
Hyphenate compound nouns when hyphenation contributes to clarity.

This rule is of necessity vaguely stated. Current practice in hyphenation of compound nouns varies widely. The trend is conspicuously toward less hyphenation and more one-word compounding. For example, the following words were once hyphenated but now are usually spelled as single words:

bypass	schoolboy
gamebag	storytelling
Midwest	sunstroke
playgoer	wallpaper
playhouse	weekend
rightwing	workshop

It seems certain that more and more once-hyphenated compound nouns will in the future be spelled as single words. But when clarity is improved by retention of the hypen, it should be retained.

When in doubt, you may, of course, follow the practice of any good dictionary, but failure to follow dictionary practice need not be taken as an error, for convention in the use of hyphens is shifting rapidly. Following are some hyphenated compound nouns found in one issue of *Harper's Magazine*. Some are standard, according to the dictionary; some just represent the preference of the individual author:

close-up	Pacific-minded
job-hunting	counter-paper
tie-ups	by-passing
kow-tow	shadow-boxing
self-interest	cross-country
dry-goods	globe-trotter
well-being	Mr. So-and-so
boss-man	passer-by
son-in-law	by-product
school-bus	opera-goers
word-counting	half-century
speech-sounds	bomb-testing
writing-convention	co-ed
Europe-firsters	half-a-mile

In the writing of other authors, some of the above compounds undoubtedly would have been written as single words and some as two separate words. There is no such thing as absolute standard practice in the hyphenation of compound nouns. Maintenance of clarity should be your chief guide.

RULE 4:
Use a hyphen to separate a prefix when the first letter of the root and the last letter of the prefix are the same vowel:

anti-industrial   re-echo
de-emphasize   semi-independent
pre-existent   ultra-articulate

Even this rule does not hold 100 percent. It is now common practice to omit the hyphen in such words as *cooperate* and *coordinate*. In all probability, in the future the use of the hyphen will further diminish.

RULE 5:
Use a hyphen to separate a prefix from a root which is normally capitalized.

crypto-Communist   post-Reconstruction
mid-August   pre-Freudian
non-Christian   un-American

Some professional writers now write such words without the hyphen and either with or without the capital letter, as *unChristian* or *unchristian*.

RULE 6:
Use a hyphen to separate a prefix when nonhyphenation might be ambiguous:

co-op *and* coop   re-sort *and* resort
re-collect *and* recollect   re-cover *and* recover
re-count *and* recount   re-create *and* recreate

Note: Traditionally, words compounded with the prefixes *self, non, pseudo, quasi, ultra, neo, post, anti,* and *infra* have been hyphenated. However, the move is toward elimination of the hyphen, as in such compounds as *nondevelopmental, selfhood, pseudomorphic, ultraconservative, neoclassic, postgraduate, antivivisectionist,* and *infrared.* Since either convention is acceptable, personal preference can be your guide.

RULE 7:
Hyphenate two or more words that serve a single adjective in front of a noun.

This is the most important single rule of hypenation and the least understood. It is important not because of convention, but because clarity calls for it. There is no ambiguity in this phrase, for example: *a two dollar bill*. But consider this one: *ninety two dollar bills*. If the phrase is mentioning ninety-two bills, then the rule governing compound numbers should be followed. But if it is mentioning ninety bills, then the above rule must be applied: *ninety two-dollar bills*. For complete clarity, the rule should be followed in the phrase *a two-dollar bill*.

Countless ambiguous phrases could be avoided if writers would universally follow this rule. The misuse of it among professional writers is often shocking. For example, in *Harper's Magazine* a company once advertised a stereo with "two-35 watt amplifiers." Obviously, the machine had "two 35-watt amplifiers." Another ad once mentioned "the new embedded in plastic printed wiring circuit" of an automobile. Once you understand the phrase, it is not ambiguous, but few readers could have read it quickly without pausing to ponder the word relationships. It would have been immediately clear to all if written this way: "the new embedded-in-plastic, printed-wiring circuit"—two clear compound modifiers before the noun. One issue of a publication entitled *School Days* spoke of "word analysis-skills." The phrase is gibberish unless converted to "word-analysis skills."

To give you live examples of this rule in action, here are a number of phrases from one issue of *Harper's*. Note how the hyphenated words form one clear modifier, not two or more. Also note how quickly the hyphens make the word relationships clear.

> martinis-and-rich-food lunches
> cradle-to-grave needs
> two-fisted gesture
> double-parked automobile
> all-too-human attributes
> long-term outlay
> long-sustained commitment
> state-supported white schools
> law-school faculty
> civil-rights battle
> management-engineering work
> a soft-spoken type
> a cartharsis-giving experience

cigar-making firm
sewing-machine manufacturers
work-measurement studies
an eight-year-old girl
dirty-gray water
high-pressure steam
the Rather-Red-Than-Dead people
a fifty-thousand-dollar-a-year man

To understand the clarifying value of the hyphen, read the following phrases as though each word is distinct in itself:

two fisted gesture
double parked automobile
long term outlay
a soft spoken type
a cartharsis giving experience
cigar making firm
dirty gray water
high pressure steam

Subrule A: *When a conjunction is entered in the compound adjective so that two or more adjectives are indicated, leave a space before and after the conjunction:*

all eighth- and ninth-grade pupils
all first-, second-, third-, and fourth-ranked candidates
air- or waterproof clothes
a heavy- but kind-hearted (*or* kindhearted) caress

Subrule B: *Do not hyphenate adjectival words when they follow the noun:*

a man who makes fifty thousand dollars a year
water that is dirty gray
a manufacturer of sewing machines
a person who is soft spoken
the faculty of the law school
a girl who is eight years old

Subrule C: *Do not hyphenate two words before a noun when one of them is an "ly" adverb modifying the adjective itself:*

an overly tired horse
a dismally unamusing play
a rapidly diminishing bankroll

Practice varies among professional writers in hyphenating compound adjectives including the adverb *well:*

> a well-known writer *or* a well known writer
> a well-equipped expedition *or* a well equipped expedition

Subrule D: *Do not use quotation marks to enclose a compound adjective.*

> a never-to-be-forgotten dance *rather than* "a never to be forgotten" dance
> an I-don't-care-what-you-do attitude *rather than* an "I don't care what you do" attitude

RULE 8:
Use hyphens to separate letters in a word that is spelled to emphasize a drawn-out pronunciation:

whoo-o-o-pee-e-e   here-e-e-e-e we go-o-o-o

Important Cautionary Note: *Do not confuse hyphens with dashes.* The dash is a mark of punctuation. It is used to clarify sentence structure; it is never used as a spelling device. The hyphen, on the other hand, is used only as a spelling device. The dash is twice as long as a hyphen: the mark (—) in contrast with the mark (-). In typewriting, two hyphens (not one) are used to indicate a dash. The result is a break in the dash in this way: (--). But that mark is preferable to the longer unbroken mark used for underlining, for the underlining mark sits below rather than in the middle of the typed line, in this way: (___). (For further information on the dash, see pages 296–298.)

EXERCISE 46. Using Capital Letters, Apostrophes, and Hyphens

DIRECTIONS: *Be prepared to explain where and why capital letters, apostrophes, and hyphens are needed in the following sentences. Some spellings may need alteration before the proper possessive spelling can be indicated.*

1. We were advised by dean merson to take introduction to political science as well as a course in history.
2. An up to date religious philosophy is a part of the pseudo intellectuals cultural paraphernalia.

3. The concert was given at the run down olympic theater, which is located on tenth street near the veterans administration building.

4. We were relieved by commander lucases damn the torpedoes attitude as he tried to maneuver his craft out of the enemys range of fire.

5. After a years service in the peace corps, I decided to enlist in the argentine navy for a year.

6. The captain had earned the name blood and guts donovan, but it was his mens blood and guts that had been spilled.

7. Jameses mother grew up in utah as a mormon, but after she read the koran she became a mohammedan.

8. Plato was so shocked by socrateses being sentenced to death that he undertook an as yet unequalled philosophic career.

9. The much reprinted second chapter of *an introduction to ethnology* is entitled "the concept of race."

10. A made in japan label no longer connotes inferior merchandise, as it did in the 30s.

11. In spring, when the robins return, I like to stroll among my fathers peach trees and observe nature.

12. His holier than thou attitude seemed rather unchristian for a bishop.

13. The long debated missouri compromise only postponed the civil war.

14. I like the smiths house better than the joneses, for the smiths has a make yourself at home look.

15. Yesterdays avant garde movement is todays commonplace art.

16. When aunt carolyns children had the mumps, her doctor prescribed borodin tablets, which are manufactured by the merck company.

17. The poem entitled "to an athlete dying young," which opens with the line "the time you won your town the race," appears in a. e. housmans *a shropshire lad*.

18. A water or airborne craft is suitable for rescues at sea.

19. A five or six months delay in delivery doesn't seem to annoy volkswagen buyers.

20. The history of western man is in large part the history of a never won battle for individual freedom.

PUNCTUATION

Punctuation is a conventional aspect of writing, for most perceptive readers can understand passages written without any punctuation at all. Even unnecessary marks of punctuation seldom destroy meaning. For example, probably not more than one case of real misunderstanding due to faulty punctuation occurs for every hundred errors in punctuation marked on freshmen themes. However, the absence or misuse of punctuation in a passage slows down a reader markedly, for then he must pause frequently to think out word relationships and to clear up momentary confusion. Hence, even though conventional, punctuation is a much more important aspect of writing than capitalization and the use of apostrophe. It is a valuable—some would say indispensable—aid to clarity.

All rules of punctuation, however, are not equally important, and in many cases expert opinion is divided as to proper usage. The existence of divided opinion will be noted in the discussion of the rules below.

The period, the question mark, and the exclamation point

The conventional use of end punctuation for sentences is too elementary for discussion in this book. But a few notations on other uses of the period, question mark, and exclamation point are in order.

Periods should be used after abbreviations unless convention allows omission.

Mr.	C.O.D. *or* COD
Calif.	A.B. *or* AB
N. Y.	U.N. *or* UN
Wash. Sq.	

When there is doubt in your mind, it is best to consult a good dictionary.

A period or a question mark may be used after a simple, routine request:

> Will you please meet with the Committee at 3:00 on Thursday.
> Will you see me at your earliest convenience?

Three periods with spaces between them (called an ellipsis) are conventionally used to show omission in a direct quotation:

> "In this literature . . . the humorous anecdote mingled with white and Negro folklore."

If the omission is at the end of a sentence, a fourth period shows the end of the sentence:

> "The transcendental law," Emerson believed, "was the 'moral law,' through which man discovers the nature of God, a living spirit. . . ."

A question mark may be used in parentheses after a word or phrase to indicate the writer's uncertainty or doubt about the information he has written:

> Geminianni's six concerti grossi were first published in Leyden (?) in 1718 (?).

A question mark may be used after an "I wonder . . ." sentence because such a sentence clearly denotes interrogation. A period after such a sentence is also correct:

> I wonder if you can send me samples of your latest engravings?
> I wonder where I put that book on Chinese pottery.

An exclamation point may be used in parentheses after a word or phrase to denote surprise or some other strong emotion:

> Our first year's sales of 25,000 copies (!) of *Neo-Gothic Art* has provided us with capital to publish a book on Sumerian art.

The comma

The comma accounts for more rules of punctuation than all other marks combined, and probably 80 percent of all errors in punctuation are due to the misuse or omission of commas. Some rules involving the comma are highly important; some are minor. All involve the separation of sentence elements that are in some way logically dissociated and between which there is more voice pause than between words in a phrase. For example, there is more logical dissociation as well as voice pause between the first two than between the last two words in this sentence: "Sam, come here." Commas are used where such logical dissociations and voice pauses occur within one sentence. Following are specific rules.

> *RULE 1:*
> *Use commas to separate three or more sentence elements in a series.*

Sentence elements can be single words, phrases, or clauses. When three or more such elements form a series with a conjunction between the last two, a comma should be placed between each two elements.

> The fans threw bottles, flashlights, and girdles at the umpire.
> The thoughtful host served beer, Scotch, bourbon, rum, and Coca Cola.
> The candidate promised to lower taxes, increase unemployment pay, and rehabilitate all welfare recipients.
> At the Fourth of July picnic, the politicians made speeches, the young couples made eyes, and the children made trouble.

Many writers omit the comma before the conjunction in a series, and such usage must be considered correct. But the most careful writers include that comma to avoid any chance of confusion or ambiguity (as in the second example above).

Sometimes a writer will use three or more elements in a series without a conjunction. Then commas are necessary between all elements. "We must strive to inculcate in our students a sense of self-discipline, an appreciation of beauty, a quest for discovery."

Sometimes a writer will also use only two elements in a series without a conjunction. In such cases the two elements must be separated by a comma. "College taught me how to observe without thinking, how to read without appreciating."

RULE 2:

Use a comma between independent clauses joined by a coordinating conjunction, unless the clauses are short and closely related.

> Edgar Allan Poe is popularly thought to have been a high neurotic preoccupied with morbid thoughts, but actually he was a dedicated genius who worked hard to achieve greatness in literature.
> The Board Chairman spoke and the yes men nodded.

Note: Regardless of the length of the clauses, always use a comma to separate independent clauses joined by *for*. Otherwise the *for* might be taken as a preposition and cause momentary confusion: "I ordered a Mercedes-Benz for my wife wanted to keep ahead of the Joneses." If the comma is omitted before the *for* in such a sentence, the reader will momentarily stumble.

RULE 3:

Use a comma to separate coordinate adjectives not joined by a conjunction.

In a phrase such as "an awkward old man," the two adjectives are not coordinate because "old" is virtually a part of the noun itself (some languages use just one word to mean "old man"). But in a phrase such as "an irascible, malicious man," the two adjectives are coordinate because they are equal in their relationship to the noun. Such coordinate adjectives have a logical dissociation and a voice pause between them and therefore should be separated by a comma. In general, adjectives are coordinate when the conjunction *and* sounds natural between them, but are not coordinate when the conjunction sounds unnatural. For example, "an awkward and old man" sounds unnatural, but "an irascible and malicious man" sounds natural. In essence, a comma is used to replace *and*.

> a beautiful, functional house
> a wasteful, poorly planned public works program
> a sneaky, ill-mannered little boy
> a grotesque red brick house

RULE 4:

Use a comma to set off an introductory sentence element if the element is long or if a comma is necessary to avoid ambiguity.

This is one of the less important rules of punctuation. For example, some knowledgeable writers would use commas and some would not in sentences like the following:

> As the moon rose, the platoon departed silently on its mission.
> In general, we must agree with our customers even when we know they are wrong.
> As a starter, we filed a petition with the Dean of Instruction.

The more careful a writer is, the more likely he is to use commas to set off initial sentence elements. But when clarity is not affected, you may include or omit such commas according to your own preference.

All careful writers, however, follow the above rule when clarity is at stake. For example, only a careless writer would omit commas in the following sentences:

As we were about to leave the restaurant manager hastened to apologize to us.
Above the buzzards circled ominously.
As I mentioned the rules may occasionally be broken.

Omission of the commas in these sentences results in ambiguity, for without a comma to make him pause, a reader first assumes that *restaurant, buzzards,* and *rules* are objects of the preceding verbs or preposition rather than subjects of the following clauses. You should always reread each of your sentences carefully enough to avoid such ambiguous constructions.

Initial verbal phrases (verb clusters) are usually set off by commas because of the distinct voice pause and logical dissociation between such a phrase and the following clause.

Not realizing the danger, the platoon crept forward.
Speaking harshly and with choppy gestures, the candidate attacked his opponent's integrity.
Failing that, we must resort to force.
To avoid ambiguity, a writer must punctuate carefully.

Introductory exclamations and introductory words of assent or doubt are also set off by commas. (But such elements are not common in exposition.)

Why, we were old friends in optometry school.
Oh darn, I suppose I'll get another demerit.
Yes, we feel that he is due compensatory damages.
Well, perhaps he intended no disrespect.
Maybe, but I'll have to consult an internist.

RULE 5:
Use commas to set off an interrupter or parenthetic element placed within a sentence.

A parenthetic element (or interrupter) is an additional word, phrase, or clause placed as an explanation or comment within an already complete sentence. Since there is a dissociated logic between such an element and the rest of the sentence, and since there is a distinct pause before and after it, commas (or, in some cases, dashes or parentheses) should be used to set it off from the rest of the sentence. Various kinds of parenthetic elements or interrupters can be identified.

Words in direct address are parenthetic and should be set off by commas. (Such phrases do not, however, appear frequently in exposition.)

> Let me tell you, sir, that your insinuations are insulting.
> Over here, ladies and gentlemen, is a replica of the Venus de Milo.
> Mother, don't be so devious in your plans.
> That's an ingenious device, young fellow.

Words and phrases denoting logical continuity or transition between ideas are usually set off when used parenthetically.

> We can conclude, then, that Rousseau was not the only fountain head of Romanticism.
> There is, indeed, ample precedent for the judge's decision.
> Senator Stoner, of course, is a Democrat in name only.
> Wheat germ, for example, is a valuable food once just discarded by flour mills.
> Thus individual human I.Q.'s, according to Becker's findings, cannot be accurately ascertained.

The words and phrases set off in these examples denote a continuation of thought from the previous sentences and thus are used parenthetically as transitions between ideas.

The so-called *logical connectives* are often used parenthetically to show logical continuity. When used in the middle of sentences, such connectives (*however, nevertheless, consequently, therefore, accordingly, furthermore, moreover,* and so on) should be set off by commas on both sides.

> Atomic energy, however, has not yet produced economical electric power for home consumption.
> The judge's decision, moreover, broke a hundred-years-old precedent.
> His net income for the year, consequently, was less than his secretary's.

Opinion is divided about the use of a comma after such words when they come at the beginning of a clause. If you feel a distinct pause after such a word, you should use a comma: "However, proof of his guilt was not adduced." If you do not feel a pause, you need not insert a comma: "Therefore the committee decided to implement their plan." But a comma after *therefore* in that sentence would not be wrong.

Appositive phrases are parenthetic identifications and should be set off by commas (or, in some cases, dashes).

The prophecies of Nostradamus, a sixteenth-century French astrologer, enjoyed a new burst of popularity in the 1930s.

Anticholinergics, drugs that reduce muscle spasm, were used by ancient physicians.

Vivisection, an indispensable aid to medical science, is strongly condemned by many fuzzy-minded reformers.

Note: Some appositives are restrictive—that is, are necessary to identify the nouns to which they are in apposition. Such restrictive appositives are not set off by commas.

The movie "Cleopatra" was filmed in Italy.
The color black is becoming to a young woman.

If the appositives *"Cleopatra"* and *black* are removed from these sentences, the nouns *movie* and *color* are left completely unidentified.

When given parenthetic status, *phrases of addition, contrast, and alternative choice* should be set off by commas.

A study of rhetoric, and of grammar too, can increase one's appreciation of literature.

Tom Paine's religious ideas, but not his literary style, have gone out of fashion.

One result of Sade's genius, or else of his psychoticism, was the introduction of new modes of psychological inquiry.

Phrases of personal opinion are set off by commas when they take parenthetic form.

Your estimate, I'm sure, is accurate enough for preliminary studies.

It was Mark Twain, I think, who said "Heaven for climate; hell for company."

My Uncle Jurgen, it seems, left me only a notebook full of good advice.

Dean Etheridge, if I understood him correctly, implied that the Administration will not bend to the pressure of extremists.

Note: A very common error in punctuation is the omission of the second comma needed to set off a parenthetic element. Commas are **erroneously** omitted after the phrases in these examples.

Madison, Hamilton, and Jay, the authors of the Federalist Papers signed their essays "Publius."

Henry David Thoreau, a member of the Transcendentalist movement said, "My mind is my church."

Inconsistency, as Emerson pointed out does not invalidate philosophic thought.

Absence of the second comma in such sentences will momentarily confuse the reader.

RULE 6:

Use a comma to set off a terminal clause or phrase used in contrast with the main clause of the sentence.

The State Department White Paper dealt with resurgent Fascism, not Communism.

Our students must learn to understand language, not just facts about it.

He is not just a man who will try his best, but who will deliver what he promises.

RULE 7:

In dates, use commas to separate the name of a day from the date of the month and the date of the month from the year.

If the sentence continues, place a comma after the date of the month and after the year.

The revolution began on Monday, July 26.

The proclamation was issued on October 22, 1962.

On Tuesday, August 13, began our long march into the jungle.

On January 14, 1859, Darwin published his *Origin of Species*.

On Tuesday, February 3, 1888, the Great Blizzard struck the Plains.

Actually, commas in all of these positions are largely ornamental, and it is likely that the future will see a gradual decrease in their use.

RULE 8:

In addresses, use commas to separate the name of a person or an establishment from the street address, the street address from the city, and the city from the state.

Opinion is divided about the use of a comma after the state.

The rioting occurred in front of the Hamburger Haven, 223 Main Street.

The assignation occurred at 345 Bourbon Street, New Orleans.

Twenty-two bomb-frightened families moved to Chico, California.

The culprit was finally located in the Palace Theater, 413 Michigan Boulevard, Chicago, Illinois, on St. Valentine's Day.

Residents of Los Angeles, California get most of their water from the Colorado River.

There is a definite trend toward omitting the comma after the state, as in the last example. In fact, even a comma between city and state is a functionless ornament. The name of city and state is like the first and last names of a person, between which no one would use a comma. Notice how cluttered the first example following is compared to the second:

The Frelighs moved from Topeka, Kansas, to Gunnison, Colorado, and on to Needles, California.

The Frelighs moved from Topeka Kansas to Gunnison Colorado and on to Needles California.

But since convention has called for a comma between city and state, you should obey the rule. It is, of course, permissible to omit a comma after the name of the state.

RULE 9:
Use commas to set off a nonrestrictive (or nonessential) adjective clause or phrase.

This is one of the most important rules governing the use of the comma. Adjective clauses (usually introduced by *who, whom, whose, which,* or *that*) and adjective phrases usually modify nouns. If a clause or phrase gives additional information about a noun that is already fully identified, it is nonrestrictive and should be set off by commas.

President Franklin D. Roosevelt, who defied tradition and ran for a third and a fourth term, died shortly after his fourth inauguration.

"The Convergence of the Twain," written by Thomas Hardy in his old age, is a powerful lyric poem about the sinking of the Titanic.

Heisenberg's Principle of Indeterminacy, which asserts that there is no strict operation of cause and effect on a subatomic level, is used by modern philosophers to refute scientific determinism.

The philosopher's stone, sought by all medieval alchemists, has in a sense been found by modern nuclear physicists.

School teachers, who are thought by many to be underpaid and oversubjected to community pressures, are not generally vociferous in their complaints.

School teachers who join unions are sometimes harassed by their administrative superiors.

The adjective clauses and phrases in the first five sentences above are nonrestrictive because they give additional information about nouns that are already fully identified. Since their removal would still leave fully meaningful sentences, they are set off by commas. Note that since example five is talking about all school teachers, its adjective clause is nonrestrictive. Example six, however, is not talking about all school teachers, but only about those identified by the adjective clause. Since the clause is needed to identify the noun it modifies, it is restrictive and therefore not set off by commas.

RULE 10 :

Use commas to set off an internal or terminal adverbial clause when a clear logical dissociation and a voice pause are apparent between it and the main clause of the sentence.

Do not set off an adverbial clause when such logical dissociation and voice pause are not apparent.

The President's first act after he took his oath of office was to send an ultimatum to Russia.

The President, after he had sent the ultimatum, ordered a call-up of 100,000 reserve troops.

The weather report was delayed because the meteorological equipment did not function properly.

The weather report must be broadcast soon, because if it isn't the farmers will suffer losses.

Adverbial clauses cannot be clearly divided into restrictive and nonrestrictive categories as can adjective clauses. Note that even without their adverbial clauses the first and third examples above are fully understandable sentences. In fact, the adverbial clause in the last example seems more essential than those in the first three examples, and yet the comma to set it off is distinctly necessary. There simply is no explicit rule to guide you in punctuating internal and terminal adverbial clauses; you must rely on your ear.

RULE 11 :

Use a comma to set off a terminal clause or phrase which in tone seems to be an afterthought.

Grammar can be an exciting intellectual adventure, and that from a fairly early age.

Grammar and rhetoric interact mutually, and in ways that we do not understand clearly.

A real study of grammar is enlightening, and not at all stuffy as most students believe.

Grammar and rhetoric are but two sides of one coin, and inseparable.

RULE 12 :

Do not add useless or obstructive commas to any sentence.

Adding an unnecessary comma usually results in a worse error than omitting a needed one. You should make it a rule of thumb not to use a comma unless you have a specific, known reason for using it. Commas are **misused** in all the following examples.

Do **not** separate a subject from its predicate or a verb from its complement with a single comma (parenthetic elements are, of course, set off on both sides).

The main cause of the friction between the new African nations, is due to tribal jealousies.

Senator Tushure's solution to the impasse with Russia was, to eliminate our bases in the Near East.

Do **not** set off a noun clause used as a subject or a complement.

That scientists will ever reach a final truth, seems doubtful.

The President's second White Paper stated, that the United States would not surrender overseas bases in order to avoid war.

Do **not** set off a restrictive noun clause used as an appositive: "The belief, that war is inevitable, seems to be widespread."

Do **not** set off a restrictive adjective clause or phrase. Violation of this rule results in one of the most serious errors in punctuation.

Nurses, who work night shift, are more likely to administer wrong drugs.

The first book, written by William Faulkner, was *The Marble Faun.*

The novel of William Faulkner's, which earned him the most money, was *Sanctuary*.

The book, most sought after in college libraries, is *God's Little Acre*.

Do **not** separate noncoordinate modifiers.

Mr. Gunn is a spirited, public servant.

I found a rare, old, vulgate Bible in our attic.

Do **not** set off nonparenthetic elements.

The manager, of the supermarket, decided to poke every woman who poked his tomatoes.

The canned music, supplied by Muzak, should never be let out of the can.

Do **not** separate two sentence elements in a series joined by a conjunction.

The patrol's duties were to locate enemy machine gun emplacements, and to cut enemy telephone lines.

The Lieutenant sent out a second patrol, and radioed headquarters to send more mortar ammunition.

Again note that all the commas in the above examples are *misused*.

RULE 13:

Do not use a comma between independent clauses not joined by a coordinating conjunction.

Violation of this rule results in the notorious **comma splice.** Actually, short, closely connected independent clauses can be joined with a comma splice. The comma splices in the following sentences are acceptable.

The wind blew, the rain poured, the wind howled.

The mayor droned on, the audience fidgited.

But normally the comma splice is faulty. In cases such as the following, either separate sentences should be formed, a coordinating conjunction should be placed between the clauses, or a semicolon should replace the comma.

In Economics 3A, students meet for a fourth hour each week in small groups, this gives them a chance to learn from each other.

The instructor continued to discuss the theory of natural

selection until nearly eleven o'clock, nobody told him the class period had ended.

Reciprocal trade agreements make for flexibility in world commerce, they are used by virtually all national governments.

Comma splices like these are serious errors.

The comma splice occurs most frequently in compound sentences with logical connectives (*however, moreover, therefore, nevertheless, consequently, accordingly, furthermore,* and so on). Independent clauses joined by a logical connective must be separated by a semicolon rather than a comma. The following sentences have comma splices.

> Senator Foreman was absent when his pork-barrel bill came to a vote, however, his colleagues saw that it passed safely.
>
> The Watch and Ward Society banned *Three on a Honeymoon* from sale in Boston, moreover they announced that the movie based on the book would not be shown in Boston theaters.
>
> English teachers are likely to have personal prejudices about little matters of usage, consequently, students often feel that they have been given conflicting rules.

A good rule of thumb to remember is that a semicolon (or a period) is necessary when the connective word can be shifted to the interior of the second clause.

> Senator Foreman was absent when his pork-barrel bill came to a vote; his colleagues, however, saw that it passed safely.
>
> The Watch and Ward Society banned *Three on a Honeymoon* from sale in Boston; they announced, moreover, that the movie based on the book would not be shown in Boston theaters.
>
> English teachers are likely to have personal prejudices about little matters of usage; students, consequently, often feel that they have been given conflicting rules.

In general, you should remember that the purpose of punctuation is to establish clarity. And if you will review each of your sentences with a critical eye—that is, as though you were the reader rather than the writer—, you will be able to punctuate for clarity.

The dash

The dash is perhaps the most misunderstood of all marks of punctuation. Many people use it as a sort of elegant or personalized period; the more personal or exciting their writing becomes, the more they substitute dashes for periods, as though such an ordinary mark as a period would diminish the charm of their self-expression. In intimate letters and *billets doux,* dashes may be used at will. But in exposition a dash should never be used as end punctuation.

Other writers (or perhaps the same ones) use dashes as an excuse for writing in fragments, as in the following passage from an essay exam:

> Emerson represented the optimistic school of Romantic thought—self-reliance, individualism and all that stuff—"hitch your wagon to a star." He believed that each person is directly in contact with the Divine—has a personal pipeline to God—so to speak. No need for clergymen—you can reach divine truth by yourself. So you should rely on yourself completely—ignore social convention—be a nonconformist.

If the writer of this passage had not been such a dash addict—had not, indeed, "dashed" off his answer—doubtless he would have written in more complete and coherent sentences. There seems to be something about the dash that leads the careless writer into fragmented discourse. Such a mode of writing makes for very weak exposition.

The dash, then, is not a mark of end punctuation and does not justify fragmented discourse. Instead, it is a mark of internal punctuation with specific uses, as illustrated in the rules below.

Conventionally, no space is left before or after a dash. On the typewriter, two hyphens (--) make a dash.

RULE 1:

Use dashes to set off a parenthetic element (1) that is especially emphatic or (2) that has several commas of its own or (3) that is a sentence construction by itself.

> Our minister—even our beloved, incorruptible minister—succumbed to the pressures of the Society for the Advancement of True and Sacred Democratic Principles.
> The threatening mob—thrill-seekers, bums, criminals, extremists, dupes—was dispersed with tear gas.
> Professor Witter—he was the leader of the faculty group that successfully resisted Midwestern University's Program for Patriotic Education—has been made Chairman of the President's new Commission on Academic Freedom.

RULE 2:
Use a dash to set off a terminal construction that has the tone of a delayed afterthought.

In the popular mind, astronomy and astrology are still often confused—like religion and occultism.

After extensive research, Professor Sackett reported that the lower a family's income, the larger percentage of it they spend on food—hardly a novel discovery.

RULE 3:
A dash may be used to introduce an explanation or explanatory series.

Normally, a colon is used in this structural position; a dash represents a more informal usage.

One alternative to war is uncomplex—surrender.

The first moon colony was plagued with difficulties—mechanical breakdowns, sudden psychological aberrations, showers of meteorites, interruption of radio communication with earth.

RULE 4:
Use a dash to set off a long series from a pronoun or nominal referring to the series.

Course work, desultory reading, social contacts, extracurricular activities, friendly conversations with professors—all of these are important in the education of a college student.

Honesty is the best policy, virtue is its own reward, innocence is its own protection, deceit destroys the deceiver—these are precepts to remember.

RULE 5:
Use a dash to indicate an abrupt structural shift.

This use of the dash is rare in exposition and appears only occasionally in narrative writing: "And then as the traveling salesman—but wait, I forgot to mention the farmer's wife."

Parentheses

The word *parentheses* is plural, for it designates both of the curved marks that go by that name; the singular is *parenthesis*. Spaces are maintained on the outside but not the inside of parentheses.

RULE 1:

Use parentheses to set off an internal or terminal parenthetic element that has a tone of isolation or that is intended as an aside rather than an emphatic addition to the sentence.

In such cases the first word of the parenthetic element is not capitalized and a period is not placed within the parentheses.

> In 1921 Trinity College (later to become Duke University) moved its campus to Durham, North Carolina.
>
> Atomic fission was first demonstrated in 1938 (a year before World War II began).

RULE 2:

Use parentheses to set off a whole sentence or group of sentences parenthetically inserted into a longer passage.

In such cases, the sentences begin with capital letters and the end punctuation is put inside the parentheses.

> In 1929, the stock market collapsed and the Great Depression began. (That was also the year that saw the publication of Hemingway's *A Farewell to Arms,* Wolfe's *Look Homeward, Angel,* and Faulkner's *The Sound and the Fury.* Though economic catastrophe loomed, literature seemed to be entering a period of greatness.) Neither President Hoover, who had been in office only a few months, nor the leaders in Congress seemed to understand the economic forces at work. . . .

RULE 3:

Use parentheses to enclose numerals or letters used to number items in a series.

> Use dashes to set off a parenthetic element (1) that is especially emphatic or (2) that has several commas of its own or (3) that is a sentence construction by itself.

RULE 4:

Use parentheses to enclose cross references and other such interpolated material.

> Epicureanism is the system of moderate and refined hedonism (see axiology) taught by Epicurus (342–270 B.C.).

Brackets

Square brackets should not be confused with parentheses.

RULE 1:

Use brackets to enclose a word or phrase inserted into a direct quotation to replace an otherwise unintelligible reference.

When such a word or phrase is the antecedent of a pronoun, the pronoun may be included or omitted, according to personal preference.

> "He [Professor Billwiller] was granted NSF funds in the amount of $15,000 to continue his researches into the 'Seasonal Changes in Blood Components of Wild Rodents.' "
>
> "[Professor Chapman] denied that he had supplied the editor of the *University Daily* with the literate and well-informed editorials that were reprinted in the *New York Times.*"
>
> "For centuries the study of the sky has been conducted under [the names of astronomy and astrology]."

RULE 2:

Use brackets to enclose the word sic *or other interpolated comments inserted into a direct quotation.*

Sic, meaning *thus* in Latin, is used to indicate that erroneous or startling material actually appeared in the original source itself. In the first example below the name *Dickinson* is misspelled.

> "The poems of Emily Dickenson [sic] are the most exquisite lyrics in American poetry."
>
> "Physicists estimate that ten billion neutrinos [weightless, chargeless particles] pass through each square centimeter on earth every second."

The semicolon

The basic condition governing the use of the semicolon is that the mark is used only between parallel or coordinate elements, that is, elements that are similar in construction.

RULE 1:

Use a semicolon to separate independent clauses in a compound sentence that has no connective word between the clauses.

An espousal of leftist causes ruined the political career of Herman Dougfield; he was even defeated recently in his race for state senator.

Even the closest stars appear only as points of light through the most powerful telescopes; astronomers must use spectroscopes to deduce information about their surfaces.

RULE 2:

Use a semicolon to separate independent clauses joined by a connective other than a coordinating conjunction.

The use of a comma rather than a semicolon in this structural position results in the comma splice.

In California there are over one million more registered Democrats that Republicans; nevertheless, the state often elects Republican officials.

Candidate Cooke felt that integrity and honesty are more important than political victory; therefore he refused to stoop to slander and mud-slinging in his campaigning.

The power of the press is perhaps overrated; for example, Democratic presidents are elected even though more than two-thirds of our newspapers and magizines are Republican.

RULE 3:

Use semicolons rather than commas to separate elements in a series when the elements are long or have internal punctuation of their own.

Note that, since such elements are coordinate, the semicolons are being used between elements of equal rank.

We sent appeals to three foundations: The Coe Fund for Academic Freedom, 925 Melrose, DeKalb, Illinois; The McCall Foundation for Anthropological Studies, 483 Main Street, Umatilla, Oregon; and the Libermann Associates Foundation, 896 Beverley Lane, Philadelphia.

Professor Reifsnyder's researches disclosed that students with I.Q.'s over 140 have a dropout rate greater than those with I.Q.'s of 120 to 125; that students with I.Q.'s of 110 to 120 make better grades in the humanities than in science; and that grades assigned in science classes correspond more closely with student I.Q.'s than grades assigned in humanities classes.

RULE 4:

Do **not** *use a semicolon to separate a dependent clause or phrase from an independent clause.*

The following examples represent an **erroneous** use of semicolons; each semicolon should be replaced by a comma.

Having confronted the Soviet Ambassador with the facts of the case; the U.S. Ambassador to the United Nations waited for his answer to the charges.

Experimental proof of Einstein's theory of relativity is difficult to establish; though almost all scientists assume the validity of the theory.

The categorical imperative; which is the key term in Kant's ethical thought; denotes the supreme moral law. It is unconditional and absolute; admitting of no exceptions since it is in no way relative to some further end.

The colon

The colon is a mark of punctuation used exclusively to introduce a sentence element, sentence, or longer discourse that follows immediately.

RULE 1:

Use a colon after the salutation in a formal letter.

When you want your letter to have a more friendly and informal tone, use a comma after the salutation.

Dear Professor Bierman: (formal)
Dear Professor Bierman, (indication of friendly acquaintance)

RULE 2:

Use a colon after introductory labels.

COLLOQUIAL: It's me.
STANDARD: It's I.

RULE 3:

Use a colon to introduce a series following a noun that establishes the series.

Professor Whitehead made three important points: that religion, like science, must be prepared to change and grow; that the idea of the brotherhood of man rather than of the chosen people must underlie all sound religion; and that a balance must be drawn between the need for a learned clergy and the need for each individual to find his own faith.

Joyce was eclectic in her choice of college subjects: literature, anthropology, physics, comparative religions, ancient history, winemaking, and typing.

RULE 4:

Use a colon to introduce a sentence that acts as an explanation of, rather than a continuation of, the preceding sentence.

The sentence following the colon may be started with a capital letter or not, according to preference.

Teaching is not a 9:00 to 3:00, nine-months-a-year job: every good teacher spends hours a day every day of the year preparing himself for his work.

Enlightened school boards and administrations should insist that every teacher take a sabbatical leave every seventh year: no teacher can stave off staleness unless he undergoes massive intellectual refreshment every few years.

RULE 5:

A colon may be used to introduce a direct quotation, especially a formal or long one.

In protesting the Puritan emphasis on continual busyness, Thoreau said: "Why should we live with such hurry and waste of life? We are determined to be starved before we are hungry. We say that a stitch in time saves nine, and so they take a thousand stitches to-day to save nine to-morrow. As for *work,* we haven't any of any consequence."

Quotation marks

Quotation marks are used to enclose not only direct quotations but also certain other kinds of units that appear within written discourse. In general these units, explained in the rules below, are not parenthetic but are integral parts of the sentence structure.

A mark of punctuation that belongs to an enclosed unit is placed within the quotation marks, as in this example: "Mary Ellen asked, 'Where have you been?' " Note that a period is not used in addition to the question mark even though the whole sentence is a statement rather than a question.

A comma or period is placed within quotation marks even when it is not a part of the enclosed unit, as in this example: " 'Let sleeping dogs lie,' a proverb from *Poor Richard's Almanac,* should have been 'let sleeping babies lie.' " The second version of the proverb could also begin with a capital letter, according to preference.

Other marks of punctuation are put outside the quotation marks when they do not belong to the enclosed unit, as in these examples. Note that the quoted units are not themselves questions.

> Do you really think "the better part of valor is discretion"?
> Why did she say she "wasn't interested"?

RULE 1:
Use quotation marks to enclose direct quotations.

Regardless of the length of a direct quotation, quotation marks are used only at the beginning and end unless there is an unbracketed interruption or unless the quoted material consists of more than one paragraph, in which case marks are not used at the end of a paragraph (except of course the last) but are used at the beginning of each new paragraph. In term papers and other such written discourse, quoted passages of six or fewer lines are usually incorporated with quotation marks directly into the text and those of more than six lines are usually entered as insets, that is, are single-spaced and indented five spaces on the left margin. Inset quotations are **not** enclosed in quotation marks.

When a single-sentence direct quotation is not reported dialogue, it may or may not, according to preference, be capitalized when it comes in the middle of a sentence. Also in such cases a comma is not necessary after the phrase identifying the author. "Thoreau said 'most men live lives of quiet desperation.' " When there is an unbracketed interruption (such as *and* in the following examples), quotation marks are placed before and after the interruption to separate it from the enclosed units.

> Professor Graybo found the book "disarmingly ingenuous" and "subtly provocative."
> We learned from Chairman Cole to "listen well" and "learn fast."

RULE 2:

Use quotation marks to enclose titles of short or minor literary works: short stories, short poems, short plays, chapters from books, articles, essays, songs, and speeches.

The normal convention is to enclose in quotation marks titles that form a part of a larger collection and italicize (underline in script or typewriting) titles of works published as, or long enough to be published as, separate entities. Thus the title *Paradise Lost* is always italicized whether the poem is published separately or as a part of Milton's works, but the title of a sonnet or other short poem from a collection is enclosed in quotation marks.

> "The Fall of the House of Usher," perhaps Poe's best story, is thought by many critics to have a significant theme.
> Have you read Melville's "Bartleby the Scrivener"?
> "Where Art the Snows of Yesteryear?" is a sonnet by Villon.
> The forty-second chapter of *Moby-Dick* is entitled "The Whiteness of the Whale."

RULE 3:

Words used as words may be enclosed in quotation marks, or they may be italicized, according to preference.

> The word "jabberwocky," meaning nonsensical but grammatical phrasing, comes from the poem "Jabberwocky" by Lewis Carroll.
> A word like "scuttlebutt" often gains respectability after a career as slang.
> The word *larruping* is sometimes heard in the Southeast.

RULE 4:

Use quotation marks to enclose a word used in an unusual or ironical sense.

> Hollywood stars feel they must belong to the "right set."
> "Correct" spelling has the sanction of the dictionary, but not of all language sophisticates.

In the first example, the writer indicates that the stars' conception of the right set is not his conception. In the second, the writer means that in his opinion the traditional unphonemic spelling of English as given in dictionaries is really incorrect, that correct spelling is phonemic spelling.

RULE 5:

Avoid enclosing slang words and phrases in quotation marks as an apology for their use.

Questionable usage:

> The heroine of the novel is a "floozy" who likes to "paint the town red."

If you feel a word is worth using, use it without apology. Note the difference between this questionable use of quotation marks and their legitimate use in Rule 4 above.

RULE 6:

Use single quotation marks to enclose a unit within a unit. This has been done in many examples in this chapter.

> Professor Doner's review calls the story "an ingenious adaptation of Poe's 'Cask of Amontillado.' "
> The librarian screamed, "Bring me the book containing 'The Gift of the Magi' right now."

RULE 7:

Use quotation marks to enclose reported dialogue.

If the phrase naming the speaker comes first, place a comma after it and capitalize the first word of the dialogue. Note the difference between this rule and Rule 1 relating to direct quotations not in the form of reported dialogue.

> Professor Connoly said, "Prepare to write on *Finnegan's Wake.*"
> Maurice had cried, "Do not borrow my slide rule, please."

If the phrase naming the speaker comes last, place a comma after the dialogue unless a question mark or exclamation point is called for. Do not use both a comma and a question mark or exclamation point.

> "Turn to page 79," said Professor Cebull.
> "Where did we leave off?" asked Professor Hunter.
> "Keep your eyes on your own paper!" shouted Professor Lowers.

Note that in the second example the whole statement is not a question and that in the third the whole statement is not an exclamation.

If the phrase naming the speaker comes in the middle of a sentence, use commas before and after it and do not capitalize the beginning of the second part. " 'In the second chapter of the text,' said Professor Monteverde, 'the authors have entered erroneous information.' "

If the phrase naming the speaker comes between two sentences of dialogue, use a period after the phrase and start the second sentence with a capital letter. " 'Don't overlook the footnote on page 72,' said Professor Hernandez. 'It is more important than the textual material itself.' "

RULE 8:
Do not use quotation marks to enclose a title used as a title.

When the title of an essay is mentioned within written discourse, it is enclosed in quotation marks, but when it is used as a heading it is not so enclosed. Of course a title may have within it a unit enclosed in quotation marks. Note also that a period is not placed after a title used as a heading.

TITLE AS HEADING: Loopholes in the Usury Laws
TITLE AS HEADING: A Study of Milton's "On His Blindness"

In spite of the rather well defined rules of punctuating written discourse, there remains, as explained above, considerable latitude for you to exercise your own preference. Always, however, clarity should be your goal. Since punctuation for all structural positions cannot be covered by set rules, you should be prepared to use (or omit) any mark of punctuation in any position when the clarity of your sentence will be improved. Punctuation is mostly a science, but it is also partly an art. The more you come to understand the complexities of English sentence structure, the more you will be able to punctuate according to personal design rather than set rules.

Note, for example, the punctuation of the opening sentence of Thoreau's *Walden:*

> When I wrote the following pages, or rather the bulk of them, I lived alone, in the woods, a mile from any neighbor, in a house which I had built myself, on the shore of Walden Pond, in Concord, Massachusetts, and earned my living by the labor of my hands only.

Now it's true that standard punctuation today is different from that of 125 years ago. But Thoreau's sentence is most artfully punctuated, even with its nine commas; not one of them (except perhaps the one after *Concord*) could be omitted without altering the emphasis somewhat. Only great skill can permit a writer to chop a sentence up into so many short phrases. But by paying close attention to sentence structure, you too can develop a more artful sense of punctuation.

EXERCISE 47. Identifying Restrictive and Nonrestrictive Elements

DIRECTIONS: *Some of the adjective clauses and phrases in the following sentences are restrictive and some are nonrestrictive. Identify each and explain why the nonrestrictive elements need to be set off by commas and why the restrictive elements should not be set off.*

1. Authoritarianism is a philosophic point of view which says that the ultimate or most valid source of knowledge is authority of some kind.
2. Philosophers who reject authoritarianism are called relativists.
3. Some philosophers who are relativists in politics are authoritarian in ethics.
4. David Hume who was the most notable English philosopher of the later eighteenth century espoused a philosophy of complete skepticism.
5. Idealist philosophers are those who maintain that the ultimate reality is mind or spirit, not matter.
6. Plato who developed the philosophy of forms is generally regarded as the fountainhead of the philosophy of idealism.
7. Transcendentalism which is a religious philosophy developed in America in the 1830s by Emerson and others is a variety of idealism.
8. Another religion based on the philosophy of idealism is Christian Science which many scholars think was an outgrowth of Transcendentalism.
9. Hawthorne who was a friend of Emerson's rejected Transcendentalism which he felt ignored the problem of evil in man's life.
10. The Book of Job written about 1500 B.C. is a literary discourse on the nature of evil in man's life.
11. Theologians who support the Calvinist doctrines believe that evil in man's life is due to the original sin of Adam and Eve.

12. No religious or philosophic doctrine that is acceptable to all has ever been devised.
13. A question often asked by psychologists is whether a particular behavior pattern manifested in an individual is due to heredity or environment.
14. Professor Newman's point of view which seems logical is that all behavior patterns are due to both heredity and environment.
15. He maintains that no event can happen to you that is not due to both heredity and environment which is to say that nothing can happen to you which your heredity did not provide for and that nothing can happen to you in a nonenvironment.
16. Biochemists and geneticists both of whom work with the chemical determinants of heredity have been carrying on experiments which show that the mechanism of heredity can be altered.
17. It is expected that scientists will soon actually create life in a test tube, an event which will have profound religious and philosophic significance.
18. Even now scientists find a borderline between life and nonlife which suggests that there is no really clear-cut distinction between the living and the nonliving.
19. Some virus-like particles seem to be living material but incapable of reproduction which suggests that the difference between life and nonlife is chemical.
20. The code that is stored chemically in the genes in a human cell is said to contain enough information to fill ten thousand encyclopedic volumes.

EXERCISE 48. Modernizing the Conventions of Usage in Seventeenth-Century Writing

DIRECTIONS: *As best you can, modernize the punctuation, capitalization, spelling, and use of the apostrophe in the following passages from seventeenth-century English writers. Do not alter the diction or word order.*

1. "Nature hath made men so equall, in the faculties of body, and mind; as that though there bee found one man sometimes manifestly stronger in body, or of quicker mind then another; yet when all is reckoned together, the difference between man, and man, is not so considerable, as that one man can thereupon claim himselfe any benefit, to which another may not pretend, as well as he."—Thomas Hobbes, *Leviathan*.
2. "Poor intricated soule! Riddling, perplexed, labyrinthicall

soule! Thou couldest not say, that thou beleevest not in God, if there were no God; Thou couldst not not beleeeve in God, if there were no God; if there were no God, thou couldest not speake, thou couldest not blaspheme the Name of God, thou couldest not sweare, if there were no God: For, all thy faculties, how ever depraved, and perverted by thee, are from him; and except thou canst seriously beleeve, that thou art nothing, thou canst not beleeve that there is no God."—John Donne, *Sermon for the Feast of the Conversion of St. Paul.*

3. "I think it is beyond Question, that *Man has a clear Perception of his own Being;* he knows certainly, that he exists, and that he is something. He that can doubt, whether he be any thing, or no, I speak not to, no more than I would argue with pure nothing, or endeavor to convince Non-entity that it were something. If any one pretend to be so sceptical, as to deny his own Existence, (for really to doubt of it, is manifestly impossible,) let him for me enjoy his beloved Happiness of being nothing, until Hunger, or some other Pain convince him of the contrary. This then, I think, I may take for a Truth, which every ones certain Knowledge assures him of, beyond the liberty of doubting, *viz.* that he is something that actually exists."—John Locke, *An Essay Concerning Humane Understanding.*

4. "The immoderate use of, and indulgence to *Sea-coale* alone in the City of *London,* exposes it to one of the fowlest inconveniences and reproches, than can possibly befall so noble, and otherwise incomparable City: and that, not from the *Culinary* fires, which for being weak, and lesse often fed below, is with such ease dispell'd and scatter'd above, as it is hardly at all discernible, but from some few particular Tunnells and Issues, belonging only to *Brewers, Diers, Lime-burners, Salt,* and *Sope-boylers,* and some other private Trades, *one* of whose *Spiracles* alone, does manifestly infect the *Aer* more than all the Chimnies of *London* put together besides."—John Evelyn, *Fumifugium.*

EXERCISE 49. Analyzing the Uses of Marks of Punctuation

DIRECTIONS: *Explain the use of each mark of punctuation in the following passages. Indicate structural positions where commas are optionally used or could be optionally used.*

1. " 'I couldn't find nobody there.' This sentence, as anybody who will read this probably knows, contains a double negative, a construction with a fascinating history. Today in all parts of the

English-speaking world, its use or avoidance is one of the clearest marks of differentiation between social groups. Among those who have had little formal schooling and whose social and occupational status is relatively low, the construction is extremely common. Among the well-educated and more 'privileged,' it is rare almost to the point of non-existence. In many circles, in fact, a double negative uttered by a presumably educated person would cause the same embarrassed silence as a loud belch in church.

"In earlier English, the doubling, tripling, or even quadrupling of negatives was frequent even in the most formal literary styles. King Alfred, for example, in a translation made late in the ninth century, writes a sentence which in modern form would read: 'No man had never yet heard of no ship-army.' A little later, in the oldest English version of the Gospels, we read: 'The five foolish maidens took lamps, but didn't take no oil with them.' In the fourteenth century, Chaucer writes of his 'gentle knight' that 'in all his life he hasn't never yet said nothing discourteous to no sort of person' (four negatives!). As late as Shakespeare's time, the construction was still possible in Standard English, particularly in speech. Thus, in *Romeo and Juliet,* when Mercutio is confronted by Tybalt he cries out, 'I will not budge for no man's pleasure.' "—Allan F. Hubbell, "Multiple Negation."

2. "The one phenomenon which has invariably accompanied [writing] is the formation of cities and empires: the integration into a political system, that is to say, of a considerable number of individuals, and the distribution of these individuals into a hierarchy of castes and classes. Such is, at any rate, the type of development which we find, from Egypt right across to China, at the moment when writing makes its debut; it seems to favour rather the exploitation than the enlightenment of mankind. This exploitation made it possible to assemble work-people by the thousand and set them tasks that taxed them to the limits of their strength: to this, surely, we must attribute the beginnings of architecture as we know it. If my hypothesis is correct, the primary function of writing, as a means of communication, is to facilitate the enslavement of other human beings. The use of writing for disinterested ends, and with a view to satisfactions of the mind in the fields either of science or the arts, is a secondary result of its invention—and may even be no more than a way of reinforcing, justifying, or dissimulating its primary function."—John Russell, tr., Claude Lévi-Strauss, *Tristes Tropiques.*

3. "Everyone knows that our sun is a star, that it has a group of planets circling around, relatively close to it—ranging from the planet Mercury nearest the sun, out to tiny Pluto, the most distant

planet. Suppose we go beyond Pluto and off toward the next star which is the nearest neighbor to the sun, the star called by the astronomers Alpha Centauri. How long would it take us to reach that star and explore its vicinity for other planets? Well, the time required, of course, would depend upon how fast we could travel. I might point out, however, that if we could get away from the gravitational pull of both earth and sun, and still have a speed of twenty miles per second, then to reach Alpha Centauri would take forty thousand years. Even if we could speed up our spacecraft, after getting away from the sun, to the unimaginable speed of two hundred miles per second, it would take four thousand years to reach the very nearest star. Other stars—even the relatively nearer ones in our own Milky Way—would require millions or hundreds of millions of years of travel time. I suggest that we cross off our list of near-term objectives any journeys to the vicinity of other stars."— L. A. DuBridge, "A Scientist Calls for Common Sense."

4.   "At this late hour of the world's history, books are to be found in almost every room in the house—in the nursery, in the drawing room, in the dining room, in the kitchen. But in some houses they have become such a company that they have to be accommodated with a room of their own—a reading room, a library, a study. Let us imagine that we are now in such a room; that it is a sunny room, with windows opening on a garden, so that we can hear the trees rustling, the gardener talking, the donkey braying, the old women gossiping at the pump—and all the ordinary processes of life pursuing the casual irregular way which they have pursued these many hundreds of years. As casually, as persistently, books have been coming together on the shelves. Novels, poems, histories, memoirs, dictionaries, maps, directories; black-letter books and brand new books; books in French and Greek and Latin; of all shapes and sizes and values, bought for purposes of research, bought to amuse a railway journey, bought by miscellaneous beings, of one temperament and another, serious and frivolous, men of action and men of letters."— Virginia Woolf, *The Second Common Reader*.

5.   "Charles Darwin was born in Shrewsbury, England, in 1809, the year in which Lamarck published his theory of evolution through the transmission of acquired characters. At the age of nine, like most English boys in families of considerable means, Darwin was sent to a near-by private boarding school. There he did nothing to suggest that he would grow up to be the prime mover in a major scientific revolution. 'Nothing could have been worse for my mind than Dr. Butler's school,' he later wrote. . . .

'Much attention was paid to learning by heart; this I could effect with great facility, learning forty or fifty lines of Virgil or Homer whilst I was in morning chapel; but this exercise was utterly useless for every verse was forgotten in forty-eight hours.'

"Darwin was not a loafer, however, and he studied even those subjects that he disliked. In the meantime he developed strong interests in extracurricular matters. He became an avid collector of shells, coins, minerals, and insects, especially beetles. He was specially fond of bird shooting and of long hikes through the beautiful English countryside. Through application to his studies, rather than an interest in them, Darwin qualified for admission to university work and spent three years at Edinburgh studying medicine and then another three at Cambridge studying theology. His spare time he devoted to learning everything he could about the subjects he really loved—botany, zoology, and geology. 'Although . . . there were some redeeming features in my life at Cambridge,' he writes in his autobiography, 'my time was sadly wasted there, and worse than wasted. From my passion for shooting and for hunting, and, when this failed, for riding across country, I got into a sporting set, some dissipated and low-minded young men. We often used to dine together in the evening, though these dinners often included men of a higher stamp . . . with jolly singing and playing at cards afterwards. . . . I know I ought to feel ashamed of days and evenings thus spent, but as some of my friends were very pleasant, and we were all in the highest spirits, I cannot help looking back to these times with much pleasure.' Actually, while cultivating these extracurricular interests, Darwin did not neglect to pass his examinations creditably, and he had 'many other friends of a widely different nature' who interested him in music and art, subjects in which, to his regret, he later lost interest almost entirely."—Thomas S. Hall and Florence Moog, *Life Science*.

EXERCISE 50.   Punctuating Written Discourse

DIRECTIONS: *All marks of punctuation except end punctuation have been omitted from the following passages. Indicate the structural positions where punctuation is needed and suggest a suitable mark of punctuation for each position.*

1.   "When we distinguished between the various kinds of general statements we noted that there are some statements which can be confirmed by observation or experimentation or both. Other

sweeping assertions seem to resist being confirmed by these means. Even though a substantial body of evidence may appear to support such truths that evidence often is capable of different interpretations depending on who does the interpreting. One man will believe a certain truth because his personal background his tastes and temperament everything that makes him an individual distinct from other men incline him to do so. Another man will reject the same assumption because he has a different background different tastes and a different temperament. In trying to understand the judgment of a person therefore we must always be aware of the way that individual differences affect the understanding and interpreting of human experience.

"If someone were to assert that Beethoven was born in the eighteenth century and someone else were to maintain that he was born in the nineteenth the two could settle the argument by consulting certain historical records which they agreed would tell the truth of the matter. But a similar disagreement over whether Beethoven was a greater composer than Brahms that is composed finer music cannot be settled so definitely. Nor indeed would the two parties be likely even to agree on a way by which they could come to a meeting of minds. It is a question of taste and a meeting of minds may be impossible."—Richard D. Altick, *Preface to Critical Reading*.

2. "There have been at different times and among different people many varying conceptions of the good life. To some extent the differences were amenable to argument this was when men differed as to the means to achieve a given end. Some think that prison is a good way of preventing crime others hold that education would be better. A difference of this sort can be decided by sufficient evidence. But some differences cannot be tested in this way. Tolstoy condemned all war others have held the life of a soldier doing battle for the right to be very noble. Here there was probably involved a real difference as to ends. Those who praised the soldier usually consider the punishment of sinners a good thing in itself Tolstoy did not think so. On such a matter no argument is possible. I cannot therefore prove that my view of the good life is right I can only state my views and hope that as many as possible will agree. My view is this The good life is one inspired by love and guided by knowledge."—Bertrand Russell, *Why I Am Not a Christian*.

3. "The overseas libraries are plagued by problems similar to those which beset libraries in the United States they are perpetually short of money manpower and space. In addition they are faced with other difficulties owing to their location abroad and

their relationship to Congress. Because their relatively small collections must retain balance the libraries are never able to stock enough books on any one subject to satisfy specialists. Visiting Americans including historians educators musicians artists religionists economists sociologists and experts in other fields frequently complain about the lack of books and magazines representing their specialites. Liberals tend to find a preponderance of material on the conservative side while conservatives see the opposite. This is particularly true of religious groups some of which go through our catalogues with great care and complain loudly if they think we lean toward Catholic or Protestant authors. Congressmen apart from expressing their own preferences are obliged to serve as outlets for opinions expressed often in strong language by their constituents. Selection of books requires a combination of common sense and courage. It is not an easy task."—George V. Allen, "Books and the American Image."

VERB FORMS

One of the most obvious distinctions between the language usage of those with and those without formal education is the verb forms that each group uses. The pattern of verb usage in standard English is rather rigidly established, while that in vulgate (or nonstandard) is variable. For example, standard usage allows only the forms in the left-hand column below, whereas vulgate usage does not distinguish between the forms in the right-hand column.

I saw	I saw, I seen
I have seen	I have saw, I have seen
I took	I took, I taken
I have taken	I have took, I have taken
I knew	I knew, I knowed
I have known	I have knew, I have knowed, I have known
they were	they was, they were

An individual unaffected, or only slightly affected, by formal education may use the variant forms above indiscriminately, without being aware that in one sentence he has said "I saw" and in another "I seen."

The reason for the considerable rigidity in standard and variability in nonstandard usage is that educated people adhere to the usage patterns established and maintained traditionally in schools, whereas the uneducated absorb variable forms from their non-school environment and use them unconsciously. A few variable forms exist in standard usage because textbooks and teachers since the eighteenth century, when grammarians began crystallizing formal English usage, have not been able to establish unanimous opinion in all cases and also because at any given point in time some language forms will be in the process of change, so that for a while two forms may exist side by side. For example, standard usage still allows these variant forms:

> I dived, I dove
> I have showed, I have shown
> I lighted, I lit (the cigaret)
> I have proved, I have proven
> I waked, I woke

The problem of verb form is strictly one of grammar, not of diction. It is grammatical form and not word choice that varies in the above examples, for the lexical (dictionary) meaning of *know, knew, known, knowed, have known, should have known,* and so forth is the same. The various forms indicate differences in time of occurrence (tense), in number involved (number), and in attitude of speaker (mood), but they do not indicate differences in word definition.

The problem is not only one of grammar rather than diction, but also of social acceptability rather than clarity, for none of the forms used in vulgate language is ever ambiguous to educated ears unless it is also ambiguous to vulgate speakers. For example, the use of *was* instead of *were* for plural meaning never results in ambiguity, for the plurality is also indicated in another way, such as "*they* was." The sentence "he knowed I taken his money" is just as clear and meaningful as "he knew I took his money." Verb form in English, then, is a matter of conventional usage. Educated Americans simply tacitly agree to accept some forms, but not others accepted by the uneducated.

Social prejudice against vulgate usage does not extend to its appearance in literature. In fact, in that context the prejudice may even be transformed into admiration. Almost everyone would agree that the following passage from "Two Soldiers" by William Faulkner is beautiful and that the short story itself is great literature:

I seen all the towns. I seen all of them. When the bus got to going good, I found out I was jest about wore out for sleep. But there was too much I hadn't never saw before. We run out of Jefferson and run past fields and woods, then we would run into another town and out of that un and past stores and gins and water tanks, and we run along by the railroad for a spell and I seen the signal arm move, and then I seen the train and then some more towns, and I was jest about plumb wore out for sleep, but I couldn't resk it. Then Memphis begun. It seemed like, to me, it went on for miles. We would pass a patch of stores and I would think that was sholy it and the bus would even stop. But it wouldn't be Memphis yet and we would go on again past water tanks and smokestacks on top of mills, and if they was gins and sawmills, I never knowed there was that many and I never seen any that big, and where they got enough cotton and logs to run um I don't know.

The language usage in this passage is perfectly acceptable to educated ears when used in literature, but not when used naturally by real human beings. Of course Faulkner transformed the vulgate usage into literary art.

The social prejudice against vulgate verb forms carries with it a suspicion that a user of such forms is not likely to know what he is talking about, since he is obviously uneducated. However, this suspicion is shown to be more social than intellectual, for whenever a sophisticated American encounters a true vulgate document that clearly is sound in subject matter—such as a diary of a common soldier or a mountaineer's account of moonshining—he is quite willing to ignore the vulgate usage (or even find it charming) in his eagerness to read the material itself.

Another interesting corollary of this social prejudice is that many highly educated Americans love to play around with vulgate usage when there is no danger of their play being mistaken for ignorance. For example, many English teachers, in the presence of their social peers, like to use such expressions as "I brung it," "have you thunk it over," "who dolt the cards," "she clang to him tightly," and "he squoze her tenderly." In a situation that doesn't permit such social freedom, most educated Americans would be as likely to belch at a formal banquet as to use vulgate forms. Language usage is perhaps more subject to social prejudice than any other noncriminal aspect of human behavior.

Verb forms in tense, mood, and voice

All finite verbs have tense, mood, and voice. *Tense* is a grammatical term having to do (chiefly) with time of occurrence. The three simple tenses are of course the past, the present, and the future, but English tenses become complicated because of such forms as past perfect, present progressive, future perfect progressive, and so forth. *Mood* is a grammatical term having to do with the attitude of the speaker. The three moods are the indicative (which makes a statement), the imperative (which issues a request or command), and the subjunctive (which indicates an obligation or a condition). *Voice* has to do with whether the subject performs the action (the verb is then in the active voice) or whether it receives the action (the verb is then in the passive voice). The forms required by tense, voice, and mood make the grammar of English verbs frightening. Consider these forms: *go, went, have gone, will go, is going, was going, will be going, will have been going, will have been gone, shall go, shall be going, shall have been going, shall have been gone, shall be gone, was gone, were gone, should go, should have gone, should have been gone, should have been going, could go, could have gone, could have been gone, could have been going, might go, might have gone, might have been gone, might be gone, might be going, ought to go, ought to have gone, ought to be going, ought to have been going, may go, may have gone, may have been gone, may have been going, can go, can be gone, can be going, can have been going, was to go, was to have gone, was to have been gone, do go, did go,* and so on.

An organization of such verb forms into coherent groups is known as *conjugation*. In years past, school children had to memorize the various perfect and progressive as well as simple tenses, and also the indicative, imperative, and subjunctive mood forms and active and passive voice forms for each of the tenses. It was enough to terrify the conscientious and to make hardened linguistic criminals of the rebellious. Fortunately, such a study of tense and mood is now abandoned. Probably not one English teacher in twenty could now give a full scheme of conjugation of any one verb, with proper terminology, without checking in an old, traditional grammar book. *The truth is that even for standard usage, verbs take care of themselves except for confusion of the simple past and the past participle forms of a few verbs.* A study of tense, mood, and voice is interesting to those who want to know grammar just for the sake of knowing it, but such a study has little value in improving the correctness of one's usage. The range of mistakes made in verb forms is really very narrow.

The so-called principal parts of verbs are the present (infinitive form without the *to*), the simple past, the past participle, and the present participle (both of these last two being used with an auxiliary, such as *have* or *are*). The forms of **regular** verbs are as follows:

Present	Past	Past Participle	Present Participle
walk	walked	(have) walked	(are) walking
explain	explained	(have) explained	(are) explaining

Regular verbs give no trouble to anyone.

The principal parts of **irregular** verbs involve more complexity and do give trouble to those who have vestiges of vulgate forms in their speech but who are trying to learn standard grammatical usage. The present participle of irregular verbs has the regular *ing* ending, and thus gives no trouble. The other principal parts are sometimes confused, as *saw* for *seen, run* for *ran, swum* for *swam,* and so forth, and this limited confusion accounts for most nonstandard verb usage. Occasionally, mistakes are also made in mood, as *if I was king* for *if I were king*. On a regular college level, however, few students make mistakes in tense and mood forms of verbs, and the whole matter may be ignored for our purposes. The following list of the principal parts of the most troublesome verbs is given here for reference, not for textual study. (Since all present participles are regular, they are not included here.)

Present	Past	Past Participle
begin	began	(have) begun
blow	blew	(have) blown
break	broke	(have) broken
bring	brought	(have) brought
choose	chose	(have) chosen
climb	climbed	(have) climbed
come	came	(have) come
deal	dealt	(have) dealt
do	did	(have) done
draw	drew	(have) drawn

Present	Past	Past Participle
drink	drank	(have) drunk
drive	drive	(have) driven
eat	ate	(have) eaten
fall	fell	(have) fallen
flee	fled	(have) fled
fly	flew	(have) flown
freeze	froze	(have) frozen
give	gave	(have) given
go	went	(have) gone
grow	grew	(have) grown
know	knew	(have) known
lead	led	(have) led
ride	rode	(have) ridden
ring	rang	(have) rung
run	ran	(have) run
see	saw	(have) seen
send	sent	(have) sent
shake	shook	(have) shaken
sing	sang	(have) sung
speak	spoke	(have) spoken
swim	swam	(have) swum
take	took	(have) taken
throw	threw	(have) thrown
wear	wore	(have) worn
write	wrote	(have) written

One distinction needs to be made between certain verb forms used in the subjunctive mood in an *if* clause.

> STANDARD: If the Governor *had* been re-elected, he would have commuted the Ripper's sentence to life imprisonment.
>
> COLLOQUIAL AT BEST: If the Governor *would have* been re-elected, he would have commuted the Ripper's sentence to life imprisonment.

> STANDARD: If I *had* had an MA degree, I would have got the job.
>
> COLLOQUIAL AT BEST: If I *would have* had an MA degree, I would have got the job.

The verb usage in the second (colloquial) examples seems to be on the increase, and it may some day be standard usage. At this time, it should be avoided.

Verb forms in subject-verb agreement

Verb forms vary not only in tense, mood, and voice, but also, in a few cases, in number.[4] *Number* is a grammatical term having to do with, obviously, the number of units involved. In English grammar there are only two numbers: singular (one) and plural (more than one). (Some languages have more than two numbers.) Nouns and pronouns[5] in English have number: *man-men, it-they, this-these.* When a noun or pronoun is used as the subject of a verb, the verb agrees in number with the subject. Fortunately, however, the singular and the plural of most English verb forms are identical, thus precluding mistakes in subject-verb agreement.

The use in English of the same form of a verb for both singular and plural usage creates very little ambiguity, for there is almost always some other aspect of the sentence that also shows number. For example, there can be no ambiguity in the following, though the same verb form is used:

The man walked.   The men walked.

Similarly, there would be no ambiguity in these forms if both were standard:

He has money.   They has money.

The reason there can be so many variant verb forms in vulgate language is that in structure English is so redundant that the necessary information is often entered in a sentence in several different ways. Hence such forms as *we was, they was,* and *he were* offer no ambiguity in number.

On rare occasions the failure to make a distinction in number in verb form can lead to ambiguity. For example, the following sentence is ambiguous because the verb form *can be* is both singular and plural: "Bathing beauties can be fun." Rewrite the sentence with a verb form that does change with number and the ambiguity vanishes:

Bathing beauties are fun. Bathing beauties is fun.

---

[4] Only one case of variation in verb form according to *person* remains in English: *I am.*

[5] In the new grammar many of the words formerly called *pronouns* or *possessive adjectives* are now called *markers* or *determiners.*

In actual practice, however, such ambiguity seldom occurs. And in fact, stress in oral language would remove the ambiguity from the first example above.

Except for the verb *to be,* verb forms in English vary in number only in the present tense, indicative mood. One form is used for the third person singular present tense:

Subject	*Verb Form*
he	walks
she	eats
it	runs
one	sneers
everybody	speaks
everyone	knows
person	flies
thing	brings
nothing	has

Another form is used for all other subjects:

Subject	*Verb Form*
I	walk
you	eat
they	run
all	sneer
persons	speak
things	fly
many	have

Such a distinction in number is made in both the present and simple past of the verb *to be:*

Subject	*Verb form*
you	are, were
they, things	are, were
he, thing	is, was

In all other past and all future tenses and in all forms involving imperative and subjunctive moods, the verb form is the same for both the singular and the plural.

The following rules cover all common structural patterns that cause trouble in subject-verb agreement. These rules are based on what actually happens in the writing of educated Americans, not on pre-established grammatical dicta.

RULE 1:

A prepositional phrase intervening between subject and verb does not affect the verb form.

A list of banned books was (not *were*) posted in the library.

The scoutmaster together with six members of his troop is (not *are*) representing Council 8 in Washington.

The Mayor as well as the Councilmen refuses (not *refuse*) to endorse Measure A.

If a noun phrase begins with *and* but is separated from the subject and verb by commas, it also has no effect on the verb. "Finite Mathematics, and other courses similar to it, has (not *have*) been widely adopted throughout the country." If the commas were removed from this sentence, the subject would then be compound and the proper verb form would be *have*.

RULE 2:

The indefinite pronouns one, each, either, neither, everyone, everybody, *and so on are singular and require singular verbs.*

Each of the buses is (not *are*) supposed to carry forty students.

Either of the answers happens (not *happen*) to be acceptable.

The indefinite pronouns none *and* any *may take either a singular or a plural verb form.*

None of you is (or *are*) qualified.

Has (or *have*) any of you read Maritain's *The Range of Reason?*

RULE 3:

The indefinite pronouns few, several, many, *and* some *take plural verb forms.*

Several were (not *was*) accepted for membership.

A few are (not *is*) sufficient for this experiment.

RULE 4:

A compound subject (two or more elements joined by and) *is plural and requires a plural verb form.* (See exceptions in Rule 6 following.)

One Republican and one Democrat were (not *was*) appointed to the committee.

A book of instructions and a pad for taking notes have (not *has*) been provided for each member.

Both a letter and a telegram have (not *has*) been sent.

RULE 5:

In the constructions either (neither) . . . or (nor) *and* not only . . . but also, *the verb agrees with the element of the subject closest to the verb.*

The conjunction *or* by itself sometimes functions as *either . . . or.*

Either the Mayor or the members of the Council are responsible for Measure A.

Either the members of the Council or the Mayor is (not *are*) responsible for Measure A.

Not only the Mayor but also the members of the Council defend Proposition B.

Not only the members of the Council but also the Mayor defends (not *defend*) Proposition B.

The maid or my parents are at home.

My parents or the maid is (not *are*) at home.

RULE 6:

Subjects which are compound in appearance but which function as singular units may take singular verbs.

Some gas and dust actually shows up in photography.— *Scientific American.*

Disparate clatter and chatter has fascinated linguists.—*Time.*

Your rattling and banging is giving me a headache.

A woman's sweetness and gentleness is a civilizing force.

Sighing and swooning is the way to attract the sentimental man.

Cussing and growling is no way to fix a flat.

When a plural verb form sounds natural, it may also be used with such a construction: "Grousing and growling are no way to curry favor with the sergeant."

RULE 7:

When a form of the verb to be *connects a subject of one number with a subject complement of another number, the verb agrees in number with the subject.*

Cars are Detroit's chief product.
Detroit's chief product is cars.
The stars were the cause of my proposal.
The cause of my proposal was the stars.

RULE 8:

The so-called collective nouns—family, crew, team, series, crowd, group, number, *and so on—may take either singular or plural verb forms, depending on which form sounds most natural to the user.*

Often either form sounds natural, and then either form must be considered correct. A singular verb form is always correct with these words unless a plural form is needed to keep the sentence from being nonsense.

A number of spectators were (or *was*) hurt in the crash.
A number of students has (or *have*) been expelled.
My family are taking separate vacations.
The crew are on their way to their battle stations.
The team is (or *are*) in good physical shape.
A series of coincidences has (or *have*) disrupted our program.

RULE 9:

Nouns that are plural in form but singular in meaning—civics, economics, mathematics, politics, physics, mechanics, acoustics, statistics, athletics, mumps, measles, checkers, *and so on* —*normally take singular verb forms.*

When a plural verb form sounds natural, however, it may be used with such a noun.

Economics is (not *are*) a difficult course for me.
Athletics is (or *are*) good for character building.
Measles is (or *are*) preventable with a new vaccine.

RULE 10:

A plural noun that establishes a weight, measurement, period of time, or amount of money normally takes a singular verb form.

When such a noun clearly indicates a plurality of units, however, it takes a plural verb form. When either a singular or plural verb form sounds natural with such a plural noun, then either must be considered correct.

One hundred and fifteen pounds is (not *are*) a good weight for an eighteen-year-old girl.

Thirty-six inches is (not *are*) not only a yard but also an ideal in beauty contests.

In the nineteenth century two years was (or *were*) not considered too long for an engagement.

Ten dollars is (not *are*) too much for a parking fine.

Three cents is (not *are*) the correct price.

Three cents were (or *was*) lying on the piano.

Three dollar bills were (not *was*) stolen from my wallet.

Two gallons of gasoline is (or *are*) all I can afford.

RULE 11:

In the there . . . *and* here . . . *constructions, the verb agrees in number with the subject, which follows the verb.*

There is one important reason why I believe in metempsychosis.

There are (not *is*) two reasons for his defection.

Here comes an expert in verbal gymnastics.

Here come (not *comes*) two petty officers properly ranked.

RULE 12:

In inverted sentence order, the verb agrees in number with the subject, which follows the verb.

Lined against the wall were (not *was*) six spies awaiting execution.

Behind the rose bushes sits (not *sit*) the complacent gardener.

RULE 13:

A verb phrase used as a subject always takes a singular verb form.

Hiring someone because he is related to you *is* called nepotism.

To expedite relief for those damaged by natural disasters *is* a primary function of the Red Cross.

Denying others the right to their opinions *makes* you a slave to your own.

RULE 14:

In a subordinate clause with a relative pronoun—who, which, that—as the subject, the verb agrees in number with the antecedent of the relative pronoun.

The *theory that was* most strongly supported was that advertising is the chief stimulant of the American desire to improve social status.

The *theories that were* most quickly discredited had already been advanced two decades earlier.

Professor Profant is one of those *critics who are* (not *is*) trying to revive certain elements of eighteenth-century esthetic theory.

Professor Nichols is one of the *supporters* of the BTAC *who urge* (not *urges*) a campaign of letter-writing to Congressmen.

Professor Freligh is the *one who seems* most reluctant to establish a precedent in promotion by seniority.

EXERCISE 51. Subject-Verb Agreement

DIRECTIONS: *Comment on the verb forms—present tense, indicative mood or past tense of* to be—*that can be used in the blanks in the following sentences.*

1. He is one professor who _____ willing to listen to students.
2. He is one of those professors who _____ dogmatic and narrow-minded.
3. Baby-sitting for the Joneses _____ an onerous task.
4. Lining the top shelf _____ twenty-odd volumes of Shakespeare's plays.
5. There _____ six Shakespeare festivals in England each year.
6. Thirteen dollars _____ a rather exorbitant price for a theater ticket.
7. Economics _____ one of my most difficult college subjects.
8. A series of fire drills _____ held yesterday.
9. Florida's chief agricultural product _____ oranges.
10. Singing and cheering _____ a habit with our football fans.
11. Not only the Joneses but also my father _____ taking the 3:30 flight.
12. Either Jackie or the twins _____ supposed to stay at home.
13. One junior and one senior _____ appointed to the Advisory Council.

14. Few if any freshmen _____ allowed to sit in the Student Council.
15. Each of the runnersup _____ given a $500 scholarship.
16. The professor as well as his students _____ happy to have a holiday.
17. A crowd of hungry orphans _____ patiently waiting for the CARE official to finish his speech.
18. The quarterback together with three others of the backfield _____ to quit before Saturday's game.
19. The Pleiades and one other constellation in the area of Andromeda _____ selected for close study during the semester.
20. The frug as well as other suggestive dance routines _____ banned from half-time shows.
21. A number of honor students _____ selected to attend a Chamber of Commerce meeting.
22. The soil in the three large plots _____ different from that in the two small ones.
23. The acoustics in our theater _____ perfect.
24. Two gallons of grape-ade _____ consumed at Billy's birthday party.
25. Lining both sides of the street _____ a stand of ancient live oaks.
26. There _____ many who will take exception to that assumption.
27. Running counter to Professor Wicklund's theory _____ the findings of Professor Frenz.
28. Hiring unreliable thugs _____ Professor Wattrous's downfall.
29. Checkers _____ more strategic skill than chess.
30. Two acres _____ a large residential lot.
31. Thirteen dollars _____ the sale price.
32. Calendars _____ a chief advertising medium for patent medicines.
33. An important local source of power _____ earth-filled dams.
34. The whole group _____ democratic.
35. A group of professors _____ interviewed on "People Are Funny."

PRONOUN FORMS

The two basic divisions of grammar are word order (syntax) and word form (morphology). To deliver meaning in any language, words must be put in proper grammatical (syntactical) arrangement and in proper grammatical (morphological) form. In delivering meaning, languages vary in their relative dependence on word order and word form. English grammar depends more on word order and less on word form than the grammar of most other languages. For example, the following two sentences, though composed of identical word forms, have different meanings:

The goat butted the sergeant.
The sergeant butted the goat.

In English, rearrangement of the words without alteration of their forms results in different meaning, for word order rather than word form determines which noun is the subject and which the object.

In many languages, such rearrangement of word order does not alter meaning. For example, the following Spanish sentences have identical meaning even though their word order varies:

La cabra pegó al sargento.
Al sargento pegó la cabra.

These two German sentences, with different word order, also have the same meaning:

Der Kater frass den Vogel.
Den Vogel frass der Kater.

These pairs of sentences in Spanish and German, though different in word order, can have identical meanings because in those languages word form rather than word order can determine whether a noun is a subject or object.

Inflection (an aspect of morphology) is the general grammatical term applied to the change of word form for different sentence functions. Inflection changes only word form, not lexical meaning. For example, the words *is, are, was, were, has been, may be,* and so forth do not vary in lexical meaning; they are all inflected forms of the verb *to be.* Tense, mood, and voice are phases of verb inflection.

The grammatical term *case* is applied to the phase of inflection that has to do with the change in form of nouns and pronouns. For example, in the previous German sentences *den Vogel* is a noun in the objective case and therefore is the object of the verb *frass* in both sentences. For that noun to be the subject of the verb, its form would have to be *der Vogel.* Similarly, the article *al* in the Spanish sentences makes *sargento* an object, regardless of its position in the sentence. Only the form *el sargento* can serve as a subject. In English, of course, the form *the sergeant* can be either a subject or an object, depending on word order.

Languages vary in their number of case forms. Classical Greek and Latin have five cases, plus vestiges of two others. Some primitive languages have more than a dozen. In English, cases have been reduced to three: (1) the subjective (or nominative), in which the noun or pronoun acts as a subject; (2) the objective (or accusative), in which the noun or pronoun acts as an indirect object or object of a verb, verbal, or preposition; and (3) the possessive (genitive), in which the noun or pronoun shows ownership.

The possessive case of English nouns calls for proper use of an ' or *'s*, as explained earlier. In the subjective and objective cases, all English nouns have exactly the same form. Thus a mistake in noun form due to confusion of the two cases is not possible, as it would be in many other languages. It is the important role of word order in modern English that allows English nouns to have identical subjective- and objective-case forms. Less than a thousand years ago, English was still a highly inflected language and depended less on word order and more on word form for meaning.

Unfortunately, all English pronouns do not, like English nouns, have identical subjective- and objective-case forms. Some do: *you* (compare the old *thou* and *thee* forms), *it, which, this, that, these,* and *those.* And the distinction between *who* and *whom* is slowly being eroded. But several English pronouns still have different subjective and objective case forms: *I-me, we-us, he-him, she-her,* and *they-them.* In theory, it may seem illogical to use the singular form *it* for both cases, while distinguishing between the plural forms *they* and *them*; but grammar though always functional, is not necessarily logical.

So far as clarity and logic are concerned, pronoun-case forms (except for the possessive) are obsolete in English. A mistake in pronoun form almost never obscures meaning; it only reduces the social acceptability of a spoken or written utterance. Thus proper choice of pronoun form is a matter of conventional usage. We are often amused to hear small children wrestle with pronoun forms, as in such sentences as "my don't like she" and "she's wagging she's tail." But when used by adults, such constructions as "just between you and I" and "John and him volunteered" may bring raised eyebrows, if not covert sneers. Pronoun usage, like verb usage, is one

of the obvious yardsticks of social and educational attainment. The
following words of caution, stated as rules, cover the main structural positions that cause confusion of pronoun forms.

RULE 1:

Compound elements do not affect pronoun-case form.

Perhaps the most common source of error in pronoun form is
due to the confusion that may arise when pronouns are used in
compound elements. The most illiterate native speaker of English
never uses constructions such as these:

> Me received a draft notice.
> Her wants to marry I.
> My father bought a watch for I.

Yet constructions like these are common in vulgate English:

> John and me received draft notices.
> Her and me want to get married.

And even highly educated Americans are often heard to use such
constructions as these:

> My father bought watches for John and I.
> Between you and I, I am glad to join the Army.

There is something about compound elements that makes the
wrong pronoun form sound correct, when a single wrong pronoun
in the same construction would not sound correct.

When in doubt, you may test for the proper pronoun form in
a compound element by dropping one part of the element and
listening to the sound of one pronoun by itself. For example, your
ear will not approve of these constructions:

> You shouldn't be seen with I.
> Him is an undercover agent.

Therefore you should also reject these constructions:

> You shouldn't be seen with Peggy and I.
> Professor Verhine and him are undercover agents.

Dropping one part of the compound element will almost always
make the proper pronoun form apparent.

Mistakes in pronoun form in compound elements usually

come after the prepositions *between* and *for*. Be careful always to use the objective-case form of pronouns after those two prepositions, as in these examples:

between you and me
between him and her
between her and them
between us and them
between Phil and me
for Phil and me
for him and us
for her and them
for you and me

Note: When *for* is used as a coordinating conjunction, pronouns in the subjective case may follow it: "John stopped for a chat, for he and I were to work on the nominating committee." The second *for* in this sentence is not a preposition and thus does not require pronouns in the objective case.

RULE 2:

In semiformal or formal writing, the subjective-case form is used after a form of the verb to be.

The verb *to be* is a linking verb, not an action verb, and therefore does not take an object. The word is literally the same as an equals mark in mathematics; what is on one side is equal to what is on the other side. Consequently a subject form of a pronoun is used on both sides of a *to be* verb.

It is I.
That was she.
Can it be he?
Was it they who called?
The chairman is she.
The guilty ones were we.
You must be he.

The subjective pronoun forms are always correct after a form of the verb *to be*. But in colloquial language, objective forms must also be considered correct. In casual conversation, even well-educated people are likely to use such forms as these:

It's me.

I do believe it's her.
Are you sure it was them?

No stigma should be attached to such colloquial usage.

RULE 3:

In semiformal or formal writing, who (whoever) *is the subjective form and* whom (whomever) *the objective form.*

In colloquial language *who (whoever)* may be used for both cases. *Whom (whomever)* should never be used as a subject.

The distinction between *who* and *whom* is disappearing; within two or three generations *who* is likely to be the only nonpossessive form (as is now the case with *you*). Currently, however, correct written language calls for proper use of the two forms.

Several structural positions cause confusion between the two forms. One of these positions occurs in questions that open with the interrogative pronoun *who* or *whom.* In conversation most educated speakers use *who* to open all such questions, because *who* sounds natural at the beginning of a question:

Who were you talking to?
Who did they choose?
Who did the Dean expell?
Who did the professor say made an A?

Actually, only the fourth example here is grammatically correct, for in the other three *who* is an object, which means that the grammatical form should be *whom.* In colloquial language, however, *who* is fully acceptable in all such questions.

In a formal situation, a distinction should be made between *who* and *whom.* You may choose the correct form by testing. First change the question into an indicative construction:

_____ were you talking to?
You were talking to _____.
_____ did they choose?
They did choose _____.
_____ did the professor say made an A?
The professor did say _____ made an A.

With such a change in structure, the subjective or objective form of the pronoun becomes clear.

If with such a change in structure, however, you still are not sure of which form to use, you may test further by substituting *he* or *him* for *who* or *whom:*

> _____ were you talking to?
> You were talking to <u>him</u>. (So use *whom*.)
> _____ did they choose?
> They did choose <u>him</u>. (So use *whom*.)
> _____ did the professor say made an A?
> The professor did say <u>he</u> made an A. (So use *who*.)

Such simple questions occur infrequently in expository writing. Therefore, since *who* as an object is acceptable in colloquial language, the distinction between *who* and *whom* in the interrogative position is a minor matter.

The structural position that causes most confusion between *who* and *whom* occurs in sentences in which such parenthetic expressions as *I think, do you think, I'm sure, he feels,* and *it seems* come between the pronoun and its verb. In such sentences the pronoun may appear to be the object of the verb in the parenthetic expression when it is really the subject of another verb in the sentence. For example, one of America's foremost publishers of English textbooks issued a pamphlet to its authors with these opening sentences:

> Every author tries to discover who among the many publishers can best assure the success of his text. He should, naturally, contract with that publisher <u>whom</u> he feels can most tastefully and appropriately produce and thoroughly and effectively promote his text.

In the first sentence, the writer clearly saw *who* as the subject of *can assure*. But in the second sentence, he apparently thought that *whom* was the object of *feels*. Actually, *he feels* is just a parenthetic expression that can be removed from the sentence. The writer incorrectly used *whom* as the subject of *can produce*.

In such sentences as the following, *who* is the correct form; the parenthetic expressions (which, incidentally, are usually not set off by commas) do not affect the case form of the pronoun:

> Professor Sherman is the man who everyone feels is best qualified to represent the faculty.
>
> Professor Beal, who I am sure takes a disinterested position, has been chosen to arbitrate the dispute.

Who do you think is a suitable replacement for Professor Ryan?

Professor Lubbe is the applicant who it seems will receive the first-place award.

Sometimes, however, the pronoun is the object rather than the subject of another verb (or preposition) in a sentence that has such a parenthetic expression. For example:

Professor Aspiz, whom I am sure we all rely on frequently, will present our grievance to President Peterson. (We rely on *him*.)

Professor Rosenberg, whom I think the Academic Council intends to promote, is considering an offer from Mideastern Theological Seminary. (The Academic Council intends to promote *him*.)

In conversation, you may find it difficult to think of the correct form of *who* and *whom* quickly enough to feel secure. The best practice is always to use *who* (except perhaps directly after a preposition), for in colloquial usage that form is now fully acceptable both as a subject and an object. When writing, you have time to test for the correct form. The simple test is to use *who* when *he* (*she, they*) also fits and *whom* when *him* (*her, them*) fits. Examples:

Professor Dodge is the candidate _____ it seems will be elected.

It seems that he will be elected. (So use *who*.)

_____ do you think will replace Professors Marcus and Stone?

They will replace Professors Marcus and Stone. (So use *who*.)

Professor Adjoka, _____ I believe the President will select for the award, is also the favorite of the faculty.

The President will select him for the award. (So use *whom*.)

Professor Walters, _____ everyone says the Board treated unjustly, has received an excellent offer from Brookline Institute.

Everyone says the Board treated her unjustly. (So use *whom*.)

This simple test can also be applied when no parenthetic expression causes confusion. Examples:

We should be friendly with those _____ we dislike.
We dislike them. (So use *whom*.)
I wonder _____ I can recommend for the job.

I can recommend him. (So use *whom*.)
It's impossible to predict _____ will be elected.
He will be elected. (So use *who*.)

The pronouns *whoever* and *whomever* should be selected on the same bases as *who* and *whom,* and the same kind of testing for the correct form can be applied. In colloquial usage, of course, *whoever* is acceptable as both subject and object. There is, however, one structural position involving these forms that can cause confusion in semiformal or formal writing. When an entire dependent clause is the object of a preposition (*to, for, with,* and so on), the preposition itself does not affect the case of a pronoun in the dependent clause. Examples:

The award will be given to whomever the Mayor selects.
The job will go to whoever is gullible enough to take it.

In each of these sentences the dependent clause is the object of the preposition *to,* which has no effect on the pronoun form. You can test for the correct form as explained above. Examples:

I am keeping the prize money for _____ makes the first valid claim for it.
He makes the first valid claim for it. (So use *whoever*.)
Mary goes out with _____ her mother selects.
Her mother selects him. (So use *whomever*.)

RULE 4:

The case form following the comparative words than *and* as *is the same as the case form of the first element of the comparison.*

When nouns form both elements of the comparison, no mistake can be made, for noun forms do not vary. For example: "The Dean of Instruction is more likely to favor the proposal than the President." But pronouns often complete the comparison, with a consequent opportunity for a mistake in grammar. For example: "The President is rather conservative. The Dean of Instruction is more likely to favor the proposal than (*he* or *him?*)." In such a sentence the pronoun should be in the same case as the first element of the comparison. In this sentence *he* is the proper form, for *Dean of Instruction* (the first element of the comparison) is a subject.

The construction *as . . . as* also shows comparison: "Professor

Lewis did not praise John as highly as (*I* or *me?*)." If this sentence intends to draw a comparison between John and me, *me* is the correct form, for *John* is an object. But if the comparison is between Professor Lewis and me, the correct pronoun is *I*, for *Professor Lewis* is a subject. Note how the two different meanings can be illustrated:

> Professor Lewis did not praise John as highly as (he praised) me.
> Professor Lewis did not praise John as highly as I (praised John).

Apparently, these sentences show that pronoun form can govern meaning, but actually such an ambiguous construction is extremely rare in writing and speaking.

The simple test to use in selecting the proper pronoun form to follow *than* and *as* is to complete the unstated part of the comparison. Note how the correct pronoun is made obvious in the following examples:

> Professor Chapman is more likely to become Dean of Instruction than he (is likely to become Dean).
> Professor Ludwig gave Sue more individual help than (he gave) me.
> Professor Saunders is as well known in scholarly circles as I (am well known).
> Professor Dickey tolerates Ambrose as readily as (he tolerates) me.

RULE 5:

The possessive form of a noun or pronoun is used to modify a gerund or gerund phrase.

A gerund is the *ing* form of a verb used as a noun and therefore denotes an action or state of being: *walking, gambling, becoming, appearing,* and so forth. When the action or state of being belongs to someone, that ownership is shown by use of the possessive case. Examples:

> Professor Steele objected to my talking.
> I objected to Professor Steele's reprimanding me.

Note that we did not object to each other *in toto*. Professor Steele objected just to the talking, and the talking was *mine*. I objected just to the reprimanding, and the reprimanding was *his*.

338 · CONVENTIONS OF USAGE

When referring just to **one** of the person's actions, use the possessive-case form, as in these examples:

> The judge was annoyed by their (not *them*) resorting to the Fifth Amendment.
> Professor Cerveney was surprised at Sue's (not *Sue*) showing up in slacks.
> Professor Cox was taken aback by our (not *us*) agreeing to write an extra term paper.
> Professor Freeman sympathized with your (not *you*) voting against Proposition 24.

When referring to the whole person as well as one of his actions, use the subjective- or objective-case form, as in these examples:

> I saw him giving a bribe to Professor Stone.
> It was they lying in ambush.
> Was that Jane leaving with Professor Ranald?

In these sentences the *ing* verbals (called participles) are modifying *him, they* and *Jane*, not vice versa.

RULE 6:

The objective-case form them *should never be substituted for the demonstrative pronoun* those.

The demonstrative pronouns *this, that, these,* and *those* are used to point out an object or objects: *this book, that car, those people, these categories.* Often the noun that is being pointed out is not stated but understood: "I'll take six of those (meaning whatever objects are being referred to)."

Even in vulgate usage the only confusion of demonstrative pronoun forms is the use of *them* for *those.* You should never use *them* to modify a noun either stated or understood. Examples:

> Professor Carey asked us to read those (not *them*) books.
> Professor Carey asked us to read those (not *them*, if a pointing action, and thus a noun, is understood).
> Professor Carey mentioned six books and asked us to read them. (No pointed action indicated.)
> Do you see those girls (pointing action)? I want to talk to them (no pointing action).

The confusion of *them* and *those* is generally accounted an especially gross error in usage.

RULE 7:

In the we men-us men *constructions, the case of the pronoun should be the same as it would be if no noun were present.*

If the noun part of the construction is mentally omitted, the correct pronoun form will be obvious. Examples:

> We (Americans) must learn to be less provincial.
>
> Many foreigners resent the provincial snobbishness of us (Americans).
>
> Many professors think we (students) take the world too seriously.
>
> Give us (students) an inch and we'll convert it into centimeters.

RULE 8:

Pronouns in apposition should be in the same case form as they would be if no nouns were present.

The simple test for this construction is to substitute the pronouns for the nouns they are in apposition to. Examples:

> Two students—Cheri and (*I* or *me?*)—were sent to the conference.
>
> Cheri and I were sent to the conference.
>
> Dean Levinson threatened to expel two students—Cheri and me.
>
> Dean Levinson threatened to expel Cheri and me.

RULE 9:

The proper forms of the reflexive pronouns are myself, yourself, himself, herself, itself, oneself, ourselves, yourselves, *and* themselves.

Note that these pronoun forms are single words; thus *its self* and *one's self* are improper forms. Also note that the plural form is *selves* rather than *selfs*.

The grossest error in reflexive pronoun usage is the confusion of *hisself* for *himself* and of *theirselves* for *themselves*. That these forms should be considered vulgar is illogical. If the possessive forms *my, your,* and *our* are properly combined with *self* and *selves* to make reflexives, why should not the possessive forms *his* and *their* also be so combined? The situation is made further ironical in that *his own self, one's own self,* and *their own selves* are correct forms. But grammar, as has been pointed out, is more functional than logical.

A reflexive pronoun form may be used as a subject or an object in colloquial usage. Examples:

> John and myself were the only members present.
> The invitation was for both my father and myself.
> Barbara and yourself may be interested.

But such usage should be avoided in semiformal and formal writing.

RULE 10:

The personal possessive pronouns are never spelled with apostrophes: its, hers, his, ours, yours, theirs. *The indefinite possessive pronouns are spelled with apostrophes:* one's, anyone's, anybody's, everyone's, everybody's, anyone else's, *and so forth.* Examples:

> The purse is hers.
> The car is ours.
> The mistake is yours.
> The book is theirs.
> Its cover is soiled.
> One's religion is important.
> Anyone's idea is worth consideration.
> Everybody's business is nobody's business.
> Do you have anyone else's book?

EXERCISE 52. Correct Pronoun Usage

DIRECTIONS: *Discuss the proper choice of pronoun in the following sentences. Indicate in which ones colloquial and semiformal usages diverge.*

1. Our dog Snoopy was asking for (its, it's) supper bowl.
2. Mr. Jones (himself, hisself) agreed to escort Cherie and (I, me) to the dance.
3. Two football players—Tom Jones and (I, me)—were assigned to the Sports Council.
4. It is clear that (we, us) students were to blame for the riots.
5. Professor Fleenor pointed to a stack of books and said, "Read one of (them, those) by Wednesday."
6. (We, Us) students objected to (his, him) acting like a martinet.

7. Tom has as high an I.Q. as (I, me).
8. Professor Williams graded Tom as harshly as (I, me).
9. We were supposed to send the money to (whoever, whomever) we felt needed it most.
10. He is the student (who, whom) I think Professor Palitz recommended for a Fellowship.
11. The two who received the largest vote were Tom and (I, me).
12. There was a telephone call for both John and (I, me).
13. It is true that both Marie and (I, me) failed the exam.
14. If it had been (he, him) at the door, I wouldn't have known (who, whom) to call for help.
15. The accident didn't injure John and (I, me) as much as (she, her).
16. Sue enjoyed (he, him, his) staring at her until she discovered (who, whom) he was.
17. The trust fund established for my brother and (I, me) is administered by one (who, whom) we both trust.
18. No matter (who, whom) the voters elect, he will not be as qualified for the job as (I, me).
19. (No ones, No one's, No ones') report was more appreciated than (hers, her's, hers').
20. Don't subject (yourself, your self) to such a strain, for your health is as important as (theirs, their's, theirs').
21. As a cat washes (its self, it's self, itself), it gets vitamin D from (its, it's) hair.
22. There is no excuse for (we, us, our) missing the surprise party given for Jane and (she, her).
23. Professor Williams appointed only two students—Janice and (I, me)—to the Central Council, and it was (we, us) two (who, whom) Dean Clark favored.
24. It is appropriate for (we, us) students to give books as Christmas presents.
25. Just between you and (I, me), I think (those, them) are of better quality than the first ones he showed us.
26. The cook resigned because of (they, them, their) continual complaining about her lack of sanitary precautions.
27. The star of the play is not as attractive as (she, her).
28. It may have been (he, him) (who, whom) the Dean was referring to.
29. The jest's prosperity lies in the mouth of (he, him) (who, whom) utters it.
30. It must have been (he, him) (who, whom) Professor Plunkett said was to parse the opening sentence of the Declaration of Independence.

MODIFIER FORMS

In grammar, a modifier is a word, phrase, or clause that qualifies, limits, describes, or restricts another word. Traditional grammar identifies two kinds of single-word modifiers: adjectives, which modify nouns and pronouns, and adverbs, which modify verbs, adjectives, and other adverbs. Actually, modification in English grammar is not nearly so simple. For example, in such a phrase as "very funny," *very* is not a true adverb, but an *intensifier*. In "this book," *this* is not an adjective, but a *demonstrative*. In "both sexes," *both* is not an adjective, but a *determiner* (or *marker* or *indefinite*). In "consolation prize," *consolation* is not an adjective, but a *noun*. In "barking dog," *barking* is not an adjective, but a *verbal*. Modification in English grammar is, indeed, very complex—even more complex than these few examples suggest. But so far as conventional usage (that is, correctness) is concerned, the range of mistakes in modifier forms is narrow, and standard usage is not difficult to master.

The following words of caution, stated as rules, cover the few common structural positions in which errors in modifier forms may occur. These rules are intended to be only a practical guide to standard usage, not an exhaustive analysis of modification in English grammar. The many phases of modification that are not a source of errors in conventional usage are not discussed here.[6]

---

[6] For illustration, however, a few examples may be illuminating. Some adverbs have two forms:

"to climb *high*" and "to value *highly*"
"to sit *close*" and "to look *closely*"
"to fly *direct*" and "to go *directly*"

Many adjective and adverb forms are identical:

"an *early* riser" and "to rise *early*"
"a *fast* walker" and "to walk *fast*"
"a *far* distance" and "to travel *far*"

Some adjectives may normally be used only in the predicate of a sentence:

The boy is *afraid*.
I was *aghast* at his crime.

Some *ly* words can be used either as adjectives or adverbs:

"a *leisurely* walk" and "to walk *leisurely*"
"a *kindly* word" and "to speak *kindly*"

Following the direct object of the verb *call*, adjective and adverb forms deliver different meanings:

He called her *sweet*.
He called her *sweetly*.

Since not even illiterate native speakers of English make mistakes in using such modifiers—and many more oddities, irregularities, and anomalies could be cited—they are of interest only in a study of grammar, not of conventional usage.

RULE 1:

Do not use an adjective form in an adverbial pattern.

Most true adjectives and adverbs are inflectional forms of the same word. Normally the suffix *ly* is added to an adjective form to convert it into an adverb. Examples:

Adjectives	*Adverbs*
rapid	rapidly
smooth	smoothly
angry	angrily
happy	happily
quiet	quietly

The adjective form fits this sentence pattern: "He is a *quiet* man." When a modifier is in that position, it is a true adjective provided the sentence structure can be altered to this pattern: "He is a man who is *quiet*." And provided the word can be compared: *quieter, quietest;* "He is a *quieter* man than I."

The adverb form fits this sentence pattern: "He spoke *quietly*." Like the adjective form, it can be compared: *more quietly, most quietly;* "He spoke *more quietly* than I."

Note how modifiers other than adjectives and adverbs will not fit these patterns.[7] Example of a supposed adjective:

> He is a circus performer.
> He is a performer who is circus (?).
> He is more circus (?) than other performers.

Example of a supposed adverb:

> He spoke very (?).
> He spoke more very (?) than I.

These grammatical complexities of modification, however, are not a source of errors in modifier forms. For the most part, errors result from confusion of true adjectives and adverbs.

No native speaker of English ever uses an adverb form to modify a noun. Such sentences as the following would sound absurd even to illiterates:

---

[7] There are some true adjectives (for example, *mere*) that do not fit this theoretical pattern and many adverbs (for example, *again, still*) and a few adjectives that cannot be compared. Such forms, however, are not a source of errors in conventional usage.

He is a quietly man.
I have a happily dog.

But in vulgate usage, adjective forms are often used to modify verbs. Such usage is nonstandard and should be avoided in all writing except dialogue. Examples of conventional errors in modifier form:

He talks <u>careless</u> about his wife.
He certainly spoke <u>courteous</u>.
Can't you talk <u>pleasant</u>?
He is breathing <u>normal</u> again.
He mixes <u>easy</u> in a group.
When he returned, he seemed to talk <u>different</u>.
He performed his tasks <u>satisfactory</u>.
You don't come as <u>frequent</u> as you used to.
The faucet is leaking <u>bad</u> again.
The train ran <u>smooth</u>.
He ate <u>considerable</u> more than I.
He didn't eat <u>near</u> as much as I.

All of the underscored modifiers in these examples are adjective forms and should be used to modify only **nouns** or **pronouns.** Examples:

He has a <u>careless</u> wife.
He is a <u>courteous</u> speaker.
We had a <u>pleasant</u> talk.
His breathing is <u>normal</u> again.

And so on. Addition of the inflectional ending *ly* changes such adjectives into adverbs, which should be used to modify **verbs, adjectives,** and **adverbs.** In all of the previous twelve examples, the underscored modifiers should be adverbs ending in *ly*.

Confusion of adjectives and adverbs also occurs occasionally because of a number of common *ly* modifiers that can be used only as adjectives. Examples:

"a friendly chat" but not "to chat friendly"
"a lively dance" but not "to dance lively"
"a manly stance" but not "to stand manly"
"a lonely girl" but not "to sit lonely"
"a lovely girl" but not "to kiss lovely"
"a holy man" but not "to behave holy"

"a deadly blow" but not "to strike deadly"
"an unsightly appearance" but not "to dress unsightly"
"a surly man" but not "to talk surly"

For the most part, native speakers of English have a natural feel for adjective and adverb forms, and therefore errors due to confusion of these forms are not especially common and are rather easily guarded against. When in doubt, ask yourself whether a noun or the action of a verb is being described, and choose the adjective or adverb form accordingly.

RULE 2:
Use adjective forms with linking verbs.

A number of verbs—*to be, to become, to grow, to seem, to appear, to remain, to act, to prove, to stay, to look, to sound, to smell, to feel,* and *to taste*—are called linking verbs because they may link the subject of a sentence with either a noun that is the same as the subject (*he became Mayor*) or an adjective that describes the subject (*he became angry*). Such adjectives are called *predicate adjectives* because they appear in the sentence predicate but modify the sentence subject. In the following sentences each adjective modifies the sentence subject, not the verb. Note that substituting the verb *was* for the actual verb in each sentence makes the modification unmistakably adjectival.

He grew restive.
He seemed contented.
He appeared calm.
He remained quiet.
He acted silly.
He proved reliable.
He stayed angry.
He looked cautious.
He sounded odd.
He smelled rank.
He felt greasy.
He tasted gamey (to the cannibals).

Many of these verbs, however, may also be used as action verbs, in which case they may be modified by adverbs rather than followed by predicate adjectives. Entirely different meanings result from the two types of modification. Example:

He looked curious.
He looked curiously.

The first sentence means that to others he had a curious appearance, whereas the second means that he himself gazed at something in a curious manner. Obviously, choosing the proper modifier form to accompany a linking verb is necessary for clear meaning. Here are other examples of adverbial modification of the above verbs:

The tree grew rapidly.
The waiter appeared quickly.
He proved constantly on the alert.
He smelled the concoction cautiously.
He felt her sprained ankle gently.
He tasted the wine eagerly.

Each of these adverbs modifies the verb rather than the subject of the sentence; thus here the verbs are used as action rather than linking verbs.

In actual practice, few errors in modifier form occur because of confusion of linking and action verbs. Students often make mistakes in choosing proper forms for sentences in textbook exercises, chiefly because such sentences are artificial, but they rarely make such errors in their own writing or speaking. The most conspicuous and most common error is the use of *badly* and other adverb forms with the linking verb *feel*. When the subject of the verb *feel* is being described, a predicate adjective rather than an adverb should be used, as in these examples:

I felt bad (not *badly*) about his stock market losses.
She feels bad (not *badly*) when her children disobey her.
I feel sad (not *sadly*) every time I read "That Evening Sun."
He felt bold (not *boldly*) enough to ask her for a date.

If you will remember always to use the phrase *feel bad* instead of *feel badly*, you will probably eliminate 80 percent or more of your errors (if any) due to improper modification of linking verbs.

Occasionally, adverb forms are misused with the "sense" verbs *taste* and *smell*. Examples:

The milk tasted sour (not *sourly*).
The rose smelled sweet (not *sweetly*).

But for the most part, the problem of modification with linking verbs is academic, not practical—important in a study of grammar, but not of conventional usage.

RULE 3:

In semiformal and formal writing or speech, distinguish between the adjective and adverb forms of good *and* well.

The inflection of a few common modifiers in English is irregular. For example, the comparative forms of *little* may be *less* and *least* and those of *ill* (as well as *bad*) may be *worse* and *worst*. Most such grammatical irregularities simply take care of themselves in usage. Some problems arise, however, in the use of *good* and *well*.

Good is a basic adjective form. If its inflection were regular, *goodly* would be an adverb; but because of an inflectional irregularity, *well* is the adverb form of *good*. However, both have the same comparative forms: *better* and *best*. Thus, according to the modification patterns of true adjectives and adverbs mentioned in Rule 1 above, *good* and *well* should be used as in these examples:

> He is a good worker.
> He is a worker who is good (at his work).
> He is a better worker than I.
> He is the best worker of all.
> He works well.
> He works better than I.
> He works best of all the workers.

The grammar of these modifiers is further complicated in that *well* is the adjective form for the meaning "in good health." Thus *I feel good* refers to a generalized feeling of physical and mental well being, whereas *I feel well* refers to a specific feeling of physical health. Or, for another example, *a well person* (as contrasted with *a good person*) means specifically "a person in good health."

So far as proper conventional usage is concerned, the main problem is to avoid using *good* to modify a verb, for in traditional usage, *good* is an adjective only. Here, however, a distinction must be made between colloquial and formal usage. On a colloquial level, *good* is commonly used as an adverb even by well-educated people. And perhaps within another generation or two, the distinction between *good* and *well* will be of no more concern than the distinction between *shall* and *will* is now. In college-level exposition, however, you should avoid using *good* as an adverb. Examples:

> I did well (not *good*) in organic chemistry.
> After taking Nasaldrin, I can breath well (not *good*) again.
> Everything is going well (not *good*) for the family business
> this year.
> My Citroen runs well (not *good*) on regular gas.
> Acting pays well (not *good*) if you can get a job.
> My twelve-year-old sister plays bridge quite well (not *good*).

In your eagerness to use *well* as an adverb, however, you should not make the mistake of using it as a predicate adjective. *Good* is the proper form to use with linking verbs. Examples:

> A massage feels good (not *well*) to tired muscles.
> Even the PX food tasted good (not *well*) to the weary G.I.'s.
> A change of climate is often good (not *well*) for a sick person.
> Adversity can be good (not *well*) for the soul.

RULE 4:
Distinguish between colloquial and formal intensifiers.

Intensifiers are modifiers (usually called *adverbs* in traditional grammar) that increase the force of other modifiers; they never (as intensifiers) modify nouns or verbs. *Very* is a typical, and the most common (and overused), intensifier. It is used to add strength to adjectives and adverbs (*very rapid, very rapidly*), but can never modify a noun or verb directly (*a very man* [?], *to talk very* [?]).

In colloquial usage, the intensifiers *real, awful, awfully, pretty, mighty,* and *plenty* are acceptable, but in college-level exposition more appropriate intensifiers are *especially, fairly, extremely, quite, fully, wholly, rather, really,* and *somewhat.* Examples:

> "especially intelligent" rather than "mighty intelligent"
> "quite appropriate" rather than "real appropriate"
> "fairly well trained" rather than "pretty well trained"
> "extremely alert" rather than "plenty alert"
> "really surprising" rather than "awfully surprising"

RULE 5:
Avoid double negatives.

Negation is expressed in English both in nouns and pronouns (*none, nothing, nobody, no one*) and in modification (*no, not, never, hardly, scarcely*). Two negatives in the same statement make, of course, the notorious double negative. Probably no other vulgate expression has been so diligently combatted in public schools, with the result that a once-useful intensive is now virtually eliminated from the speech of those with as much as a high school education.

The double negative is, of course, an intensive, for it is not true that "two negatives make an affirmative," as many grammarians have said. No one in the history of English has ever interpreted a double negative as an affirmative. To everyone, the statement "I don't have no money" means that I have no money—and it will always mean that. Therefore, from a linguistic point of view, a double negative is never an affirmative—just an intensive. It once was a useful intensive, but prejudice against it is so strong now that you should not use it even colloquially (except for the special constructions noted below).

The only unacceptable double negatives likely to appear in college writing are those involving the modifiers *scarcely* and *hardly*. Since these words are themselves negatives, an additional negative should not be used with them. Examples:

> I have scarcely (not *haven't scarcely*) any work done yet.
> He knows scarcely anyone (not *scarcely no one*) at camp.
> I have hardly any (not *haven't hardly* or *have hardly no*) grades below a B.

A grammatically interesting double negative occurs in this construction: "He *won't* be eligible next semester, I *don't* think." In colloquial conversation, such a construction is acceptable. It should be avoided in writing, but then it virtually never appears in writing, anyway.

Another fully standard double negative involves the word *but*, which, when not a conjunction or preposition, expresses negation. Examples:

> There is *no* doubt *but* that political pressures caused his resignation.
> I *can't* help *but* feel that we should negotiate disarmament.

These constructions are fully acceptable, but note that the negative *but* can be removed without change of meaning (in the second example *feel* must be altered to *feeling*).

RULE 6:

Make a distinction between colloquial and formal adverb forms.

Slow, quick, loud, and *sure* are adjective forms; the inflectional *ly* ending converts them into adverbs. But all four adjective forms are commonly used as adverbs in colloquial language. Examples:

> Drive *slow* through this neighborhood.
> Finish as *quick* as you can.
> Don't talk so *loud.*
> He *sure* is an expert malingerer.

Such colloquial usage is fully acceptable, and even in semiformal usage *slow, quick,* and *loud* are acceptable adverb forms. *Sure* as an adverb is colloquial at best. In formal usage, *slowly, quickly,* and *loudly* are more appropriately used as adverbs.

RULE 7:

Avoid awkward comparative forms of adjectives and adverbs.
Examples:

> "more famous" rather than "famouser"
> "more quickly" rather than "quicklier"
>
> "most consistent" rather than "consistentest"
> "most admirably" rather than "admirabliest"

RULE 8:

Avoid awkward use of nouns as modifiers.

In English, nouns are frequently used to modify other nouns (in which case they may be called *adjectivals*). When an awkward construction results from such modification, a revision for smoothness is advisable. Examples:

> "The Dean of the University of Minnesota Law School" rather than "The University of Minnesota Law School Dean"
> "Instruction in architecture" rather than "architecture instruction"
> "An interruption in construction" rather than "a construction interruption"
> "An appeal to the State Supreme Court" rather than "a State Supreme Court appeal"
> "A death from pneumonia" rather than "a pneumonia death"

EXERCISE 53. Choosing Proper Modifier Forms

DIRECTIONS: *In the following sentences, identify modifier forms improper for college exposition and explain in grammatical terms why a different form is needed. Some sentences may be correct.*

1. Information regulation by the press is considered undemocratic.
2. She was the beautifullest girl in the pageant.
3. The Senator sure did talk loud.
4. I hadn't hardly begun the experiment when my assistant said she felt badly.
5. Professor Benston gave an awfully difficult final exam.
6. Nevertheless I did good on the exam.
7. He sounded oddly on the telephone, but he spoke clear.
8. Professor Willard doesn't give tests now as frequent as he used to.
9. When you become a homeowner, you will think different about property taxes.
10. We talked friendly for a while, but then he spoke abusive about my Alma Mater.
11. When you eat is not near as important as what you eat.
12. Your Alfa-Romeo runs smoother than my Sunbeam Alpine.
13. Schoenberg's music sounds oddly to my ears.
14. Professor Duax felt uneasily about taking over Professor Lefevre's classes.
15. Professor Liberman stepped cautiously into the Yucatan jungle.
16. Mayor Sullivan felt safely enough to accuse the commissioner openly of bribery.
17. Professor Eley stared angrily at the innocent-looking student.
18. There are scarcely no old-fashioned classicists left even in the big universities.
19. The freshman defended his thesis well against the criticism of Professor Fleishcher.
20. After a night in the open desert, we all felt miserably.

SENTENCE FRAGMENTS

Conventionally acceptable fragments

Except for the imperative (request) sentence, a normal English sentence has a subject and predicate. In ordinary conversation, however, many of our utterances consist of sentence fragments rather than full sentences. Such utterances are usually meaningful and in conversation are conventionally acceptable, as an examination of the dialogue in almost any modern realistic short story will show. For example, a bit of dialogue might run like this:

> "I know the man you're talking about," Pete said. "Big fellow with ham-like hands. Always wearing a pious smile like a fake evangelist. Probably an undertaker."

Casual conversation would, in fact, often sound awkward to our ears if every utterance were a complete sentence.

In expository writing some sentence fragments are conventionally acceptable. An answer to a rhetorical question may be expressed in a fragment. Examples:

> Why should a respectable citizen resort to pretty shoplifting? In all probability because of an unconscious psychological abnormality.
>
> Where was the Senator when his Committee met to consider the new tax reform bill? In conference with six NAM lobbyists.

The logical relationship between questions and answers is so clear that the fragmentary structure is fully acceptable—even desirable.

Fragmentary exclamations and repetitions used for emotional impact, though not common in exposition, are conventionally acceptable. Examples:

> And finally, at about 9:00 P.M., the Senate adjourned after having passed ninety-seven bills in a row. What a day!
>
> In protest against what he considered to be steamroller tactics by the Administration, the Senator did not attend even one of his Committee meetings. Not a single one!

The tone implied in fragments of this sort could hardly be achieved with full sentences.

Fragments to indicate the continuation of a series or of a line of thought are also conventionally acceptable in exposition. Such phrases as these are examples:

> And so on.
> And so with medical doctors also.
> And other such indefinite remarks.
> No question about that.

At one time, *which* clauses were commonly used fragments in high-level exposition, and, though less commonly used nowadays, they must still be considered conventionally acceptable. Examples:

> The Senator expressed moral objections to the new tax bill. Which is to say that his most powerful constituents opposed it.
> At the end of the session Senator Powers facetiously asked that every committee member immediately phone Drew Pearson. Which is exactly what Senator Snopes intended to do.

The logic of these acceptable fragments is that the relative pronoun *which* is made to function like the demonstrative pronouns *this* or *that*.

Unacceptable sentence fragments

You should use a sentence fragment in college exposition only when you are sure of its acceptability, since, except for a few special uses, fragments are not conventionally acceptable in expository writing. One common kind of unacceptable fragment is the **detached clause** or **phrase** that logically should be attached to the sentence preceding it. Examples:

> Professor Steinmann wrote an unfavorable review of *Joyce's Literary Influence*. Since he found it contained errors in fact.
> Professor McCall was wary of discussing Marxism in class. Because several students had misquoted his comments on the Counter Reformation.
> Professor Sackett agreed to give the Memorial Lecture on Elizabethan drama. Having just finished writing a new book on Shakespeare's comedies.
> William Faulkner's *Sanctuary* is a study of good *v.* evil. Not just a cheap, sensational novel.

Since a period is a signal for a full pause, a reader at first assumes that he is beginning a new sentence when he comes to such a detached clause or phrase. Consequently, he is momentarily confused and loses reading time because of the fragment.

A second common kind of unacceptable fragment occurs **when a finite verb is omitted** from a proposed sentence. A finite verb is one that can be used as the verb of a sentence predicate. Some examples are *spoke, was expressed, has disappeared, are talking,* and *will arrive.* A nonfinite verb form is one that, by itself, cannot be used as the verb of a sentence predicate. Some examples are *being, having been, to express,* and *being expressed.* When a nonfinite verb form is used as a regular sentence verb, an unacceptable fragment occurs. Examples:

> The ballots being recounted by a nonpartisan committee.
> The committee having been dissolved by executive fiat.
> The student wanting to express a dissenting opinion.

Even though the meaning of such fragments may be clear, a reader will momentarily stumble when he encounters one, for his ear is not used to accepting that kind of construction as complete. Such fragments, then, are conventionally unacceptable.

The phrase "sentence sense" is applied to the unconscious feel for grammatical completeness which we develop because of our familiarity with our language. When we are not careless, most of us will instinctively reject an incomplete sentence pattern. Those who are deficient in their sentence sense can best improve it through careful reading of good writing.

COMPARISONS

Logically, a comparison must involve two elements: more *money* than *brains; books* are better than *movies;* clearer *now* than *before.* A comparison is incomplete when one of the two elements is neither stated nor clearly implied.

Incomplete comparisons are commonly used in advertising slogans: *Green's beer is lighter; Cornsilks smoke smoother; Flimsey's underwear costs less; Butterfinger's service saves you more; Polkadot toothpaste is different; Slurry Cola is so refreshing.* The general implication of such incomplete comparisons is clear, and therefore the slogans, though perhaps not truthful, are conventionally acceptable. In expository writing, however, such generalized comparisons are not conventionally acceptable. The second part of the comparison must be specifically clear, either through unmistakable reference to a preceding sentence or completeness of the comparison within the sentence. Examples:

> INCOMPLETE: Cultural Anthropology is so interesting.
> COMPLETE: Cultural Anthropology is interesting.
> COMPLETE: Cultural Anthropology is so interesting that I advise all my friends to take it.

> INCOMPLETE: Attending a community college is different.
> COMPLETE: Attending a community college is different from leaving home to go to school.

> INCOMPLETE: Professor Gorrell tells more funny jokes.
> COMPLETE: Professor Gorrell tells many funny jokes.
> COMPLETE: Professor Gorrell tells more funny jokes than any other professor I have.

Not only should the second element of a comparison be stated, but a necessary part of a comparative structure should not be omitted. The structure words *other* and *as* are the ones most frequently omitted. Examples:

> INCOMPLETE: Theodore Roosevelt was younger than any President.
> COMPLETE: Theodore Roosevelt was younger than any other President.
>
> INCOMPLETE: Professor Wicklund is as learned or perhaps more learned than Professor Frenz.
> COMPLETE: Professor Wicklund is as learned as or perhaps more learned than Professor Frenz.

Conventions of usage call for complete comparisons in expository writing even when colloquial usage may condone the incomplete structure.

ABBREVIATIONS, CONTRACTIONS, ITALICS, NUMBERS, MECHANICS

Abbreviations

Many abbreviations are standard in all levels of writing. Abbreviations designating individuals:

Mr.	St. (Saint)
Mrs.	Sr.
Messrs.	Jr.
Mmes.	Esq.

Abbreviations indicating degrees and honors:

A.B. *or* AB *or* BA	LL.D. *or* LLD
M.A. *or* MA	D.H.L. *or* DHL
M.D. *or* MD	O.M.
Ph.D. *or* PhD	D.S.C. *or* DSC
D.D. *or* DD	

Abbreviations in designating time:

2100 B.C.	9:00 A.M. *or* 9:00 a.m.
A.D. 1688	2:10 P.M. *or* 2:10 p.m.

Abbreviations of governmental agencies and certain organizations and foundations:

UNESCO	WAVES
NRA	CARE
CAB	FOUR
CIA	ILGWU

The abbreviations *no*. and *$* with numerals:

no. 324821	$612.86

In technical writing many abbreviations are common. Consult a good dictionary when in doubt. Examples:

oz.	BTU
gr.	MPH
cc	MPG
cm	RPM

The abbreviation *etc*. may be used in exposition when the writer's intent is to give representative samples from what could easily be a long list. *Etc*. should not be used as a cover-up when the writer can think of no more examples.

Most other abbreviations should be avoided in college-level exposition. Avoid abbreviations of titles, such as *Pres*., *Prof*., and *Rev*.; of first names, such as *Benj*., *Jas*., and *Geo*.; of the names of states and countries, such as *Ala*. and *Can*.; of months and days of the week, such as *Jan*. and *Tues*.; of streets and avenues, such as *Main St*. and *First Ave*.; of the word *company*, as in *Standard Oil Co*.; of Christmas, as in *Xmas*; of weights and measurements, such as *oz*., *lbs*., *in*., and *yds*.; and of common words, such as *yrs*. and *gov't*. Avoid the ampersand (&) unless it is, in fact, a part of a business name.

The use of full words rather than abbreviations (except for standard usage given above) is not desirable because of increased clarity, but because the use of full words adds an aura of politeness to writing. Where politeness is of no consequence, clearly used abbreviations are fully acceptable.

The capitalization of abbreviations should follow that of the full words.

Contractions

Contractions are colloquial in flavor, but they need not necessarily be avoided in college-level exposition. In general, contractions should be avoided when the full spelling sounds natural and smooth. They may be used when they sound more natural than the full spelling. See the section in Chapter 5 on proper level of diction in college writing.

Italics

In print, italics are used to distinguish certain kinds of written units from the main body of discourse. In longhand or typing, italics are designated by underlining.

Words, phrases, and whole sentences may be italicized for emphasis. This use of italics is often thought to have such a personal or sensational tone that it is out of place in high-level exposition. But it is a technique commonly used in good exposition, as a glance through almost any issue of, say, *Harper's* or *The Atlantic* will disclose. Examples:

> Given all this, I still do not think that the demand by the Soviet Union to liquidate *all troops and bases on foreign soil* in the first stage of disarmament is a plausible first step.—P. M. S. Blackett, *Harper's Magazine.*

> Hence our anxiety to picture Eichmann as a monster. It is easier than believing him guilty *while accepting his defense.*—A. Alvarez, *The Atlantic.*

> Slightly more responsible is the writer who tries to convey opinion *to* the reader rather than express it *from* himself.—John F. Huntley, *CCC.*

Capitalization for additional emphasis may also be used. Example: " 'I have *hung this fantasy on the Bureau of Internal Revenue precisely because it does NOT operate in this way.'*—Bernard de Voto, *Harper's Magazine.*" Proper use of italics for emphasis calls for intelligent judgment. An indiscriminate, false-alarm use of them greatly weakens exposition.

Italics for emphasis may be supplied in direct quotations when the writer using the quotation wants especially to call attention to a particular part of the quotation. The fact that the italics have been added must then be noted in brackets. Example:

> The board shall have the power and authority to elect heads of various institutions of higher learning and to contract with all deans, professors, and other members of the teaching staff and all administrative employees of said institutions *for a term of not exceeding four years* [emphasis supplied].—E. Philip Trapp, *AAUP Bulletin*.

The titles of books, plays, long poems, magazines, newspapers, musical compositions, works of art, and names of ships and aircraft are commonly italicized in exposition, though in journalism and casual writing such italicization is often omitted. The whole title, not just individual words, should be underlined. Examples:

> Faulkner's last novel was The Reivers.
> W. Somerset Maugham's most famous play is The Circle.
> More people talk about Paradise Lost than read it.
> The New Yorker is America's most sophisticated magazine.
> The Portland Oregonian is noted for its crusading editorials.
> Handel's most popular oratorio is The Messiah.
> The Mona Lisa was brought to the United States for public display.
> The Titanic sank on its maiden voyage.

Foreign words and phrases which have not been fully anglicized are usually italicized in exposition. Examples:

> The *sine qua non* of astrological forecasts is ambiguity.
> The *raison d'être* of many education courses seems to be to provide employment for professors of education.

Do not italicize foreign words and phrases which are well established in English usage, such as *bona fide, et cetera, gratis, tour de force,* and *verbatim.* Examples:

> James Jones's first novel was a tour de force.
> Many foreign jokes cannot be translated verbatim.

There are too many words and phrases of both types to be listed here. Any good collegiate or unabridged dictionary is a reliable guide.

Words used as words should be italicized in exposition, but the more casual the writing, the less need for such italicization. Examples:

The word *autointoxication* was once important in medical terminology.

Was his use of *tomato* slang?

Sometimes such italicization is necessary for clarity in any writing, as in this oddity: "James, where John had had *had had,* had had *had; had had* had had the teacher's approval." The italicized *had's* are words used as words; the others are normally used verbs.

Numbers

In exposition, it is customary to spell out numbers from zero to ten. Usage varies in handling numbers from eleven to ninety-nine and round numbers: some writers spell them out and some use figures. Figures should be used for numbers that require more than two words in spelling. Examples:

> Casey won election by nine (not *9*) votes, and would have lost if 39 (or *thirty-nine*) absentee ballots had not been disqualified. He can usually depend on a margin of at least 200 (or *two hundred*) votes, and once he won by 423 (not *four hundred and twenty-three*) votes.

Whichever method you choose, be consistent within any one paper.

Figures should not be used to start a sentence. Example: "Eight hundred and thirty-three (not *833*) Democrats registered."

Always use figures for dates, street and room numbers, pages of a book, percentages and decimals, hours of the day when used with A.M. or P.M., numbers involving dollars and cents, and a series of numbers. Examples:

> I live in room no. 6 (not *six*) at the Mariners' Boarding House at 322 (not *three hundred and twenty-two*) Westlake Street.
> The quotation appears on page 9 (not *nine*) of *Fox's Martyrs.*
> Only 43 (not *forty-three*) percent of the voters voted.
> According to my figures, you should get a remainder of .0432 (not *four hundred and thirty-two ten-thousandths*).
> The countdown began at 9:00 A.M. (not *nine o'clock* A.M.).
> The net cost is $4.23 (not *four dollars and twenty-three cents*).
> The daily results for a week were 66, 9, 101, 2, 6, 13, and 10 (not *66, nine, 101, two, six, 13, and ten*).

There is no need to use figures in parentheses with spelled-out numbers. In technical and mathematical writing, figures may be used exclusively.

Mechanics

When writing longhand, use blue or black ink and write on one side of the paper only. Use wide-spaced, 8½-by-11-inch notepaper and do not skip every other line; avoid narrow-spaced paper that might, for legibility, require skipping alternate lines. Make corrections neatly; do not leave errors enclosed in parentheses, for parentheses may be used to enclose pertinent parts of the discourse itself.

When possible, type papers prepared outside of class, in which case use unruled, 8½-by-11-inch typing paper. Typed papers should be double spaced, except for inset quotations and footnotes. Two spaces should be used after all end punctuation and colons, but one space after commas and semicolons. No spacing should precede or follow dashes. In typing, two hyphens (--)—not the underlining mark (____)—make a dash and the small letter l—not a capital I—makes the figure 1. Capital letters are used for Roman numerals, except for numbering the pages of a preface or table of contents, for which lower-case Roman numerals may be used. Arabic rather than Roman numerals are used to number the pages of a paper other than the prefatory matter; the first page need not be numbered. All typed papers should be carefully proofread for typographical errors.

No quotation marks, underlining (italics), or punctuation should be used in a title unless other rules call for them. Examples of titles:

> A New Approach to Disarmament
> The Dual Theme of "Richard Cory"
> Visual Imagery in *Paradise Lost*
> Where Are the Snows of *This* Year?

Always skip a line or double space between your title and the first line of your paper. Maintain at least a one-inch, but no more than a 1½-inch, margin on all four sides of each page.

Appendix 1:

The Research Paper

THE PURPOSE OF THE RESEARCH PAPER

In everyday usage, the term *research* (preferred pronunciation: re-search') has two common meanings. First, it means the discovery through investigation or experimentation of new knowledge —something that people now living have not known before. For example, a researcher in literary history might find evidence to show that Shakespeare wrote a play never before attributed to him. Or a researcher in American history might discover documents that prove that a great Confederate general sold military information to the Union forces (or vice versa). Such research discoveries would add to our available store of knowledge. The term *original research* can be applied to this first meaning. Very little original research goes on in school work below the advanced graduate level, for (though there are rare exceptions) one must have considerable training before he is competent to discover really new and important knowledge.

The term *research* is also commonly used to mean the process of seeking out information known by some but not by the person seeking it. Such research is not the discovery of new knowledge, but of established information new to the person seeking it. For example, a student in American literature might ask his professor whether William Faulkner really fought in the Canadian Air Force in France during World War I. The professor might in turn say, "Why don't you do some research and find out?" The actual information is already known to some people and is recorded in reliable reference works in any good library. Looking up the information in the library, then, would constitute a minor piece of research in the second meaning of the word. The term *practical research* can be applied to this meaning of the word. Practical research is quite important in college work, for one of the most distinguishing skills of the college-educated person is his ability to find out information—complicated, involved information, not just isolated facts—that he does not have readily available in his memory. A considerable amount of originality may be involved in practical research, as will be explained below.

Term papers are common assignments in college work. Of the two broad kinds of term papers, one, the so-called *critical paper,* usually requires little research. The purpose of such a paper is to present the student's own evaluation and interpretation of a book or an issue. The writer may gather some information through practical research, but mostly he evaluates on the basis of his current knowledge and set of values. Such a paper is usually more subjective than objective. It may not even send the student to the library.

The second kind of term paper is called the *research* or *reference* or *library paper*. (The name *reference* means that the paper refers to the sources of its information; the name *library* means that the materials for the paper are gathered in the library.) This kind of term paper is based mostly on practical research; it relies more on objective presentation of discovered information and less on subjective interpretation than does the critical paper. A critical paper may be based on the reading of only one book or article; a research paper usually sends the student to a dozen or more sources.

The research paper assigned in freshman composition is often used as a training device designed to prepare students to write term papers in such content courses as history, anthropology, sociology, economics, philosophy, and literature. *The techniques of preparing this kind of paper are rather well standardized. The better you learn how to follow these techniques step by step, the more successful (and easier) your work in academic courses will be.* The composition-course term paper is intended to train you to (1) find source materials in the library; (2) take usable notes from them; (3) evaluate their soundness and reliability; (4) digest and assimilate the source materials rather than let them bypass your mind in their transference to your own paper; (5) draw sound conclusions from the evidence found in the source materials; (6) organize your findings into a coherent whole; (7) present your evidence and conclusions in an effective expository style; and (8) give credit to your sources and to distinguish between your own original work and your source materials.

SELECTING A RESEARCH PAPER TOPIC

In such fields as history and anthropology, term paper topics are often assigned by the professor, and in any case they must pertain to the subject matter of the course. But term papers in freshman composition can hardly be written on the subject matter of the course itself, for not much research can be undertaken in the simple principles of expository writing.[1] Thus term-paper topics in freshman composition may come from any subject-matter field. If your professor assumes the burden of providing you with a topic, you can relax and handle it as best you can. If you are asked to choose your own topic, you must exercise careful judgment.

Limiting the topic

The first criterion of a good term-paper topic is that it be limited enough so that it can be adequately handled in the 2000 to 4000 words accorded it. Even 4000 words are not very many (and the length commonly suggested is about 2500). Only a closely limited topic can be thoroughly developed in so short a paper. Topics such

---

[1] In advanced work in language and literature, there is much opportunity for research.

as "The Napoleonic Wars," "The Development of Democracy," "The Life of Beethoven," and "Space Exploration" are hopelessly broad and general. A good topic must be quite narrowly limited.

The process of limiting a topic involves the principle of subdividing. The first topic you think of will undoubtedly be too general; your task is to investigate the possibilities of limiting it. You do this by seeing if you can isolate just one coherent aspect of the general topic that first entered your mind; and then you continue the process of isolating coherent aspects until you feel your topic would vanish if it were further reduced. Then you **may** have a sufficiently limited topic.

Here is an example of such a process of subdividing: General topic: "Slum Problems in the United States." First reduction: "Slum Problems in Washington State." Second reduction: "Slum Problems in King County, Washington." Third reduction: "Slum Problems in Seattle." Final reduction: "Slum Clearance Projects in Seattle from 1956 to 1959."

Here is another example: General topic: "Integration Problems Outside the South." First reduction: "Integration Problems in the West." Second reduction: "Integration Problems in California." Third reduction: "Integration Problems in San Francisco." Final reduction: "Controversies over *de facto* segregation in San Francisco High Schools in the Early 1960s."

Though you may jump from a general to a sufficiently limited topic in one leap, the need for such a process of subdividing a topic cannot be overstressed. The choice of too broad a topic will invariably result in a poor paper. Always ask yourself if your topic can be further subdivided. Overlimited topics are almost unheard of in term-paper writing, whereas overbroad ones are in the majority.

One of the best ways to test your topic for proper limitation and to understand just what information you want to put into your paper is to *turn your topic into a few specific questions*. Once you can do this successfully, you will know whether your topic is sufficiently limited and will also know much more clearly what you are to look for in your source materials. For example, suppose you decide to write on "President Truman's Administration." What kind of questions can you turn that topic into? Obviously it is a wholly worthless topic for a term paper. Through a process of subdivision, however, you might arrive at this topic: "The Reasons for President Truman's Dismissal of General MacArthur." Then you could formulate these questions: "When and under what conditions did the dismissal occur? What reasons did President Truman and his spokesmen give for the dismissal? What reasons did Republicans or opposition leaders give? What reasons did various news analysts give? Did highly placed military leaders venture opinions? From the evidence, which spokesmen do I think expressed the real reasons for the dismissal?" Actually, such a topic as this is fairly broad and could command many times 4000 words. But freshmen research papers must be allowed some license in dealing with generalities because of the limited knowledge of young students. Any topic that you can convert into four or five such specific questions is likely to be sufficiently limited for a term paper.

If you know precisely the few specific questions for which you are seeking answers, you will not only feel secure in having a limited topic, but will also be able to work rapidly in gathering material for your paper. If you are hazy about the answers you are seeking, or if your questions are too broad or numerous, you will waste time on irrelevant material and will probably turn in a paper that is weak because it is too general. Occasionally, of course, you may want to revise your questions as your work progresses.

Detective work in research papers

A second important criterion of a good research paper topic is that it require you to select information from several sources. A topic for which all the material can be found in one source is not satisfactory for a research paper. Ideally, even a freshman research project should result in the presentation of a body of material that has never before been presented in that form. Thus, though millions of words have been written about President Truman's dismissal of General MacArthur, perhaps no one has yet prepared a paper that presents the basic views of Truman's spokesmen, of his enemies, and of reasonably objective news analysts. A student taking this topic, then, would not engage in original research in that he would be discovering actually new knowledge, but he could show originality in putting together known information that had never before been put into that exact arrangement.

A good research-paper topic, then, requires a certain amount of detective work. If you can find all the evidence you need for your paper in one encyclopedia article, you don't have a research-paper topic. Your topic should require you to seek different pieces of information from various sources. Then you prepare your paper by merging these pieces of information together into one coherent whole—ideally, a kind of whole work that has never before been created. Success in this task will give you great intellectual pleasure and will markedly improve your college work.

Factual and controversial topics

Research-paper topics fall into two broad classifications: those that call for an orderly presentation of factual or hypothetical material about which there is little if any controversy and those on controversial issues. Some examples of the first type are "Seventeenth-Century Theories of Tidal Action," "The Critical Reception of Faulkner's *The Sound and the Fury* in 1929," and "The Growth in United Nations Membership from 1950 to 1960." In writing on a factual topic, you are not called upon to take sides but simply to present—and comment intelligently on—the information that you discover. In preparing a paper on the second topic, for example, you would read all the contemporary reviews of the book you could find and would report the varying critical opinions. You would mention that critics now are virtually unanimous in their praise of the book, and you might explain the biases that brought unfavorable reviews in 1929, but it would not be your task to take sides in any controversy that raged in 1929. You would not evaluate evidence in order to reach a debatable conclusion.

Other research-paper topics are of an argumentative or controversial nature. Some examples are "The Therapeutic Value of Vitamin C," "The Value of Required Foreign Language Study in Elementary Schools," and "The Deterrent Value of Capital Punishment." There is no general agreement among experts on these issues. In writing a paper on one of them, you would seek out and present the established evidence for both sides and then either present a conclusion of your own or express the opinion that not enough evidence is yet available for a sound conclusion to be reached. This kind of topic puts considerable demand on the writer's ability to evaluate the evidence he seeks out, about which more will be explained below.

Topics that simply call for factual reporting may be highly informative and interesting. Controversial topics are likely to be more exciting and to give the writer a greater sense of his own worth as a thinking human being.

Following are a variety of possible research-paper topics for freshman composition:

1. The Nutritional Value of Spinach (Questions: What has been the folklore of the nutritional value of spinach? What experimental evidence has been presented in recent years? Have modern researchers all reached the same conclusions? Does it seem that enough research has been done for positive conclusions to be drawn now? If so, what are these conclusions?)
2. Abraham Lincoln's Religious Views (Questions: What general definition of religion will I use in writing this paper? What comments have been made by historians and biographers about his religious views? From his own words what do I think his views were? Do his writings indicate that he changed his views during his adult life?)
3. The Use of Hypnotism as an Anesthetic (Questions: How do doctors describe the anesthetic effects of hypnotism? In what kinds of medical treatment has it been used as an anesthetic? Do medical doctors and dentists disagree about its value as an anesthetic? What seems to be the majority opinion?)
4. Some Feature of Soviet Public Education
5. The Emergence of One New African Country in the 1960s
6. The Advantages of Steam Automobiles over Gasoline Automobiles
7. The Contribution of Religious Music to Jazz
8. The Essential Features of the Theory of Continuous Creation
9. The Possibilities of Biological Warfare
10. The Effectiveness of Translating Machines
11. The Views of Leaders of the Protestant Churches on Birth Control
12. The Use of Artificial Satellites in Communication
13. Therapeutic Uses of Music
14. The Controversies that Have Centered Around Diego Rivera
15. Recent Attacks in Books and Magazines on the Advertising Industry
16. The Building of Brazil's New Capital, Brasilia
17. Some Celebrated Cases of Quackery in Cancer Cures
18. The Success of Central Malls in Big Cities
19. Featherbedding Practices on the Railroads
20. Some Cases of Fraudulent Practices in Fund-Raising for Charities
21. Controversies in the Career of Admiral Hyman Rickover

22. The Case For or Against Any One Type of Psychical Phenomena
23. Important Archeological Discoveries in the Near East since 1960
24. Albert Einstein's Religious Views
25. Mark Twain's Philosophic Outlook in the Last Ten Years of His Life

After the selection of a properly limited topic, the procedure in preparing a research paper follows rather rigidly a set pattern of steps. The kind of brilliance that can produce a prize-winning critical paper may increase your success in following these steps, but it cannot be substituted for them. You should learn and patiently adhere to the disciplined routine explained below. Once you have mastered the pattern, you will find term-paper writing both easy and rewarding. And the basic procedure presented here is the foundation of the highest-level scholarly research.

SOURCE MATERIALS FOR RESEARCH PAPERS

Whether your research-paper topic is of a factual or controversial nature, you will gather information for it from library sources. Practical research calls for a systematic use of materials that are given standard arrangement and accessibility in all good libraries. An orderly approach in using these materials is essential for good term-paper work.

The general encyclopedias

The most available and reliable source of established factual information is a good general encyclopedia. The three most notable ones are the *Britannica,* the *Americana,* and the *New International.* They are available on the open shelves in the library's reference room.

Though they are monumental works, the general encyclopedias have a limited use in research-paper work and are not usable at all for many topics. *Any topic for which you can gather most of your material from a general encyclopedia is not a satisfactory term-paper topic.* For example, if you decided to write on "The Origin of Language" and simply used the material you found in the *Britannica,* you would produce an unacceptable paper. Furthermore, many of the best topics pertain to issues or events of such recent occurrence that no encyclopedia has material on them.

But when a general encyclopedia can contribute some minor pieces of information that will help you build your paper, you should not hesitate to use it. Suppose, for example, you decided to write on "The Use of the Sinking of the *Titanic* in Imaginative Literature." You could certainly use a general encyclopedia to secure factual information about the sinking of the *Titanic*. General encyclopedias, then, are not a major source of research-paper materials, but they need not be avoided just because they contain established factual information on alphabetically arranged topics.

Special encyclopedias and reference books

On the open shelves of the library are also many special encyclopedias and reference books. These works, like the general encyclopedias, are limited in their usefulness for term-paper work. They may occasionally contribute specific bits of factual information, but, since they are themselves the product of research, they cannot by themselves provide complete materials for a good term-paper topic. When you need to verify or establish a fact, use any appropriate reference work, but do not consider these works a prime source of materials for term papers. Following is a list of some of the most useful reference works.

Biography:
American Men of Science
Contemporary American Authors
Current Biography
Dictionary of American Biography
Dictionary of National Biography (British)
International Who's Who
Twentieth Century Authors
Who's Who (mostly British)
Who's Who in America
World Biography

Business:
Encyclopedia of Banking and Finance

Education:
Cyclopedia of Education
Encyclopedia of Educational Research

History, Political Science, and Social Science:

Cambridge Ancient History
Cambridge Medieval History
Cambridge Modern History
Cyclopedia of American Government
Dictionary of American History
Dictionary of Philosophy and Psychology
Dictionary of Political Economy
Encyclopedia of Psychology
Encyclopedia of the Social Sciences
Encyclopedia of World History

Literature and the Arts:

A History of Architecture
Cambridge History of American Literature
Cambridge History of English Literature
Columbia Dictionary of Modern European Literature
Dictionary of Music and Musicians
Dictionary of Painters and Engravers
Dictionary of World Literature
Harper's Encyclopedia of Art
International Cyclopedia of Music and Musicians
Oxford Classical Dictionary
Oxford Companion to American Literature
Oxford Companion to Classical Literature
Oxford Companion to English Literature

Religion:

Catholic Encyclopedia
Dictionary of the Bible
Encyclopedia of Religion and Ethics
Jewish Encyclopedia
New Schaff-Herzog Encyclopedia of Religious Knowledge

Science and Agriculture:

Cyclopedia of American Agriculture
Dictionary of Applied Chemistry
Scientific Encyclopedia
Technical and Scientific Encyclopedia

Yearbooks:

The American Yearbook
The Americana Annual
The Britannica Book of the Year
The New International Yearbook

Social Work Yearbook
Statesman's Yearbook
United Nations Yearbook
World Almanac

Not all libraries have all of these reference works, but any college library will have several for most subject-matter fields. All such books are available on the open shelves in the reference room. When you cannot find a potentially useful reference book, consult the card catalogue or ask the reference librarian for help.

Though the general and special reference works may make minor contributions to your term papers, they are not major source materials. Most of your information you must collect from books, pamphlets, newspapers, and articles from magazines and learned journals. These materials are also given standard arrangement and accessibility in all libraries.

The card catalogue

The library card catalogue guides you in finding books and pamphlets that may provide source materials for your term papers. Most books are entered three times in the card catalogue: once under the name of the author, once under the title, and once by subject heading. (All the cards are arranged alphabetically.) Occasionally you will know the name of an author who has written on your subject or the title of a possibly useful book, in which case it is a simple matter to discover whether your library has the book.

Here is a sample card that lists a book alphabetically by author's name; it was found under the N's.

341①.672   Nogee, Joseph L②
N68   ③ Soviet policy towards international control of atomic
                      energy. [Notre Dame, Ind.] University of Notre Dame
                      Press, 1961.
                      ⑦xiv, 306 p. 24 cm. (Notre Dame international studies)
                      ⑩ Bibliography: p. 286–297.

                      ⑪ 1. Atomic power—International control. I. Title.
                      ⑫ (Series: Notre Dame, Ind. University. Committee on International Relations. International studies)

                      ⑬ HD9698. A22N6   341.672   61–10850
                         Library of Congress   [61F5]

The small numbered circles do not appear on the card; they correspond to the following explanations:

1. Library call number
2. Author
3. Title
4. Place of publication
5. Publisher
6. Date of publication
7. Number of pages in prefatory material
8. Number of pages in text of book
9. Height of book in centimeters
10. Indication that the book contains a 12-page bibliography
11. Subject heading
12. Indication that the book is one of series
13. Information for librarians only

Here is a sample card that lists the same book alphabetically by title; it was found under the S's.

341.672   Soviet policy towards international control of atomic
N68   energy
          Nogee, Joseph L. [Notre Dame, Ind.] University of
          Notre Dame Press, 1961.
              xiv, 306 p. 24 cm. (Notre Dame international studies)
              Bibliography: pp. 286–297.

              1. Atomic power—International control. I. Title.
          (Series: Notre Dame, Ind. University. Committee on In-
          ternational Relations. International studies)

          HD9698.   A22N6   341.672   61–10850
          Library of Congress   [61F5]

With knowledge of either the author's last name or of the title of the book, you can quickly see if it is in your library's holdings.

In gathering materials through the card catalogue, however, your main reliance must be placed on subject-heading cards, for you will seldom know many authors or titles to investigate. For example, suppose you chose the topic "Methods of Inspection in International Control of Atomic Weapons." What useful titles or authors would you already know about? Probably few, if any. Therefore you would need to look for books and pamphlets by subject-heading cards. Here is a sample card that lists the same book by subject heading; it was found under the A's.

341.672
N68
	Atomic power—International control
	Nogee, Joseph L
	    Soviet policy towards international control of atomic energy. [Notre Dame, Ind.] University of Notre Dame Press, 1961.
	    xiv, 306 p. 24 cm. (Notre Dame international studies)
	    Bibliography: p. 286–297.
	
	    1. Atomic power—International control. I. Title. (Series: Notre Dame, Ind. University. Committee on International Relations. International studies)
	
	HD9698. A22N6 341.672 61–10850
	Library of Congress [61F5]

Since subject headings are so important in term paper research, most libraries type subject headings in red for quick identification.

Cross references

In using the card catalogue for practical research, you will frequently be plagued with the question "What subject heading should I look under?" For example, if you were to choose the topic mentioned in the preceding paragraph, which subject heading would you look for: atomic energy, atomic weapons, international control, inspection, or some other? All too frequently you will feel baffled. But **cross-reference** subject-heading cards will give you good guidance. Often in front of the first book listed under any subject heading, you will find a cross-reference card that suggests other headings that may be fruitfully investigated. For example, before the first book listed under the subject heading "Astronomy," which usually appears in red above the author and title of the book, you will find several cross-reference cards suggesting the following as possible alternatives for investigation:

Astronomy
   See also

Calendar	Cosmography
Comets	Earth
Constellations	Geodesy

Mechanics, celestial	Planets, and names of planets
Meteorites	Seasons
Meteors	Solar system
Milky Way	Spectrum analysis
Moon	Stars
Nautical almanacs	Sun
Nautical astronomy	Also headings beginning with
Orbits	the word Astronomical

Of course not all subject headings will have such extensive cross references, but most will have a few, and you will find it absolutely essential to investigate cross-reference subject headings if you are to do successful term-paper research.

The periodical indexes

Most research-paper topics require some source materials from articles in magazines, learned journals, and newspapers; and topics on recent issues or events often draw on those sources only. The periodical indexes list articles just as the card catalogue lists books and pamphlets. In fact, there are only two essential differences between the indexes and the card catalogue: the indexes print many entries on a single page rather than one entry per card, and most of them list articles only by author and subject heading, not also by title. As with the card catalogue, you will find most use for the subject headings in the indexes.

Since articles appear by the millions (it is estimated that about one million articles on science alone appear each year), not all articles can be listed in one periodical index. Hence there is a periodical index for each major subject-matter field. There is, however, one important general index: *The Readers' Guide to Periodical Literature*. This is the index you will find most useful in seeking source materials for your term papers. *The Readers' Guide* lists articles from about 200 general, wide-circulation magazines, but not from the thousands of small-circulation learned journals. However, it may often be the only index you need to consult for term-paper work—that is, until you undertake advanced work, at which time you will probably not use *The Readers' Guide* at all.

Issues of *The Readers' Guide* appear in pamphlet form about every month, and these in turn are incorporated into volumes that list articles for one or more years. The inclusive dates are clearly imprinted on the spine of each cumulative volume. *The Readers'* *Guide* lists articles since 1900 (first volume published in 1905).

Following is a sample selection of entries from *The Readers'* *Guide:*

PARKER, William Riley
Refocusing the English program. NEA J 50:
38–40 N '61

PARKES, A. S. and Bruce, H. M.
Olfactory stimuli in mammalian reproduction.
bibliog Science 134: 1049–54 O 13 '61

PARKING, automobile. *See* Automobile parking

PARKING lots. *See* Automobile parking

PARKING meters
Fast figuring of parking charges. il Am City
76: 120 Jl '61
Newport Beach's parking policy. T. H.
Childs. il Am City 76: 119+ Mr '61
This hitching post makes a profit for many
communities! Sat Eve Post 234: 10 Ap 1 '61
Tight parking enforcement: Huntington, W.
Va. E. F. Duff. il Am City 76: 96–7 Mr
'61

PARKINSON, Cyril Northcote
Art of being no. 2. Fortune 64: 123–6+ S '61
Mr Upton-Cumming, of the establishment.
NY Times Mag p 43+ Ag 20 '61
On the ball. New Yorker 37: 22–3 Ja 20 '62
Parkinson's lore. il pors Arch Forum 114:
92–5 Mr '61

PARKINSON, Margaret B.
And from now on, no hooky. Mlle 53: 154–5 +
S '61

PARKINSONS disease. *See* Paralysis

In this sample, items 1, 2, 6, and 7 are entries by name of author; item 5 includes four entries under one subject heading; the other entries are cross references. As in the card catalogue, cross references in the periodical indexes are often extensive. For example, the cross references for "Astronomy" in one volume of *The Readers' Guide* are as follows:

ASTRONOMY
> See also
> Comets
> Constellations
> Cosmography
> Earth
> Galactic systems
> Meteorites
> Nebulae
> Radar in astronomy
> Radio astronomy
> Stars
> Telescope
> Television in astronomy

In other volumes, even more cross references might be listed. In seeking source materials for your research paper, you must depend heavily on cross references both in the card catalogue and the periodical indexes.

The entries in *The Readers' Guide* include many abbreviations, which are explained in prefatory material for each volume. For example, in the first entry reproduced, NEA J means that the article appeared in the *NEA Journal;* the figure *50: 38–40* means volume 50, pages 38 to 40; and N '61 means the November issue of 1961. In the fourth entry under C. N. Parkinson, the *il* means that the magazine *Architectural Forum* is illustrated and the *pors* means that it has portraits. You consult the prefatory material in *The Readers' Guide* for abbreviations that you don't understand.

There are several other general periodical indexes that are often useful in term-paper research:

> *International Index* (covers American and foreign periodicals in the humanities, from 1907)
> *Poole's Index to Periodical Literature* (covers American and English periodicals, many now defunct, from 1802 to 1906)
> *Public Affairs Information Service* (covers books, periodicals, and pamphlets in economics, government, and public affairs, from 1915)
> *United States Government Publications* (covers all government publications, from 1895)

Periodical indexes for special subject fields are the following:

> *Agriculture Index* (includes books, pamphlets, and articles, from 1916)

Art Index (from 1929)

Biography Index (from 1946)

Book Review Digest (lists book reviews by author, title, and subject, from 1905)

Dramatic Index (American and English, from 1909)

Education Index (includes books, pamphlets, and articles, from 1929)

Engineering Index (from 1906)

Index to Legal Periodicals (from 1926)

Industrial Arts Index (from 1913)

Quarterly Cumulative Index Medicus (covers medical literature from many countries, from 1927)

The chief index to newspaper articles is *The New York Times Index,* which is published monthly and has annual volumes dating from 1913. Most libraries have files of *The New York Times,* but even when that newspaper is not available, the *Index* can be useful, for it will indicate the approximate date news items were published in other newspapers.

The periodical card file

Since many hundreds of magazines and journals are covered in the periodical indexes, many libraries will not have copies of all of them. Every library, however, has a card file listing the magazines and journals that it does have, with the inclusive dates of its holdings. Small libraries often file these periodical cards in the regular card catalogue; larger libraries usually have a separate card catalogue for periodicals only. In either case, it is easy for you to determine whether your library has the magazines in which you are interested.

Many aids to research other than those listed are available, but few undergraduate term papers require research beyond the sources listed here.

THE WORKING BIBLIOGRAPHY

Once you have selected a suitable research-paper topic, your next step is to prepare a working bibliography by canvassing the library sources discussed above. A **bibliography** is a list of books, articles, and other source materials on any particular topic. At the end of your research paper you will have a bibliography that lists all the sources from which you gathered information for your paper. But of course you must have a list of these sources before you can begin work on your paper, and so you compile a working bibliography.

You can compile a complete working bibliography before you read a single item of your list; and it is wise to compile as full a bibliography as you can before you begin intensive work on your paper. However, if you know little about your topic, you should first read some general material pertaining to it in order to be certain of its suitability. Also you should be prepared to add to your working bibliography after you begin intensive work, for one piece of source material will sometimes lead you to others that you did not discover originally.

Be systematic in compiling your working bibliography. First, come to as full an understanding of your topic as you can by converting it into a few specific questions. For example, suppose you chose the topic "The Scandals that Destroyed the Pacific Coast Conference in the Late 1950s." Your questions might be these: "What was the constitution of the Pacific Coast Conference? What charges of irregularities in sports activities were made against which universities and who made the charges? How did the defendant universities try to refute the charges? What punishments were inflicted on the supposedly guilty schools? How and when did the disintegration of the Conference occur?"

After converting your topic into a few such specific questions you should then make a list of key terms that might be used as subject headings in the periodical indexes (including *The New York Times Index*) and the card catalogue. For the above topic you might list these possible headings:

1. Pacific Coast Conference
2. Football
3. The names of the universities in the Conference
4. Sports
5. Recruiting in sports
6. Sports scandals
7. The name of any university official prominent in the controversy

After compiling a list of possible subject headings (and of course any specific authors and titles you may know that are pertinent to your topic), you should begin canvassing the library sources for items to put in your working bibliography. If you think the general and special encyclopedias and reference works may have usable information for you, investigate them first. Then try the card catalogue, making sure that you exhaust all cross references. Finally you canvass *The Readers' Guide* and, if necessary, other periodical indexes, also being sure to examine every cross reference.

As you follow this ordered process, fill out a separate bibliography card for each item you think may provide you with information; never list two items on the same card. Use 3-by-5-inch note cards and number each card sequentially in the upper right-hand corner. (You will need these numbers later in your note-taking.) Be sure to list on each card full information about the item: (1) the library call number of a book or periodical; (2) the full name of the author; (3) the exact title of the book or article; (4) the exact name of a magazine, journal, or reference work; (5) the date, place of publication, and publisher of a book; (6) the date and volume number of a magazine; (7) the page numbers of the article in a magazine; (8) the volume and page numbers of an article in a reference work; and (9) a notation on whether the item has a bibliography of its own or any other feature that might be of additional help to you. All of this information can be secured from the card catalogue or a periodical index; you do not check out an item in order to prepare a working bibliography card for it.

Here is a sample bibliography card for the book illustrated above in the discussion of the card catalogue:

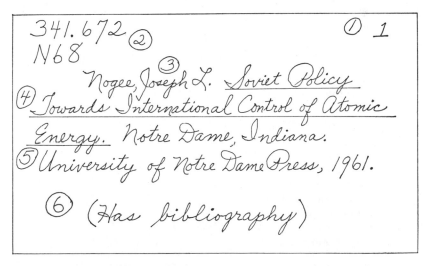

Explanation of the encircled numbers on the bibliography card:

1. The number of the bibliography card
2. The call number of the book
3. The author
4. The title
5. Publication data: place, publisher, date
6. Informational note

Here is a sample bibliography card for a magazine article listed in the sample above taken from *The Readers' Guide:*

Explanation of the encircled numbers on the bibliography card:

1. The number of the bibliography card
2. The call number of the periodical (You will obtain this information from the periodical card file or card catalogue rather than from the periodical index. In smaller libraries, periodicals may not be given call numbers, in which case they are placed in the stacks alphabetically and thus are easily found.)
3. The author
4. The title of the article
5. The name of the magazine
6. Publication date
7. Volume and page numbers
8. Informational note

For two reasons it is very important to enter all of the above information on each bibliography card: (1) so that you can check out a book or periodical without returning to the card catalogue or periodical index and (2) so that you can write footnotes and bibliographic entries for your paper without checking out the item a second time. If you omit any of the information, you will be forced to do useless rechecking later on.

In preparing your working bibliography, you will often have to judge from titles, subject headings, or other scant information whether a particular item will be useful. Since you will not be preparing an exhaustive paper for publication, you need list only those items that seem to have a reasonable chance of furnishing you information. After you begin reading the articles and books on your working bibliography, you should watch for references to other works that may have pertinent information for your paper. Often your most important source materials will be discovered in this way.

Different topics will of course require various quantities of source materials, and thus there can be wide variation in the number of items on working bibliographies. With almost any topic you should feel unsafe with fewer than ten items as a starter; not many topics should require more than thirty.

PRELIMINARY OUTLINING

As you gather material for your paper, you should keep in mind the need for organizing it into a coherent whole. Your paper is not to be a mere compilation of facts selected at random; it is to be a new, organic whole of its own. It should not read like a series of excerpts, but should have a clear beginning, middle, and end. It must be organized, and this means that its parts must fit together clearly and logically and in the proper sequence.

An outline is concrete evidence of organization. You will present a formal outline with your finished paper (see Appendix 2), but that kind of outline is best prepared after the paper is written. You need a working (scratch) outline to help you write your paper. How much you already know about your topic will determine how much of a scratch outline you can prepare before you actually begin taking notes from your source materials. *You should, however, make as much of an outline as you can as soon as you can and then revise or add to it periodically as you do more reading and note-taking.*

Turning your topic into a few specific questions will help you prepare a general scratch outline before you do much reading. For example, suppose you should choose the topic "Communist Brain-washing of American Prisoners in the Korean War." You might formulate these questions: "What was the aim of the brainwashing attempt? What techniques were used? How many American prisoners were involved and what were some of the notable cases? What success did American officials think the Communists had in their brainwashing? What official judgment was passed on those who were brainwashed?" From these questions you might decide, tentatively, that your paper could take this form:

    I. A definition and explanation of the aims of brainwashing
   II. The techniques of brainwashing practiced by the Communists in Korea, with examples
  III. The results of their program as officially admitted by American government officials
  IV. Governmental action toward American soldiers who were brainwashed

With a preliminary scratch outline like this to begin with, your actual work on a paper will be greatly simplified. As soon as you can, you should list in scratch form the three, four, or five main parts around which your paper will be organized. Then you should revise and amplify your outline as your work progresses. Preparing a preliminary outline, however scant, will make your task of note-taking much easier.

NOTE-TAKING

After you have a working bibliography compiled and, if possible, a scratch outline prepared, your next step is to begin taking notes from your sources, notes from which you will develop your finished paper. Since your materials are gathered from sources and not created out of your imagination, note-taking is perhaps the most important part of your research-paper work. The accuracy and skill with which you can take usable notes will in large part determine the success of your paper.

Evaluating source materials

If your topic is of a factual nature, such as "Current Theories about the Neutrino," your chief task is to be accurate and complete in taking notes. But if your topic is controversial, such as "The

Role of General Walker in the University of Mississippi Riots of 1962," then you must use in your note-taking all your powers of evaluating the reliability and soundness of your sources.

One of the most important aspects of your college education is learning to pass valid judgment on what you read. You can't rely on the truthfulness of a statement just because it is in print; in fact, probably more untruth than truth is in print. Evaluating source materials, then, is a very important part of research-paper writing, particularly if the topic is controversial.

Evaluating source materials does not mean just determining whether they pertain to your topic, but whether they are sound, reliable, and truthful. For example, if you were writing on "The Controversy over Bombing in the Vietnam War," you would need to distinguish between Republican and Democratic propaganda and objective and truthful materials. Making such a distinction is very difficult (often impossible, for truth can be very hard to find or recognize), but as a researcher you must do your best to be objective and honest and you must be willing to take pains in trying to find the truth. In evaluating source materials, you must take into consideration (1) the reliability of the author, (2) the recency of the material, (3) the completeness of the material, and (4) the distinction between verifiable facts and opinions. Complete success in evaluation is, of course, impossible; you can only do your best.

Digesting source materials

As you take notes, you must use your mind as well as your pen and paper. Many students try to escape work by merely transferring information from the source material to the finished paper without letting it register in their minds. Consequently, many research papers are no more than compilations of sentences and paragraphs taken at random from various sources and put together in a haphazard fashion. Such work can by no means receive a passing grade as a research paper. You must not only seek out source materials, but you must assimilate them into your mind. You should make yourself a bona fide expert on your topic by reading your materials carefully and retaining the essence of what you read. If your paper is to be really good, you must come to know a great deal more about your topic than you put in your paper. You must digest your materials, not merely transfer them from the original sources to the typewritten page.

Techniques in note-taking

Note-taking is, in a large degree, an individual matter. Some people can successfully take notes in an apparently disordered fashion, and some have excellent memories which enable them to take only sketchy notes. But most students need to take notes systematically. You should follow these suggestions closely:

1. As best you can, arrange your bibliography cards in a sequence of general importance to your paper and take notes on the various sources in that sequence. Be prepared, of course, to add new bibliography cards.
2. For your note cards, use half-sheets of notebook or typing paper. You may also use 3-by-5-inch or 4-by-6-inch cards, but half-sheets give more flexibility in space, are cheaper, and are just as handy to arrange for use in writing the paper.
3. Identify the source of the information on a note card by entering in the upper right-hand corner the number of the bibliography card which lists that source. (Remember, your bibliography cards should be numbered in sequence.) This short method of identification will eliminate a lot of tedious recopying.
4. In addition to the number of the bibliography card, be sure to put on each note card the exact page numbers from which you take the information. Failure to enter page numbers can only result in tedious rechecking.
5. Do not put on one note card information from two distinct parts of your paper, even though both pieces of information come from the same source. Instead, use two note cards.
6. Do not put information from two different sources on one note card, even though both pieces of information belong to the same part of the paper. Each note card should be identified with only one bibliography card. This simplifies the writing of footnotes.
7. Take most of your notes in a condensed, summarized form so that you can re-expand them later in your own words. However, you will want to take some notes verbatim, and then you must take care to be absolutely accurate. (The section following on paraphrasing and the use of direct quotations will further explain this aspect of note-taking.)
8. As you develop your working outline, try to identify on each note card just to which part of your outline the information belongs. This will simplify your task when you begin to convert your notes into your finished paper, for you can then arrange your note cards to correspond with your outline headings.

9. Learn to skim through source materials so that you will not waste time in concentrated reading of useless material. Having turned your topic into a few specific questions or having a good working outline will help you examine materials rapidly without overlooking pertinent information. As soon as you find useful material, slow down and be thorough and accurate in your reading and note-taking. After you begin systematically examining the items listed on your bibliography cards, you will find that some of them are of no use to you at all. Such minor frustrations are just a part of research and investigation. Consider the research chemist. Can he always discover a useful product on his first experiment? Research means separating the usable from the useless.

10. Be as neat and legible in your note-taking as your own abilities require. Don't be too hasty for your own good and don't crowd too much material on one note card. Be sure to get everything accurate the first time: bibliography card reference, page numbers, direct quotations (if any), and the information itself.

Following is a sample of note-taking. Topic: "Controversy over the Existence of Extrasensory Perception." Questions: "What is a definition of extrasensory perception? On what bases do some notable scholars claim that it exists? What are a few specific experiments that they have conducted? On what bases do other scholars refute these claims? What is my objective conclusion on the basis of the evidence?"

Let us examine this passage from a source listed on a hypothetical bibliography card:

> . . . Whether or not there is enough material left to sustain Dr. Rhine's case, one comes away from his account with the feeling that, much as he believes in the necessity for rigor, he is not always willing to insist upon it.
>
> Dissatisfaction with the controls is increased by the long list of conditions with which he finds it necessary to surround his experiments. Extrasensory perception is a "delicate and subtle capacity" something like the creation of poetry in its instability. The experimenter must be "friendly, almost fraternal" and the experiments "casual and informal." The situation must appeal to the subject; he must not be reluctant or feel hurried. There must be a spirit of play; a monetary reward is destructive. Strong emotions, illness, fatigue, over-intellectual analysis, or pre-formed beliefs may interfere. And so on.—B. F. Skinner, "Is Sense Necessary."

A note card based on this source would look as follows:

Explanations of encircled numbers on the note card:

1. The number of the corresponding bibliography card, which will contain all the information about the source: author, title, facts of publication
2. Heading that identifies where the information fits in the paper
3. Actual page numbers that the information is taken from
4. A condensed summary of the information

If the information from this source had seemed usable as a direct quotation, the note-taker would have copied it verbatim and would have indicated on his note card that it was a direct quotation.

DIRECT QUOTATIONS;
PARAPHRASING; PLAGIARISM

Paraphrasing

A direct quotation is, of course, an *exact* reproduction of the words of another writer. A paraphrase is the statement in your own words of information or ideas you have taken from source materials. It is most important in term-paper work for you to distinguish between direct quotations and paraphrasing. Using someone else's words as your own is **plagiarism**—literary theft—which alone justifies a grade of F. Your professor can easily distinguish between professional writing and your own, and he will not tolerate plagiarism. The best way to guard against it is to take condensed, summarized notes (except when you take verbatim notes for probable use as a direct quotation). Then when you use your notes you will expand them in your own words.

Look again at the condensed notes on the sample note card. In preparing his paper, a writer might use these notes to compose this passage for his paper:

> In addition to maintaining that Dr. Rhine does not practice the rigor in experimentation that he says he believes in, this reviewer feels that Rhine fails to control his experiments sufficiently because he attaches too many conditions to them. For example, he believes that Rhine loses scientific rigor when he insists on the experimenter being "friendly" and "casual and informal" with the subject of the experiment. He also believes that Rhine attributes too many of his failures to such causes as payment for services, illness, fatigue, and prejudice or emotionalism on the part of the subject.

A comparison of this finished passage for inclusion in a term paper with the original source quoted above will illustrate proper paraphrasing: remaining true to the spirit and facts of the source material, but using one's own style of writing. *The process is from source material to condensed notes to re-expression in one's own style.* Of course beginners in academic research must be allowed some freedom in imitating the style of their sources, but deliberate plagiarism cannot be tolerated.

Uses of direct quotations

Direct quotations have two minor and two major roles in research papers. One minor role, which usually calls for a short quotation, is to emphasize a point or fact; quoted material is naturally emphasized by virtue of being quoted. Another minor role is to share with the reader material that is striking and original in its phrasing; this is an esthetic use of direct quotations. These uses should not be overworked.

The two important uses of direct quotations are (1) to make use of the direct words of an authority to sanction a point of view and (2) to present original evidence for a conclusion you draw. These two uses differ. For example, suppose you wrote a paper on "Natural Control of Insect Pests." You might quote a famous entomologist to the effect that natural control eliminates many of the dangers of pesticides. His eminence in his field would lend weight to this point of view. Now suppose you wrote on "Jeffersonian Ideas in the Speeches of Franklin D. Roosevelt." You would, of course, first become acquainted with Jeffersonian ideas and then would read the speeches of Roosevelt to discover Jeffersonian overtones. In writing your paper you would quote from the Roosevelt speeches simply to give evidence for your conclusion that he expressed Jeffersonian ideas. You would not be quoting Roosevelt because he was an expert on Jeffersonian ideas, but as evidence of the fact that he used the ideas.

When a direct quotation appears in a research paper, it must fulfill one of these definite purposes. *It must not be aimlessly tossed into the paper.* The paper is your creation; the direct quotations in it must be used creatively. Do not quote commonly known information such as can be found in several sources. For example, you should not quote birth and death dates, statistics that can be found in various good reference works, or scientific information that any good teacher might be expected to know. Few practices give as gauche an appearance to a term paper as a direct quotation of this sort: "Beethoven was born in Bonn, Germany, on December 16, 1770, and died there on March 26, 1827." (accompanying footnote) Also be wary of using a direct quotation to open a term paper, for such a practice is usually awkward.

There are two methods of entering a direct quotation into a paper. When it will take up five or fewer normal lines of your text, you should enclose it in quotation marks and incorporate it directly into the text of your paper.

Sometimes you will want to leave out part of the original in using a direct quotation. You indicate such an omission by putting three spaced periods (. . .) in place of the omitted material. If you omit the last part of a sentence, or a whole sentence, use four periods. If you enter a word or words not actually in the original quotation, such as a name for clear reference, enclose them in square brackets [like this].

```
    The second method--called the inset or
block  method  of  quotation--is  illustrated
here. You should use it when a quotation will
take up six or more lines of your paper. You do
not enclose an inset in quotation marks, for
the inset form itself indicates a direct quo-
tation. Indent each line of the inset five
spaces. Give the first line additional para-
graph indentation only if a paragraph actually
began  there  in  the  source  material.  Single
space the inset (the rest of the paper, except
footnotes, to be double spaced); in longhand,
skip a line before and after it. An inset need
not be--usually is not--a separate paragraph.
```

When using a direct quotation as evidence for a conclusion you draw or to establish authority for a point of view, use an *introductory phrase or sentence* which will make the quotation an integral part of the paper. Even such a short, simple phrase as "according to the well-known geneticist So-and-so" will tie a quotation in with the rest of the paper and provide coherence. You should never just abruptly enter an important quotation without announcing its purpose. Such a practice makes a paper appear disjointed.

Always be absolutely accurate in using direct quotations. Get the habit of checking carefully as you take verbatim notes for possible use as direct quotations. Be sure to paraphrase when you do not quote material directly.

DOCUMENTATION

In a research paper, documentation means the acknowledgement of the sources used. One aspect of documentation is the appendage of a bibliography of items used in preparing the paper; another is footnoting.

Uses of footnotes

There are three main uses of footnotes. The first is to acknowledge the source of direct quotations. Every direct quotation must be absolutely accurate and either enclosed in quotation marks or identified as an inset. The footnote tells the reader exactly where he can find the quotation. Well-known quotations (such as from Shakespeare or the Bible) and common dictionary definitions should not be footnoted when they are used for embellishment rather than as evidence.

The second use of footnotes is to acknowledge the source of evidence or important information even when it is not quoted directly. Here you must distinguish between important information or evidence that builds your paper and relatively unimportant information or easily ascertained facts. Obviously the source of every single fact in a paper should not be acknowledged, else the paper would be cluttered with excessive footnotes. But the source of evidence and information of central importance must be cited. In general, it is difficult to learn when and when not to footnote unquoted (paraphrased) material. *The crux is to avoid footnoting material that will pass without question*—that is, that a critical reader will accept without doubt or suspicion. Information that is central to the paper or that a critical reader might question or that can be found in just one source should usually be footnoted.

The third use is to put in the paper explanatory material that would be out of place in the text of the paper. An explanatory footnote is likely to begin with such a phrase as "an interesting sidelight in this connection . . ." or "a consequent result that had no bearing on cancer research itself. . . ." Explanatory footnotes are not common in term papers. Using them to be impressive is not a recommended practice.

Location of footnotes

There are three ways of entering footnotes in a research paper, though one of the methods doesn't actually involve footnote forms. The traditional method, most frequently used in freshman composition because the term paper in that course is often a training device, is to place the footnote at the bottom of the page on which appears the source material being acknowledged. Under this method a two- or three-inch line should separate the text from the footnotes on any one page, and a one-inch margin should be maintained at the bottom of each page.

Typing footnotes at the bottom of a page presents difficulties, for even the most careful typist will often forget to leave enough space for the footnotes of any particular page. A good way to prevent this trouble is to insert a guide sheet under your sheet of typing paper. On an 8½-by-11-inch sheet of typing paper you can prepare for yourself a guide sheet like the one illustrated here. The numbers and lines of the guide sheet will show through and will guide you in leaving enough space for your footnotes. If you are also typing a carbon copy, be sure to place the guide sheet on the inert side of the carbon paper.

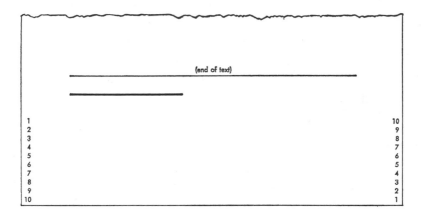

The second method is to place all footnotes at the end of the paper. This method makes the typing of a paper much easier.

In both of these methods (a necessity in the second) footnotes should be numbered consecutively throughout the paper (1, 2, 3, and so on). Each footnote should be single spaced, with double spacing between footnotes. Raised numbers (without periods) should be used both in the text immediately **after** the material being acknowledged and with the footnote itself. Each footnote should be indented as a paragraph—that is, the first line indented five spaces and successive lines flush with the established margin.

The third method of acknowledging source materials is the simplest, but the least used in term papers. In using this method, you number the items in your bibliography, and then in place of a footnote number in the text of your paper you place in parentheses the number of the bibliographic entry that is the source of the material and the page numbers on which the material appears. For example, (4, pp. 21–22) after a quotation would indicate that it appears on pages 21 and 22 of the bibliographic entry number 4. A variation of this method is to use the name of the author rather than the number of the bibliographic entry—for example, (Morton, p. 14). Under this variation, the bibliographic entries are not numbered, the full name of the author is given if two in the bibliography have the same last name, and both the author's name and the title are given if that author is represented more than once in the bibliography.

Which of these methods of footnoting you use will depend on your professor's preference.

Footnote forms

Various footnote forms are in common use, and any standard form, if consistently used, is satisfactory. The forms recommended here emphasize simplicity. You should not make a special effort to memorize the forms, though if such memorization comes easy for you, you can certainly profit from your talent. Even experienced writers of term papers usually just check the proper guide form each time they write a footnote. Since there are so many commas, periods, quotation marks, underlinings, and parentheses in footnotes, you can insure accuracy best by patiently copying a guide form. Accuracy in form has the same importance that conventions of usage have in writing.

GUIDE TO FOOTNOTE FORMS

Though you will refer to these forms as you write footnotes, you should first study them all carefully so that you will know how to use them as guides. Remember that the use of italics here is equal to underlining in a typed paper.

Form for a Book:
   [1] John F. Bateson, *A New Look at Vocational Education* (New York, 1968), p. 106.

Form for a Magazine Article:
   [2] Jasper S. Jackson, "Education in the Atomic Age," *The Atlantic,* CII (June 1959), p. 97.

Form for an Encyclopedia Article (Anonymous):
   [3] "Education," *Encyclopaedia Britannica* (12th ed.), IV, 642.

Form for a Newspaper Article:

[4] *Portland Oregonian,* 17 August 1960, sect. G, p. 7.

Note: If the name of the newspaper does not clearly identify its city, put the city and state in parentheses after the name of the newspaper. If the paper consists of only one section or part, give only the page number. If the reference is to a newspaper article with a by-line, put the author's name and the name of his column before the name of the newspaper, as in the form for a magazine article.

Form for a Later Edition of a Book:

[5] Herbert Schwimp, *The Philosophy of Education* (New York, 1956; 2d ed.), pp. 18–21.

Form for an Edited Book:

[6] Helen Fogle (ed.), *Tributes to John Dewey* (New York, 1940), p. xiv.

Form for a Component Part of an Edited Book:

[7] E. Z. Morales, "Wealth and Education," in *Essays in Philosophy,* edited by P. G. Wall (Caldwell, Idaho, 1968), p. 275.

Form for a Work in Several Volumes:

[8] Harry Speigle, *A History of Education* (Chicago, 1955), III, p. 90.

Form for a Work by Two Authors:

[9] Thomas Jones and Alfred Hill, *Perspectives in Education* (New York, 1964), p. 66.

Form for a Work by Three or More Authors:

[10] Mary Blake and others, *Educational Studies* (New York, 1968), p. 48.

Form for a Translated Book:

[11] Julio Petrillo, *Education and Class Structure,* trans. by John Moon (New York, 1962), p. 290.

Form for a Pamphlet:

[12] *Higher Education for Democracy,* Report of the President's Commission on Higher Education (Washington, 1957), p. 26.

Short Forms:

Once a work has been referred to, any subsequent footnote for it should be of a **short form.**

If the footnote is the same (except for page number) as the immediately preceding footnote the abbreviation *ibid.* (meaning "in the same place") should be used as the short form. *Ibid.* may be used any number of times in succession, and intervening pages without footnotes do not limit its use. Practice is now divided on underlining *ibid.;* it is always capitalized as a footnote; it always has a period after it. Note that a comma separates *ibid.* from a new page number.

> [13] Norman Harris, *Education and Technology* (London, 1964), p. 98.
> [14] *Ibid.,* p. 119.
> [15] *Ibid.*

When there has been an intervening footnote, *ibid.* cannot be used. In such a case the **short form** can be just the author's last name, plus a page number.

> [16] Speigle, p. 39.

The short form can be a title (if anonymous) plus a page number.

> [17] "Education and Earnings," p. 43.

If the paper has footnotes referring to two authors with the same last name, then the short form should list the author's whole name, plus the page number.

> [18] Bertrand Smith, p. 42.

If the paper has referred to two works by the same author, then the short form should give the author's last name and the title, plus the page number.

> [19] Harris, *Industrial Education,* p. 346.

Always use *ibid.* as a short form when the footnote is the same as the immediately preceding one. Use the author's name as a short form when there has been an intervening footnote. The abbreviation *op. cit.* (work cited) is totally unnecessary in a short-form footnote.

In the form for a magazine article, the Roman numeral refers to the volume number of the magazine. Most good magazines have volume numbers. However, if you use a magazine that does not have a volume number, just refer to it by date.

> [20] Jerry Bildt, "Be Educated and Healthy," *Modern Health,* June 1962, pp. 54–55.

Bibliography

At the end of your research paper you will place a bibliography, a list of all the sources you have used in preparing your paper. You need not necessarily have referred to a work in a footnote to place it in your bibliography, but you should have found definite use for it in preparing your paper. Enter your bibliography on a separate sheet or sheets of paper and center it for neatness. Number the entries in it *only* if you are to use the numbers as explained above in the third method of footnoting. Do not separate entries into categories, such as books and magazine articles. Alphabetize the entries according to last name of author or, if the work is anonymous, the first word of the title (except *a, an,* or *the*); do not use the word *anonymous* in the bibliography. If you have two or more entries by the same author, you may substitute a long dash (————) for the author's name after its first use. Indent the bibliographic entries just the opposite of footnotes; begin the first line with the established margin and indent all succeeding lines five spaces. Single space each entry but double space between entries.

As with footnotes, you should not try to memorize the bibliographic forms. Just refer to the guide as you write each entry. All the information needed should be on your working bibliography cards.

GUIDE TO BIBLIOGRAPHIC FORMS

Form for a Book:
Jackson, James Thomas. *Tank Warfare in Africa.* New York: The Macmillan Company, 1968.

Form for a Magazine Article:
Bates, Thomas H. "The American Army in Africa," *Harper's Magazine,* CCXXV (April 1964), 89–101.

Form for a Newspaper Article:
Spokesman Review (Spokane, Washington), 14 July 1963, part A, p. 6.
Note: See note under form for a newspaper article in the section on footnote forms.

Form for an Encyclopedia Article (Anonymous):
"Tank Warfare," *Encyclopaedia Britannica,* 13th ed., XXI, 906–13.

Form for a Later Edition of a Book:
Mosely, Ivan. *Tanks and Men*. 2d ed. Chicago: Claxton Press, 1968.

Form for an Edited Book:
Hill, James T. (ed.). *Stories of Tank Warfare*. New York: Home Press, 1958.

Form for a Component Part of an Edited Book:
Ruiz, Richard. "Panzer Units," in *Essays on Warfare*, ed. by Harley S. Jones. Chicago: Mobile Press, 1954.

Form for a Work in Several Volumes (All Used):
Jones, Harley S. *A History of Tank Warfare*. New York: S. S. Filtch, Inc., 1956. 3 vols.

Form for a Work in Several Volumes (One Used):
Jones, Harley S. *A History of Tank Warfare*. New York: S. S. Filtch, Inc., 1956. Vol. I.

Form for a Translated Book:
Gerhardt, Erich. *Blitzkrieg*. Trans. by Abner Porter. New York: The Dial Press, Inc., 1943.

Form for a Work by Two Authors:
Field, Robert and Charles Foreman. *Ancient Tanks*. Ann Arbor, Mich.: Adoption Press, 1962.

Form for a Work by Three or More Authors:
Field, Robert and others. *Modern Tanks*. New York: World Press & Co., Inc., 1963.

Form for a Pamphlet:
American Preparedness and International Tension. Washington: National Association of Pacifism, 1968.

In research-paper work, follow your professor's directions (1) in preparing a title page; (2) in entering a table of contents or prefatory material; (3) in providing an outline (see Appendix 2); (4) in entering appendixes, charts, graphs, and so on; and (5) in method of submitting paper.

The following specimen paper is an actual, undoctored freshman research project prepared by a good college student. It is intended to represent the real work of a college freshman, not an ideal product that ordinary students cannot hope to emulate. Its defects might be found in the work of the best college freshmen; its virtues are worth study.

THE SCIENTIFIC AMERICAN PSYCHICAL INVESTIGATION:

A CASE AGAINST SPIRITUALISM

by

William Wolfe

English 1A -- Section 12

Professor Willis

January 1968

OUTLINE

I. The <u>Scientific American</u> Psychic Investigation was well organized.

    A. Its committee was composed of five open-minded, level-headed men, who were sincerely interested in psychic research.

    B. It offered a $2500 prize to the medium who produced a genuine psychic phenomenen under laboratory conditions.

    C. It used scientific techniques in detecting fraud.

II. The majority of America's mediums did not cooperate with the committee.

    A. Only five mediums presented themselves before the committee during its two years of work.

    B. The mediums who entered were not among the nation's best or best known.

    C. The remainder of the mediums refused to enter or ignored the psychic competition.

III. The committee's findings were well founded.

    A. All five mediums investigated were declared to be fraudulent.

    B. The findings were borne out, in two instances, by subsequent developments.

        1. Peroraro confessed to being a fraud seven years later.

        2. Margery was exposed by two subsequent investigatory committees.

    C. In two years, the <u>Scientific American</u> Psychic Investigation Committee saw no genuine phenomena and found no actual medium.

THE SCIENTIFIC AMERICAN PSYCHICAL INVESTIGATION:

A CASE AGAINST SPIRITUALISM

Perhaps the Scientific American Psychical Investigation Committee was doomed to frustration from the very beginning. Before the investigation was over, friction developed between several members, and as a result, one person resigned and later left his job with Scientific American. The drama behind the findings, however, in no way lessens their validity. In two years of investigation into psychic phenomena, the committee saw no manifestation that they considered to be genuine. Their $2500 prize was not awarded. They found no real medium.

Spiritualism, as it is known today, began in 1848 with the famous fraud rappings of the Fox Sisters. From that time spiritualism snowballed until, as America roared into the twenties, it had attained stupendous proportions.[1]

By this time the leading magazines could no longer ignore it, and in January of 1922 Scientific American began a series of articles dealing

---

[1] Harry Houdini, Houdini on Magic, ed. by William B. Gibson and Morris N. Young (New York, 1953), pp. 122-123.

1

with spiritualism. The first article was authored by Hereward Carrington, a noted psychical researcher. His article, citing mysterious facets of the human body,[2] started the magazine's own snowball that was to produce an article a month for the following two-and-a-half years. Other articles were by Walter Franklin Prince who explained the problems of the psychic investigator.[3]

Harry Houdini, the magician and escape artist who had become quite a psychic exposer, was asked to write some of the articles in the series. He had to refuse because he could not spare the time necessary. He did, however, suggest to the magazine that they form an investigatory committee on which he would serve without pay.[4] The magazine accepted Houdini's suggestion and in December 1922 it was announced in Scientific American. The committee consisted of Dr. William McDougall, of Harvard University; Dr. Daniel F. Comstock, formerly of the Massachusetts Institute of Technology; Dr. William Franklin Prince, of the Society of Psychical Research; Hereward Carrington, a psychic investigator; and Houdini. J. Malcolm Bird, an associate editor of the magazine was appointed secretary. Scientific American offered $2500 to the first medium who could produce psychic phenomena under laboratory conditions to the satisfaction of four out of five of the committee members.

---

[2]Hereward Carrington, "The Mechanism of the Psychic," Scientific American, CXXVI (January 1922), p. 60.

[3]Walter Franklin Prince, "The Psychic Detective," Scientific American, CXXVII (July 1922), p. 6.

[4]Houdini, pp. 134-135.

2

The mediums were given two years--until December 1924--to decide if they wanted to enter.[5] Shortly afterward, Houdini offered $5000 of his own money, to go to the medium who could produce a psychic manifestation that he could not duplicate by normal means.[6]

The following month Sir Arthur Conan Doyle, who could always be counted upon to have something to say about psychic matters, had a letter published in the Scientific American in which he stated his objections to the committee's organization. He disagreed with the offer of the large sum of money, because, as he said, it would bring out "every rascal in the country."[7] There was probably little disagreement with this statement, but the money had to be offered to give weight and importance to the committee's findings. With such a large amount of money at stake, the decisions would not be hasty. Sir Arthur also disagreed with the make up of the committee. He disliked the skeptical, probing scientist type, and stated that the committee should have been composed of "gentle, quiet, courteous, sympathetic" men who are the most "useful" at a seance.[8] But again the magazine made a good choice. If the committee had been composed of just quiet gentlemen off the street it would not have been taken seriously. All the men on the committee were open minded and interested in an accurate appraisal of phenomena and, in addition,

---

[5]J. Malcolm Bird, "Square Deal for Psychics," Scientific American, CXXVII (December 1922), p. 375.

[6]William Lindsay Gresham, Houdini: The Man Who Walked Through Walls (New York, 1959), p. 234.

[7]Sir Arthur Conan Doyle, "Answer to Psychic Competition," Scientific American, CXXVIII (January 1923), p. 57.

[8]Ibid.

were distinguished enough in their own field to make their decisions acceptable to the public.

The committee's policy of investigation was that no "rough house" tactics would be used. They felt that if the medium was a fraud, they could prove him so by honorable means. It was agreed that the lights would not be flashed on suddenly during the dark seance, nor would any member attempt to tackle a spirit in an editorial. In 1923 the Scientific American said, "...Our investigation is a matter of science, not of assault and battery; and...any medium may come before us with the expectation of proper and courteous treatment."[9] In addition, the committee decided to provide conditions under which the medium could produce. As they stated, "The last thing we want is to be obliged to report that no phenomena were produced. If the medium is a fraud, our task is to make him think that it is safe for him to do his stuff, while at the same time providing means for detecting him."[10]

In all, five psychics entered the competition, the first seances being held nearly six months after the committee's organization. The mediums, Valiantine, Josie K. Stewart, Mrs. Tomson, Nino Pecoraro, and Margery, were each met with different receptions; but all failed to win the $2500.[11]

---

[9]"Our Psychic Investigation," Scientific American, CXXIX (August 1923), p. 84.

[10]J. Malcolm Bird, "Another Mediumistic Failure," Scientific American, CXXIX (December 1923), p. 391.

[11]Harry Price, Fifty Years of Psychical Research (London, 1939), p. 112.

The first seances were held in May, 1923, with a medium referred
to as Mr. X,[12] but later revealed to be Valiantine.[13] The phenomena
produced--voices and touches in total darkness--did not particularly
impress anyone concerned. The only good thing to come from these sittings was the chance for the investigators to test various fraud detection
devices. Because they believed that the medium moved from his chair, they
designed a system using a luminous button, between books on the wall
shelves, directly opposite a member of the committee. The button was invisible to anyone slightly to the left or right of this committeeman. If
the medium left his chair, this button would be eclipsed. On the night
of the second seance, the person observing the button found he could
easily predict when a phenomenon would occur by merely waiting for the
button to be eclipsed.[14]

The most conclusive evidence came from a diabolical device introduced secretly at the third sitting. It was a pressure plate under the
medium's chair that would light a lamp in the adjoining room if the medium
stood up. In addition a microphone in the seance room sent the proceed-
ings to a stenographer in the same adjacent room. The events taking
place in the seance room along with the blinkings of the light were recorded in a single transcript. When the committee members studied the
record, they found that every phenomena had been produced while the

---

[12]J. Malcolm Bird, "Our First Test Seances," Scientific American,
CXXIX (July 1923), p. 14.

[13]Price, p. 112.

[14]Bird, "Our First Test Seances," p. 56.

medium was out of his chair.[15] The first seances were disappointments, but they proved that the committee could work together and function effectively.[16]

In October, 1922, another medium, Mrs. Y[17] (Josie K. Stewart[18]), was tested; and another disappointment was had. Mrs. Stewart came before the committee to produce independent writings under laboratory conditions on cards supplied by the committee. She failed miserably. The messages (described as "platitudinous atrocities") were all produced on cards brought into the seance by her and substituted for the committee's cards. She produced no genuine phenomena and was ruled a fraud by the committee.[19] Even Sir Arthur Conan Doyle was inclined to agree. In a letter to The New York Times, Doyle stated that although he was bound to act in defense of the mediums, he found the case of Mrs. Stewart indefensible. Mrs. Stewart was, however, adamant. She demanded more sittings and even threatened to sue for libel. The magazine stated that the only way that she could obtain her sittings was for her to sue them. She did not.[20]

The investigation of the next medium turned into a comedy of errors and never progressed to a formal sitting. Mrs. Elisabeth Tomson was the first medium to reply to the magazine's offer and the most reluctant to

---

[15]Ibid., p. 14.

[16]Ibid., p. 69.

[17]Bird, "Another Mediumistic Failure," p. 390.

[18]Price, p. 112.

[19]Bird, "Another Mediumistic Failure," p. 445.

[20]J. Malcolm Bird, "Our Psychic Investigations," Scientific American, CXXX (April 1925), p. 236

6

perform under laboratory conditions. When Mr. Tomson began proposing conditions under which his wife would appear (which included replacing several members of the committee with personal friends of the medium), the magazine withdrew and officially stated that Mrs. Tomson had not permitted a proper investigation and had no claim to the $2500 prize.[21] Of course Mrs. Tomson still had her followers, and she even ran ads in a Philadelphia newspaper saying that the seances for the American were triumphs and that the published accounts were "false stories of jealous people."[22]

In the February, 1924 issue of Scientific American, the bold subheading of the investigation article proclaimed, "We Find a Medium Whom We Cannot Characterize as a Conscious Fraud." The medium was Nino Pecoraro, a 24-year-old Italiam who was supposedly controlled by the spirit of the long dead table-tipper Palladino. Pecoraro was discovered and managed by Dr. Anselmo Vecchio, who also acted as interpreter. Pecoraro did his tricks while tied in a chair in semidarkness. When Houdini tied Nino at the second seance, no phenomena were observed. At the end of three sittings the committee had not prepared a formal statement and said that they could not be sure until further sittings were held.[23]

The sittings were never held. Dr. Vecchio did not realize the importance of scientific conditions, and he wrote to the magazine only of conditions under which he would allow further sittings. So, like the

---

[21] J. Malcolm Bird, "Psychic Adventures at Home," Scientific American, CXXX (January 1924), pp. 20-21.

[22] Bird, "Our Psychic Investigations," p. 291.

[23] J. Malcolm Bird, "Our Psychic Investigation Advances," Scientific American, CXXX (February 1924), pp. 86, 115, 133.

case of Mrs. Tomson, the matter was formally dropped.[24] In 1931, Nino

Pecoraro made a full confession that he had faked all of his seances

under the direction of Dr. Vecchio. By then Nino had had enough and

announced, "I am sick and tired of giving seances and having others reap

the profits."[25] They found out just seven years too late.

By this time (April 1924) the committee and the magazine were

thoroughly disgusted with the quality of mediums that had entered the

contest. With less than seven months remaining they made an appeal to

the major mediums of the country. The magazine agreed to pay passage to

and from New York and living expenses, if some big name medium would

kindly present himself. None did. The appeal concluded, "It applies

specifically to an American lady of very large mediumistic repute who

sincerely seeks anonymity."[26] This lady was known as Margery,[27] one of

the most versatile mediums in history, whose phenomena included just about

everything that had ever been reported.[28] She was not only quite a

medium, but also quite a woman, and quite a match for a committee accus-

tomed to Mrs. X's and Mrs. Y's.

Margery was the pseudonym of Mrs. Le Roi G. Grandon, wife of a noted

Boston surgeon. She could not be called a professional medium because

she never accepted money for her seances, and she announced that if she

---

[24]Bird, "Our Psychic Investigations," p. 292.

[25]"Truth Will Out," Scientific American, CXLIV (June 1931), p. 374.

[26]Ibid., p. 295.

[27]Price, pp. 110-111.

[28]Gresham, p. 238.

8

won the <u>Scientific American</u> award she would not accept it but rather disperse it in psychic research.[29]   She and her husband were always extremely generous--to the believers, that is.   Mr. Bird, the secretary of the committee, wrote favorable articles and was their house guest for months.[30]

The committee's investigation began in April of 1924.   By mid-June, Bird began releasing news stories that the committee had found a genuine medium.   Houdini was angered to find that there had been over fifty seances held, and that Bird had not notified him of one.[31]   Houdini stormed to the editorial offices to confer with Bird and Mr. O. D. Munn, publisher of <u>Scientific American</u>.   When asked bluntly if Margery was genuine, Bird replied that she was at least fifty or sixty percent genuine.[32]   Houdini then and there declared to Mr. Munn that if he could not prove Margery a fraud, he would forfeit $1000.   Accordingly, Munn and Houdini set off for Boston on the 22nd of July.[33]

The conditions of the sittings were much less strict.   Instead of holding the seances in their office in New York, as with Valiantine, Mrs. Stewart, and Pecoraro, the Margery sittings were held in her home in Boston.[34]   The procedures at the sittings were rigidly controlled by

---

[29]G. H. Estabrooks, <u>Spiritism</u> (New York, 1947), p. 201.

[30]Houdini, p. 146.

[31]Gresham, p. 245.

[32]Houdini, p. 137-138.

[33]Gresham, p. 245.

[34]William McDougall, "The Margery Mediumship," <u>Scientific American</u>, CXXXII (May 1925), p. 339.

Margery's very autocratic spirit control "Walter."[35] In fact his rules were so strict that Dr. McDougall later stated that they hampered the investigator's freedom because he was under the constant threat of exclusion from further sittings. Dr. Crandon always sat immediately to his wife's right, so that he, as well as his wife, had to be controlled.[36]

When Houdini and Munn arrived in Boston, they were invited to join Mr. Bird and Hereward Carrington as house guests of the Crandons. They refused, stating that it would be impossible to retain their objectivity if they did.[37] The seances commenced on July 23rd with, as Long John Nebel describes them, ". . . Margery conducting, Houdini debunking, and a group from the Scientific American refereeing."[38]

During the three seances of July, Houdini was able to detect Margery ringing bells with her feet and lifting tables with her head. It was decided during a committee conference that nothing would be said to the Crandons while Houdini and Munn returned to New York to prepare further tests. Munn stopped the presses already printing the September issue and killed an article by Bird in praise of the Medium.[39]

Already with his publisher angry at him, Bird risked a storm by releasing more statements to newspapers. One was published under the headline: "Experts Vainly Seek Trickery in Spiritualist Demonstration,

---

[35]Houdini, p. 144.

[36]McDougall, p. 339.

[37]Gresham, p. 247.

[38]Long John Nebel, The Way Out World (New York, 1962), p. 147.

[39]Houdini, pp. 144-147.

10

Houdini the Magician Stumped."[40] For Houdini this was the last straw.
He called a meeting of the committee that forced Bird's resignation as
secretary. At the same meeting the proposition was put forth by Comstock
and Prince that Houdini design some kind of foolproof, humane confinement
for the medium. Houdini put his assistant Jim Collins to work on it, and
in late August the piano-box-like contraption that completely enclosed
the medium except for her head and hands was ready.[41]

At the first seance, the medium forced the lid open with her shoul-
ders and was able to ring the bell on the table in front of her with her
head. At the end of the evening she stated that "Walter" had forced the
box open.[42] The second night the box was reinforced with brass strips
which made it impossible to force open. Before the seance, Houdini had
cautioned the committee to keep careful watch that the medium had nothing
with her in the cabinet. Shortly after the seance opened, "Walter"
snarled that Houdini had placed a carpenter's folding rule in the cabinet
to discredit the medium. After Houdini swore that he knew nothing about
it, and after Jim Collins produced his own rule and swore he knew nothing
about a rule in the box, the seance continued; but it was a blank.
Shortly the box was unlocked, and under the cushion for medium's feet
was found a two-foot rule folded to the easily concealed size of six
inches.[43] Houdini later wrote, "I accuse Mrs. Crandon of having smug-
gled it in with her. Mrs. Crandon, knowing that she had been caught,

---

[40]Gresham, p. 250.

[41]Houdini, pp. 149-152.

[42]Ibid.

[43]Ibid., p. 156.

made the accusation to clear herself."[44]

In November, 1924, Houdini and Dr. Comstock published formal statements refuting Mrs. Crandon's mediumship. Finally in April, 1925, Drs.
Prince and McDougall issued statements. This constituted a four-to-one
vote against the medium. Mr. Carrington was convinced of supernormal
production. Mr. Bird, the secretary of the committee, left his job as
editor with Scientific American and wrote an entire book supporting
Margery's mediumship; but since he was not a voting member of the committee, his opinion made no difference. She was not awarded the prize.[45]

Margery was later examined by a group from Harvard, which was unanimous in its verdict of fraud,[46] and a group from the American Society of
Psychical Research.[47] In 1933 Dr. Prince published Margery's "box score."
In all she had been examined by twenty-three competent persons. Twenty-
one voted in favor of fraud while only two were convinced that they had
witnessed genuine psychic phenomena.[48]

In two years of investigation with a distinguished committee,
Scientific American could not find a genuine medium. They sincerely tried
to give away their $2500. The only problem was that there was no one who
could earn it. The Scientific American's investigation occurred many

---

[44]Ibid., p. 157.

[45]Walter Franklin Prince and William McDougall, "The Psychic
Investigations," Scientific American, CXXXII (April 1925), p. 229.

[46]Hudson Hoagland, "Science and the Medium," Atlantic Monthly,
CXXXVI (November 1925), pp. 666-678.

[47]Walter Franklin Prince, "The Case Against Margery," Scientific
American, CXLVIII (May 1933), p. 261.

[48]Prince, "The Case Against Margery," p. 261.

12

years ago and there have been many other investigations since, but not one has been able to prove spirit communication. The <u>American</u>'s was but one of many that have convinced Americans that mediums and spiritualism are frauds.

BIBLIOGRAPHY

Bird, J. Malcolm. "Another Mediumistic Failure," _Scientific American_, CXXIX (December 1923), 390-391, 441-445.

_____. "Our First Test Seances," _Scientific American_, CXXIX (July 1923), 14, 56, 64-69.

_____. "Our Psychic Investigation Advances," _Scientific American_, CXXX (February 1924), 86, 115, 133-139.

_____. "Our Psychic Investigations," _Scientific American_, CXXX (April 1924), 236, 291-295.

_____. "Psychic Adventures at Home," _Scientific American_, CXXX (January 1924), 20-21.

_____. "Square Deal for Psychics," _Scientific American_, CXXVII (December 1922), 375.

Carrington, Hereward. "The Mechanics of the Psychic," _Scientific American_, CXXVI (January 1922), 60, 80.

Crandon, L. R. G. "The Psychic Investigation," _Scientific American_, CXXXII (January 1925), 29, 62, 65.

Doyle, Sir Arthur Conan. "Answer to Psychic Competition," _Scientific American_, CXXVIII (January 1923), 57.

Estabrooks, G. H. _Spiritism_. New York: E. P. Dutton and Co., Inc., 1947.

Gresham, William Lindsay. _Houdini: The Man Who Walked Through Walls_. New York: Henry Holt and Co., 1959.

Hoagland, Hudson. "Science and the Medium," _Atlantic Monthly_, CXXXVI (November 1925), 666-678.

Houdini, Harry. _Houdini on Magic_, ed. by Walter B. Gibson and Morris N. Young. New York: Dover Publications, Inc., 1953.

McDougall, William. "The 'Margery Mediumship'," _Scientific American_, CXXXII (May 1925), 339-341.

_____. "The Psychic Investigation: Formal Statement by Dr. McDougall," _Scientific American_, CXXXII (April 1925), 229.

Nebel, Long John. _The Way Out World_. New York: Lancer Books, 1962.

"Our Psychic Investigation," _Scientific American_, CXXIX (August 1923), 84.

14

Price, Harry. <u>Fifty Years of Psychical Research</u>. London: Longmans, Green and Co., 1939.

Prince, Walter Franklin. "The Case Against Margery," <u>Scientific American</u>, CXLVIII (May 1933), 261-263.

_____. "The Psychic Detective," <u>Scientific American</u>, CXXVII (July 1922), 6-7, 71.

_____. "The Psychic Investigation," <u>Scientific American</u>, CXXXII (February 1925), 93.

_____. "The Psychic Investigation: Formal Statement by Dr. Prince," <u>Scientific American</u>, CXXXII (April 1925), 229.

"Truth Will Out," <u>Scientific American</u>, CXLIV (June 1931), 374.

15

Appendix 2:

Formal Outlining

A **working** or **scratch outline** is the record of a writer's thought processes as he plans the organization of a paper before he begins writing. The use of such an outline is to guide the writer as he composes paragraphs and sentences; it need not conform to conventional patterns. A **formal outline** is for the reader. It summarizes for him in heading form the central points of a finished paper; it is a record of a completed rather than a proposed organization. Since it is intended for public consumption, a formal outline is best prepared after the paper is written, and it must conform to conventional patterns.

There are two kinds of formal outlines. In a **topic outline** the headings are expressed in phrases; in a **sentence outline** they are expressed as complete sentences. The chief advantage of a topic outline is that it is more direct and pithy and less cumbersome than a sentence outline. The chief advantage of a sentence outline is that it compels the writer to express points fully and prevents him from composing vague or indefinite headings that may be virtually meaningless to a reader. Personal preference (yours or your professor's) must dictate which kind of outline you compose. Both kinds should observe the following six principles of good outlining, which are illustrated in topic outline form. Remember: This appendix illustrates how to prepare an outline of a paper or essay *already written*. It does not illustrate how to prepare a scratch or working outline; for material on that kind of outlining see Chapter 2 on preparing a basic organization for a paper.

Principle 1: balanced development of outline

The purpose of a formal outline is to give the reader a quick understanding of the main points of a paper and the order of their development. It must not be so sparse or general in its headings that it omits or obscures main points, and it must not be so detailed in its headings that it goes beyond a presentation of main points. It should present the full essence of the paper, but not its individual details. A properly developed outline will adequately fit the subject matter of its paper.

Here is an example of an outline that is so sparse and general in its headings that it fails to express the essence of the paper.

PORTUGUESE OPPRESSION OF NATIVES
IN ANGOLA IN THE 1950s

    I. Portuguese military rule
   II. Slave labor
  III. Censorship

Such an insufficiently developed outline is virtually useless to a reader.

Here is an example of an outline that is so detailed in its development that it goes far beyond the purpose of outlining.

PORTUGUESE OPPRESSION OF NATIVES
IN ANGOLA IN THE 1950s

  I. Portuguese military rule as the force behind oppression
    A. The organization of military forces in Angola
      1. Soldiers organized in a classic system of command

        a. Squad
        b. Platoon
        c. Company
        d. Battalion
        e. Brigade
    2. A three-year tour of duty required of soldiers
    3. Supplies shipped from home bases
    4. Promotions passed on by local commanders
  B. The power of the military force in Angola
    1. The permanence of military law
        a. Presence of soldier-police squads in every village
        b. Curfew for all natives at sundown
        c. Right of any officer to act as judge at any time
            (1) In disputes between natives
            (2) In disputes between Portuguese civilians and natives
            (3) In disputes between Portuguese soldiers and natives
    2. The use of soldiers as straw bosses
        a. To work gangs on plantations
        b. To work road gangs
        c. To work gangs for personal profit
    3. The power of the individual soldier
        a. Is always armed
        b. Can recruit native work force on his own authority
        c. Can enter any native dwelling for any purpose
        d. Can take produce from any native market

An so on. Such excessive detail defeats the purpose of a formal outline, which is to present to the reader in capsule form the central points of a paper. If the above outline were continued, it would be as long as the paper itself.

Here is an example of an outline properly balanced in development.

PORTUGUESE OPPRESSION OF NATIVES IN ANGOLA IN THE 1950s

  I. Portuguese military rule as the force behind oppression
    A. The organization of the military force
    B. The power of the military force
      1. The presence of permanent military law
      2. The use of soldiers as straw bosses
      3. The oppressive power given to individual soldiers

  II. The reduction of the native population to slave labor
    A. Complete absence of civil rights for natives

       B. Governmental expropriation of native economic production
       C. Physical abuses resulting from slave status of natives

  III. The government's use of police-state tactics to prevent world protest
       A. Supervision and restriction of travel by foreigners
       B. Censorship of all news releases
       C. Intimidation of businessmen who might express protest

In a properly developed outline, each heading is a capsule summary of—a sort of title for—a part of the accompanying paper. It is a generality derived from the paper's organization. Headings should not be mere details that occupy as much space in the outline as they do in the paper itself.

Principle 2: meaningful headings

Since the purpose of a formal outline is to give the reader a quick summary of a paper before he reads it, each heading must be meaningful. An outline heading that is understandable only to one who has read the accompanying paper is useless.

    Here is an outline composed of near-meaningless headings.

THE DEVELOPMENT OF THE FIRST NUCLEAR SUBMARINE

    I. Introduction
   II. Rickover's fight
 III. The Navy's capitulation
  IV. Troubles
   V. Conclusion

First note that the headings *Introduction* and *Conclusion* are worthless in an outline. If a central point is made in the introduction or conclusion, then it should be given meaningful summary in a real heading. Introductory sentences that explain the purpose of a paper should not be given an outline heading, for they do not express one of the main points that will be developed in the paper. And so with concluding statements that give the paper a sense of completeness. It really is unnecessary for an outline to tell the reader that the paper opens and closes. Only main points should be given outline headings.

    The other headings in the above outline are far too vague and indefinite to be useful to a reader. Here is a more meaningful version.

THE DEVELOPMENT OF THE FIRST NUCLEAR SUBMARINE

    I. Admiral Rickover's demonstration of the feasibility of nuclear submarines
   II. Rickover's controversies with the Navy over his proposal to build a nuclear submarine
 III. The capitulation of the Navy because of Eisenhower's intervention
 IV. The technical difficulties that Rickover encountered in building the submarine
  V. The completion of the first nuclear submarine and demonstration of its capabilities

The purpose of outline writing is not to reduce a heading to the fewest possible words, but to express in compact, meaningful form a central idea of the paper. Meaningfulness in an outline heading is much more important than brevity.

Principle 3: parallelism of content

An outline is composed of **levels,** and the headings in any one level represent a division of a previous level. Thus the title of a paper is the point of origin of its outline. A division of the title produces the Roman-numeral headings, which are the **first level** of the outline. For example, in the discussion of meaningful headings above, the title "The Development of the First Nuclear Submarine" is divided into five Roman-numeral headings. As presented there, the outline has only one level—the five equal headings derived from the title.

When a Roman-numeral heading (the first level) has subheadings, they represent a division of the Roman-numeral heading and are thus on the **second level.** For example:

THE DEVELOPMENT OF THE FIRST NUCLEAR SUBMARINE

    I. Admiral Rickover's demonstration of the feasibility of nuclear submarines
      A. His pilot nuclear-reactor power plant

  B. His demonstration of the practicality of power transmission from the reactor
  C. His solutions to the problems of sustained underwater cruising

Headings A, B, and C here are divisions of Roman numeral I and represent the second level of the outline.

A division of any of these headings would represent the **third level** of the outline. For example:

  C. His solutions to the problems of sustained underwater cruising
   1. Provisions for a continuous supply of oxygen
   2. Provisions for physical comfort of the crew
   3. Provisions for psychological adjustment of the crew

Headings 1, 2, and 3, being divisions of a second-level heading, represent the third level of the outline. And so on. Generally, only the outline of a very long paper needs to be taken to more than three levels, and two levels are usually sufficient for most college papers.

In writing, the word *parallelism* means equality in rank. In an outline, all the headings on any one level should be parallel in content—that is, the parts of the paper that the headings summarize should be equal in importance. Thus all the Roman-numeral headings, being divisions of the title, should be equal in rank, and all the subheadings under any one Roman-numeral heading should similarly be equal in rank. And so on.

Faulty parallelism of content occurs when the headings placed on one level are not really equal in rank. For example:

THE PRACTICAL VALUE OF A LIBERAL ARTS EDUCATION

  I. Its development of one's flexibility in adapting to new business or industrial techniques
  II. Through providing an understanding of historical perspectives and the evolution of human knowledge
  III. Through providing a mastery of theory rather than of just specific techniques

Parallelism of content is violated here because headings II and III are not two more divisions of the title but are really divisions of heading I. They should be headings A and B under I.

Thus when an outline heading is out of place, faulty parallelism of content occurs. You can keep headings properly parallel only by thinking clearly enough to see how the Roman-numeral headings derive from the title, how second-level headings derive from Roman-numeral headings, how third-level headings derive from those on the second level, and so on.

You should not think, however, that headings parallel in content must necessarily represent parts of the paper that are equal in length. For example, in a paper on "Methods of Soil Analysis" the part represented by Roman-numeral I (the first method) might cover only two pages, whereas the part represented by Roman-numeral II (the second method) might cover five pages. The two Roman-numeral headings, nevertheless, would be equal in importance (parallel in content), for each would pertain to one whole method of soil analysis.

Balanced development, meaningful headings, and parallelism of content are the three most important principles of outlining, for they pertain to the subject matter of the outline. The following three principles are of lesser importance, for they pertain to the mechanical rather than the logical aspects of outlining. They bear the same relationship to outlining that conventions of usage bear to writing, and you should observe them in outlining for the same reasons you maintain correctness in writing.

Principle 4: parallelism of structure

An outline maintains parallelism of structure when all the headings of **any one level and division** are in the same grammatical structure. One of the advantages of the sentence outline is that parallelism of structure is no problem since all the headings are sentences. In topic outlines, faulty parallelism of structure occurs when two or more different kinds of phrases are used for one level and division.

There are several kinds of phrases that may be used as headings in a topic outline. When the head word of a phrase (the key word around which the phrase is built) is a noun, verb, adjective, adverb, participle, infinitive, or gerund, the phrase is named after the head word. The prepositional phrase is another kind that may be used as a topic heading. The writer's problem is to use only one kind of phrase for the headings in any one level and division.

In the following outline, phrase names are substituted for

actual headings to illustrate how parallelism of structure is maintained.

I. Noun phrase
   A. Participial phrase
      1. Prepositional phrase
      2. Prepositional phrase
   B. Participial phrase
II. Noun phrase
   A. Adjective phrase
      1. Infinitive phrase
      2. Infinitive phrase
   B. Adjective phrase

Headings I and II are on the same level and in the same division (of the title) and thus are parallel. Headings A and B under I are on the same level and in the same division (of heading I) and thus are parallel. Headings A and B under II are on the same level as A and B under I, but they are in a different division (of heading II) and thus, though they are parallel to each other, they do not need to be parallel to headings in another division. And so on.

The following outline **violates** parallelism of structure.

METHODS OF REHABILITATING DELINQUENTS

I. The use of psychiatric therapy to rehabilitate delinquents
   A. In out-patient clinics
   B. Institutionalization
II. Giving delinquents vocational rehabilitation
   A. Through on-the-job training
   B. Putting them in a vocational school
   C. Use of the armed services
III. To remedy defects in delinquents' homelife
   A. By economic rehabilitation of parents
   B. Marriage counseling of parents
   C. To relocate delinquents in new homes

Headings I, II, and III are not in parallel structure, for I is a noun phrase (the noun *use* is the head word), II is a participial phrase (*giving* is the head word), and III is an infinitive phrase (*to remedy* is the head word). Identify the kinds of phrases in the subheadings, and suggest ways of establishing parallel structure for the whole outline.

Principle 5: avoidance of single subheadings

Mechanically, the process of outlining is subdividing. The title of a paper is divided into first-level (Roman-numeral) headings; a first-level heading is divided into second-level headings; and so on. The principle of division, then, says that a single subheading in an outline is illogical, since if you divide a heading at all, you must divide it into at least two parts.

For example, an outline with only one Roman-numeral heading is faulty:

PUBLIC RECREATIONAL FACILITIES IN MY HOME TOWN

   I. What my home town does to provide public recreation
      A. A senior-citizens recreational center
      B. A summer camp program
      C. A winter sports program
      D. A system of well-equipped parks

Heading I of this outline does not divide the title, but merely repeats it in different words. Headings A, B, C, and D are proper divisions of the title and therefore should form four first-level (Roman-numeral) headings under the title.

Sometimes an outline writer will use a single subheading that is really just a part of the heading it is placed under. Example:

   II. A summer camp program
      A. In conjunction with the YMCA Camp

Heading A is not a division of II, but a continuation of it. The faulty single subheading can be eliminated in this way:

   II. A summer camp program in conjunction with the YMCA Camp

Normally, you must divide a heading into at least two subheadings or not divide it at all.

A single subheading may be logically acceptable when it presents a single example to illustrate the heading it is placed under. Example:

URBAN RENEWAL

I. The economic success of central malls in big cities
   A. Example: Detroit, Michigan's central mall

Heading A indicates that in the general discussion of the economic success of central malls one extended example will be given. Such a legitimate single subheading should be labeled with the word *example*.

Principle 6: consistency of form

An outline should be consistent in its numbering system, its capitalization, and its punctuation. Any clear, consistent system is satisfactory. The most common numbering system uses Roman numerals (I, II) for the first level; capital letters (A, B) for the second level; Arabic numerals (1, 2) for the third level; and lower-case letters (a, b) for the fourth level. Normally in a topic outline only the first word of a heading is capitalized. In a sentence outline end punctuation is of course used, but the most commonly used system in topic outlines omits end punctuation.

Appendix 3:

A Glossary of Usage

accept, except *Accept* is a verb meaning "to receive"; *except* is a preposition indicating that something is excluded; *except* can be used as a verb meaning "to leave out or exclude."
> *right:* I cannot accept your gift.
> *right:* Everyone except me came to the party.
> *right* (though rare): The professor excepted those who had perfect attendance.

accidentally The spelling *accidently* is substandard.

affect, effect *Affect* is a verb meaning "to influence"; *effect* is a noun meaning "the influence exerted on something"; *effect* is also a verb meaning "to bring about."
> *right:* The bad weather affected my morale.
> *right:* The bad weather had an effect on my morale.
> *right:* The prisoner effected an escape.

all ready, already   *All ready* is an adjectival idiom meaning "everyone or everything is prepared"; *already* is an adverb meaning "at this time or before this time."

all right, alright   The spelling *alright* is now accepted by dictionaries, but careful writers still use only *all right*.

all together, altogether   *All together* is an adverbial idiom meaning that "everyone acts in unison"; *altogether* is an adverb meaning "wholly or completely."

> *right:* Let's sing all together now.
> *right:* That solution is altogether unsatisfactory.

allude, refer   *Allude* is a verb meaning "to mention indirectly"; *refer* is a verb meaning "to mention specifically and directly."

> *right:* He alluded to his drinking problem when he spoke of Alcoholics Anonymous.
> *right:* He referred to *Hamlet*, act IV, scene II.

allusion, delusion, illusion   *Allusion* is a noun meaning "an indirect reference"; *delusion* is a noun meaning "a false belief"; *illusion* is a noun meaning "a deceptive appearance." Don't confuse *delusion* and *illusion*.

> *right:* His allusion to *Das Kapital* made him suspect.
> *right:* He is under the delusion that he will be a great baseball player.
> *right:* Her apparent beauty was a mere illusion.
> *wrong:* His illusion that he was another FDR irritated the political pros.

almost, most   *Almost* means "nearly"; *most* means "to the greatest extent." *Most* is colloquially used for *almost*.

> *colloquial at best:* Most all the players were declared ineligible.

among, between   Use *among* when three or more items are designated; use *between* for two items. Occasionally *between* is used colloquially for *among*.

amount, number   *Amount* designates a quantity that cannot be numbered; *number* designates a quantity that is divisible into units.

> *right:* an amount of sugar
> *right:* a number of books
> *colloquial at best:* a large amount of nails

and etc.   Do not use the redundant *and* with *etc.*

and, but   It is not wrong to begin a sentence with *and* or *but*.

anxious, eager   *Anxious* means "uneasy or apprehensive"; *eager* means "strongly desirous of."

colloquial at best: I was anxious to go to the party.

anyway, any way   *Anyway* is an adverb meaning "in any case"; *any way* is a noun phrase.

> *right:* I was broke, anyway.
> *right:* I couldn't find any way to solve the problem.

as, like   Some authorities think that *like* as a conjunction is colloquial or unacceptable, but most authorities now accept *like* as a conjunction.

> *colloquial to some:* It looks like it may rain.

awful, awfully   Both *awful* and *awfully* should be avoided as intensifiers.

> *low colloquial:* I'm awful (awfully) sorry about your accident.

bad, badly   Use *bad* after the verb *feel*.

> *right:* I felt *bad* about your failure.

because of, due to   Many authorities prefer *because of* as an adverb and *due to* as an adjective.

> *preferred:* Because of the rain I was late.
> *preferred:* My failure was due to my poor study habits.

being as, being that   Avoid these low-level constructions. Use *since* instead.

beside, besides   *Beside* is a preposition meaning "at the side of"; *besides* is a preposition or adverb meaning "in addition to."

> *wrong:* We brought everything beside beer.

between   See *among*. Never use "between you and I", "between you and he," and so on. The object form of a pronoun must be used after *between*.

born, borne   *Borne* is the past participle of *bear* when it is in the active voice; *born* is the past participle in the passive voice.

> *right:* She has borne six children.
> *right:* She has borne her poverty with elegance.
> *right:* He was born in France.

burst, bust   *Burst* is the standard usage; *bust* is at best low colloquial. The principal parts of *burst* are *burst, burst, burst*. There is no such word as *bursted*.

cite, site, sight   *Cite* is a verb meaning "to indicate or mention"; *site* is a noun meaning "a place where something is, was, or is to be"; *sight* is a noun or verb having to do with vision.

> *right:* He cited a chapter from the Bible as proof.
> *right:* The site for the new building was poorly chosen.

colloquialism, localism, regionalism A *colloquialism* is "a word or phrase suitable for informal usage"; a *localism* or *regionalism* is "a word or phrase used only in one locality."

> *wrong:* I heard many colloquialisms (meaning localisms) in the hills of North Carolina.

complement, compliment *Complement* means "something that completes or a number or amount that makes a whole"; *compliment* means "to give praise." Each can be used as a verb or a noun.

> *right:* He complimented her on her dress.
> *right:* The fourth Division had a full complement of troops.

conscience, conscious *Conscience* is a noun meaning "a knowledge or feeling of right and wrong"; *conscious* is an adjective meaning "aware or alert."

contemptible, contemptuous *Contemptible* means "deserving contempt"; *contemptuous* means "showing contempt."

> *right:* He is a contemptible person because of his bad habits.
> *right:* I was contemptuous of his pomposity.

continual, continuous *Continual* means "occurring at close intervals"; *continuous* means "without interruption or cessation."

could of, would of Illiterate misspellings for *could have* and *would have*.

council, counsel *Council* is a noun meaning "an official group"; *counsel* is a verb meaning "to give advice" or a noun meaning "advice or advisor." *Counselor* comes from counsel.

> *right:* The city council voted new taxes.
> *right:* I asked my teacher to counsel me.
> *right:* He gave me good counsel.

credible, creditable, credulous *Credible* means "believable"; *creditable* means "worthy of praise"; *credulous* means "willing to believe readily or easily imposed upon."

> *right:* Your story is credible.
> *right:* His kind actions were creditable.
> *right:* A credulous person is an easy mark for a con man.

data *Data* is a plural and most writers use a plural verb with it.

> *right:* The data support his conclusion.

delusion See *allusion*.

different from, different than *Different from* is the preferred usage; *different than* is colloquial.

> *preferred:* John's book is different from mine.

disinterested, uninterested   *Disinterested* means "impartial"; *un-interested* means "having no interest in."
>   *right:* The judge was disinterested.
>   *wrong:* John was disinterested in his studies.

due to   See *because of*.

eager   See *anxious*.

effect   See *affect*.

enthuse   Many authorities prefer *be enthusiastic*.

except   See *accept*.

expect, suspect   *Expect* means "to look forward to or anticipate"; *suspect* means "to think probable or likely."
>   *right:* I suspect he will fail.
>   *colloquial:* I expect he will fail.

farther, further   *Farther* relates to physical distance; *further* refers to degree and quantity. More and more, *further* is being used as synonymous with *farther*.
>   *right:* I cannot walk any farther.
>   *right:* Do you have anything further to say?

fewer, less   *Fewer* refers to separate items; *less* refers to a quantity that cannot be divided into separate items. *Less* is used colloquially for fewer.
>   *right:* I have fewer marbles than you.
>   *right:* I have less sugar than you.
>   *colloquial:* I have less marbles than you.

good, well   These words are difficult to separate, for both are adjectives and *well* is also an adverb. But most usages are acceptable now. You should, however, avoid using *good* for *well* in such examples as these:
>   *right:* The car runs well.
>   *right:* John did well in algebra.
>   *right:* John carried the joke off well.

hanged, hung   Use *hanged* in referring to persons being suspended in a noose. Use *hung* for other uses.
>   *right:* The criminal was hanged.

hardly   Never use the double negative *can't hardly, won't hardly*, and so forth.

he, she   Use *he* when the sex is indefinite or mixed. Avoid using "he or she."

height, heighth   The preferred spelling and pronunciation is *height*.

if, whether   Use *whether* to introduce a noun clause.

> *right:* I don't know whether I can come.
> *colloquial:* I don't know if I can come.

illusion   See *allusion*.

imply, infer   *Imply* means "to suggest or hint"; *infer* means "to draw a conclusion about."

> *right:* As he talked, he implied I was a fool.
> *right:* From the conversation I could infer that John was displeased with Joan.
> *wrong:* As he talked, he inferred I was a fool.

in, into   *In* shows location; *into* shows direction.

> *right:* He was in the house.
> *right:* He walked into the house.

incidentally   Avoid the spelling *incidently*.

incredible, incredulous   The negative of *credible* and *credulous*. See *credible*.

infer   See *imply*.

inside of   Colloquial for *within*.

> *preferred:* I will see you within a week.

invite   Do not use as a noun.

> *substandard:* I received an invite.
> *right:* I received an invitation.

irregardless   Avoid altogether. Use *regardless*.

its, it's   *Its* is possessive; *it's* is a contraction of *it is* or *it has*. Never use the illiterate misspelling *its'*

> *right:* Its waterbowl is empty.
> *right:* It's raining.

it's me, it's I   *It's me* is colloquial. In formal situations use *it's I*.

kind of, sort of   Colloquial. Prefer *rather* or *somewhat*.

later, latter   *Later* is an adjective or adverb meaning "at a time after a specified time"; *latter* is an adjective or noun meaning "nearer the end or the last mentioned."

> *right:* He came later than you.
> *right:* Of the three methods described, I chose the latter.

lay, lie   *Lay* is a transitive verb meaning "to place an object somewhere"; *lie* is an intransitive verb meaning "to be in or take a reclining position." The principal parts of *lay* are *lay, laid, laid;* the principal parts of *lie* are *lie, lay, lain. Lay* is used colloquially for *lie,* but most teachers oppose such usage.

> *right:* I will lay the book on the table.

right: Yesterday I laid the book on the table.

right: I have laid the book down many times.

right: The book is lying on the table.

right: I will lie down this afternoon.

right: Yesterday I lay down.

right: I have lain down every day this week.

less See *fewer.*

liable, libel *Liable* is an adjective meaning "responsible or legally bound or likely to have"; *libel* is a noun meaning "slanderous references" or a verb meaning "to slander."

right: A man is liable for debts contracted by his wife.

right: The gossip columnist was sued for libel.

lie See *lay.*

like See *as.*

localism See *colloquialism.*

loose, lose *Loose* is an adjective meaning "unfastened"; *lose* is a verb meaning "to mislay or to be deprived of."

maybe, may be *Maybe* is an adverb meaning "perhaps or possibly"; *may be* is a form of the verb *to be.*

moral, morale *Moral* is an adjective meaning "right or ethical"; *morale* is a noun meaning "a mental attitude or condition."

right: All moral acts are recorded in Heaven.

right: The troops' morale was high.

most See *almost.*

nohow A vulgate term. Avoid in all writing except dialogue.

nowhere near Low colloquial. Avoid in semiformal writing.

number See *amount.*

oral, verbal *Oral* means "spoken"; *verbal* means "pertaining to written or oral language." *Verbal* is now much used for *oral.*

passed, past *Passed* is the past tense and past participle of the verb *pass; past* is an adjective and a noun meaning "of a former time."

right: I passed calculus.

right: The time for reconciliation is past.

prepositions It is not wrong to end a sentence with a preposition.

principal, principle *Principal* is an adjective meaning "chief" and a noun meaning "the head of a school or money used as capital"; *principle* is a noun meaning "rule, law, or doctrine."

right: Stockholm is the principal city of Sweden.

right: Algebraic principles are not difficult to learn.

quiet, quite *Quiet* is an adjective meaning "not noisy, calm"; *quite* is an adverb meaning "entirely." The words are pronounced differently, *quiet* having two syllables.

> *wrong:* Children, keep quite.

raise, rise *Raise* is a transitive verb (takes an object) meaning "to put something in a higher position"; its principal parts are *raise, raised, raised. Rise* is an intransitive verb meaning "to go to a higher position"; its principal parts are *rise, rose, risen.*

> *right:* Will you raise my salary?
> *right:* Smoke does not always rise.

reason is because Though in widespread use, this expression is still frowned upon by some authorities, especially for semiformal writing. *Reason is that* is preferred.

> *right:* The reason I resigned was that I need to devote more time to my studies.
> *colloquial:* The reason she failed was because she didn't study.

refer See *allude.*

regionalism See *colloquialism.*

scarcely Avoid the double negative *can't scarcely.*

set, sit *Set* is a transitive verb (takes an object) meaning "to place something in a position"; its principal parts are *set, set, set. Sit* is an intransitive verb meaning "to occupy a seat or to be in a sitting position"; its principal parts are *sit, sat, sat.*

> *right:* Yesterday I set the phonograph on the floor.
> *right:* Will you sit in this chair?
> *right:* I have sat here all day.
> *wrong:* He set down.
> *wrong:* He has set here all day.

site See *cite.*

sort of See *kind of.*

split infinitive Some stylists oppose the placing of a modifier between the *to* and the verb of an infinitive, such as "to better understand." They prefer "better to understand." Nevertheless, split infinitives are not errors. But usually the style will sound better if the modifier is placed before the *to* or after the verb.

> *awkward:* I want to learn to better play the game.
> *smoother:* I want to learn to play the game better.

suppose, supposed To omit the "d" of the past participle is a serious error. When the "d" is needed, the word will normally be preceded by a form of the verb *to be* and will be followed by an infinitive. The same distinction is to be made for *use* and *used*.

> *right:* I was supposed to vote today.
> *wrong:* Was he suppose to come?

suspect   See *expect.*

than, then   *Than* is a conjunction used in comparisons; *then* is an adverb of time.

> *right:* John has a higher I.Q. than Shirley.
> *right:* First we ate; then we went to the opera.

toward, towards   There is no essential distinction between these words.

try and, try to   *Try to* is preferable.

uninterested   See *disinterested.*

used to   See *suppose.*

well   See *good.*

where . . . at   Avoid the *at* if it is unnecessary.

> *right:* Where is he?
> *colloquial at best:* Where is he at?

whether   See *if.*

whose, who's   *Whose* is a possessive pronoun; *who's* is a contraction for *who is* or *who has.*

> *wrong:* Who's book do you have?

would have   Avoid using for *had.*

> *right:* If he had studied, he would have passed the exam.
> *colloquial at best:* If he would have studied, he would have passed the exam.

would of   An illiteracy. Use *would have.*

your, you're   *Your* is a possessive pronoun; *you're* is a contraction for *you are.*

> *wrong:* Your supposed to come at eight.

Index

HANDBOOK OF USAGE
REFERENCE CHART

SPELLING RULES
253–258

THE HYPHEN
277–282

THE DASH
290–298

QUOTATION MARKS
303–308

VERB AGREEMENT
321–327

ABBREVIATIONS
355–356

MODIFIER FORMS
342–350